MENDING THE
WEB OF LIFE

The character "Mai" as used in Chinese medicine may
mean pulse, arteries, veins and channels.
It can also mean the veins of a leaf.
"Mai" used here reminds us that,
as the pulse and channels reflect a person's health,
each creation is a vibrant thread in the web of life and
that their mutual health determines the health of
our living Earth.

IFAW
www.ifaw.org

AMERICAN HERBAL PRODUCTS ASSOCIATION

Foundation for Education and Research on Botanicals
(AHPA-ERB Foundation)

MENDING THE WEB OF LIFE

Chinese Medicine
&
Species Conservation

—

By
Elizabeth Call
Managing Editor: Mary Maruca

—

With Additional Contributions By:
Sandra Altherr
Sandra Cleva
Sarah Foster
Grace Ge Gabriel
Jean Giblette
Andrea Heydlauff
Michael Spencer

The substitutions recommended here are meant to be utilized and disseminated by properly trained practitioners of Chinese medicine. Practitioners bear the responsibility for using these substitutions appropriately and in accordance with the indications, contraindications, dosage and duration of use, as stated in the Chinese medical literature.

ISBN 0-9786008-0-0

Call, Elizabeth A., 1955-
    Mending the Web of Life: Chinese Medicine and Species Conservation: ETC.

    ISBN 0-9786008-0-0
1. Chinese medicine. 2. Endangered Species. 3. Species Conservation.

Cover Design by Yan Jiang at YOUnME Studio, Beijing, China
Text design: Signature Book Printing, Inc.
Printed by: Signature Book Printing, Inc.

To Stuart whose name means steward...

And to

*William and children everywhere, whose future resides
in the magnificent diversity of nature.
E.C.*

Fifteen percent of the profits from the sale of this book will be donated to conservation initiatives that benefit Chinese medicinal species.

In the *Ling Shu* Chapter Eight, (*Ben Shen*) the Yellow Emperor asks Qi Bo to define several concepts.

Qi Bo replies...

The power of individuated existence (te) is the presence of Heaven within my being.

The energy (qi) to become form is the presence of Earth within my being.

When power and energy stream and surge through one another, living beings arise.

Thus, the origins of life are the essential yin and yang.

When these two essences collide and couple this is the expression of life force or spirit.

That which follows the comings and goings of the spirit is called the hun (yang aspect).

That which accompanies the exits and entrances of the essence is called the po (yin aspect).

That which interacts with the world is called the heart-mind.

When the heart-mind reflects, this is called consciousness.

When consciousness persists this is called will.

When will is resilient and adaptable, this is called thought.

When thought is far-reaching this is called foresight.

When foresight is exercised in managing the affairs of the world this is called wisdom.

Therefore, wisdom is the way to nourish life, by following the four seasons, adapting to their climates, harmonizing the emotions, living in peace and contentment, and fine-tuning the yin and yang and hard and soft.

And in this way avoid pernicious influences to live a long and healthy life.

Translated by: Andrew Gamble

Table of Contents

Preface by Ted J. Kaptchuk i
Foreword by Grace Ge Gabriel iii
Acknowledgments vi

Part I

1. Prologue: "Primordial" Beginnings..................................... 3
   Elizabeth Call

2. Conservation Framework: "Anatomy of the Loom" 7
   Elizabeth Call

Part II

3. Introduction: Chinese Medicine and The Web of Life 21
   Elizabeth Call

4. Animal Species Profiles: The "Warp"................................... 41
   Introduction: *Elizabeth Call*
   Asian Tortoises and Freshwater Turtles: *Sandra Altherr*........... 55
   Asiatic Wild Ass: *Andrea Heydlauff* 74
   Bears: *Grace Ge Gabriel*... 81
   Musk Deer: *Andrea Heydlauff* 93
   Pangolins: *Michael Spencer*... 99
   Rhinoceros: *Michael Spencer* 106
   Saiga Antelope: *Grace Ge Gabriel*................................... 113
   Seahorses: *Sarah Foster* 123
   Tigers: *Andrea Heydlauff* 134

5. Plant Species Profiles: The "Weft".................................... 143
   Introduction: *Elizabeth Call*
   Agarwood: *Michael Spencer* 149
   Aloes: *Jean Giblette* 157
   American Ginseng: *Jean Giblette*.................................... 163
   Chain Fern Rhizome: *Jean Giblette* 170
   Euphorbias: *Jean Giblette* 175
   Orchids: *Jean Giblette*... 184

Part III

6. United States Laws and Treaties: Support for the Web 199
   Sandra Cleva

Part IV

7. Rationale for Replacements: "Weaving Variations".................... 219
   Elizabeth Call

8. Survey of Replacements: Mending The Web 223
   Elizabeth Call

Part V

9. The Role of Cultivation in Conserving Medicinal Plants:
   Nurturing the Web 251
   Jean Giblette

10. Epilogue: "A Spiritual Pivot"...................................... 261
    Elizabeth Call

Contributors and Partner Organizations............................... 273
Resources.. 277

Preface

East Asian medicine is not as much about treating disease as it is about aiding the entire human being to dynamically respond to challenges in the environment. Practitioners of Asian healing do not primarily conceptualize their healing work as a specific intervention that has a cause and effect relationship to a well-defined outcome. Rather, the Asian intervention – be it herbal, acupuncture, exercise, or counseling – is designed to help human beings adjust their internal milieu or balance to more effectively interact with bodily, emotional, social, moral, or cosmological disturbances. Healing is achieved by balancing the relationship between a person's inner and external environment. This balance is dynamic and individualized. A ballerina needs different herbs than a construction worker, even if they have the same western medical disease and a similar Asian pattern of disharmony. Adjustments are made to a person or the environment based on a gestalt of relationships.

This volume points to a paradoxical and potentially tragic situation. The human usage of selected plant and animal herbs, even from a "natural" non-technological tradition such as Chinese medicine, is threatening the survival of many species of plants and animals. The act of aiding the human response to their environment has become a threat to the environment itself. Even within a "natural" system, the self-sustaining relationship of humans using their environment is collapsing. The increased human population and the systematic exploitation of the environment to meet a growing Asian, and now global, desire for "natural" medicine threaten the source of these medicines. Chinese medicine has become a growing source of disturbance and destruction of the natural order. In order to avert such a tragedy, Chinese medicine must turn its tools for establishing dynamic equilibrium on itself. Chinese medicine must make its own internal corrections to its balance and become a tool for its own healing. The dynamic of global humanity and its impact on the environment through the practice of Asian medicine needs to be re-harmonized.

Mending the Web of Life could not have come at a more critical time. It synthesizes great scholarship with concern for clinicians' effectiveness and patients' health. *Mending the Web of Life* is itself a *serious* health "intervention" into the natural, cosmic, and moral dynamic between Chinese medicine and the environment. In a well-researched manner, this book describes critical threats to plant and animal species created by a demand for natural products that cannot be sustained without destruction of these same species. By examining textual sources and getting feedback from current experts in the field, the book makes insightful suggestions for substituting herbs that can be used in a sustainable manner. Practitioners of Asian medicine have always known how to make substitutions of herbs based on current availability and exorbitant expense. Now it is clear that substitutions must also be made based on species conservation. Chinese medicine needs to re-orient and re-align its focus because of this new crisis, and it should become a more clearly defined morally and ecologically minded profession. We need to dynamically balance ourselves as a health resource for the planet. We have used the planet; now we need to protect the planet. We need to embody our values not only on the patient-practitioner level, but also as a collective profession. *Mending the Web of Life* provides a powerful vision for legitimate, natural, and sustainable healing in the future.

We owe these authors our deep-felt gratitude.

Ted J. Kaptchuk
Harvard Medical School, Boston

Foreword

As I write this foreword, another crisis is befalling the world's remaining wild tigers that may finally push this beautiful species to extinction. In India, where conservationists believed just a few years ago that 3,500 tigers still lived in the wild, poaching has completely wiped out tigers in some nature reserves.

In a further blow to the preservation of these animals, the government of China is contemplating limited trade of tiger bone for use in Traditional Chinese Medicine (TCM). Such action would revoke a ban that has been in place since 1993. Alarmingly, legalizing the tiger trade will make law enforcement of illegal trade impossible, stimulate more poaching, and aggravate the crisis for tigers in the wild. Devastating consequences for tigers aside, reopening the tiger trade sends a message to the world that TCM and species conservation are inherently contradictory. Should wild tigers become extinct, Chinese medicine would be solely to blame.

As a Chinese, I believe in TCM and have great respect for it, both as part of my cultural heritage and as a sensible health care method. I admire its way of treating the root of the problem, instead of just the symptoms. I believe in its wisdom of disease prevention, and that its nurturance of health is just as important as its treatment of illness. I am particularly proud of its underlying philosophy, which encourages achieving harmony within one's own body, as well as with the external world, a practice that may have contributed to its sustainability during its long history spanning thousands of years.

As a conservationist, I am saddened to see the name and the reputation of TCM soiled by the role it plays, advertently and inadvertently, in ecosystem destruction, species extinction, the suffering of animals, and in one of the largest international criminal activities—the illegal wildlife trade. During the last century, particularly the past few decades, technology and other hallmarks of modern commerce have globalized international trade, making products containing wild animal and plant species obtainable and affordable worldwide. Consequently both legal and illegal trade in wildlife has escalated, raising alarm about the global disappearance of species and biodiversity.

It is this alarm that prompted the establishment of the Convention on International Trade in Endangered Species of Fauna and Flora (CITES)—a conservation convention set up to "ensure that international trade in specimens of wild animals and plants does not threaten their survival." In signing this convention, CITES countries, now more than 160, recognize and agree that "wild fauna and flora in their many beautiful and varied forms are an irreplaceable part of the natural systems of the earth which must be protected for this and the generations to come."

Considering the expanding popularity and use of TCM worldwide, the tremendous threats to ecosystem health from the international medicinal trade in animal and plant species no longer can be ignored. A resolution on "Traditional Medicines" was adopted at the CITES 10th Conference of the Parties in 1997, urging countries to enact stricter regulations on the trade of species used in all types of traditional medicine. Since then, more and more species used in TCM have joined tigers, rhinos, and bears on CITES Appendices that either ban their use or regulate their international trade for commercial purposes.

If we put this problem into the larger global context, we realize that trade bans and regulations are only a means of addressing the symptoms. The international community resorts to these tools as a last desperate effort to save a species.

Sometimes, in desperation, mistakes are made, producing a domino effect as one endangered species is replaced with another, thereby threatening the survival of the replacement. Examples of this include replacing rhino horn with saiga antelope horn, and replacing tiger bone with leopard bone, actions that have put saiga antelope and leopards in grave danger of extinction.

The practice of TCM suffers as well. The loss of biodiversity results in reduced availability and quality of the ingredients the profession uses for healing. In addition, the reputation and integrity of this ancient healing art continues to be challenged, as media attention generated by trade bans, regulations, and law enforcement paints TCM as the "culprit" responsible for species extinction.

For both TCM and global biodiversity to survive and thrive into the future, a holistic and precautionary approach is needed to address the problem of biodiversity loss at its roots. *Mending the Web of Life* applies the ancient wisdom of Chinese medicine to the healing of the Earth, on which all species, including humans (*Homo sapiens*), depend for survival.

Using the Five Phase theory, *Mending the Web of Life* superimposes the health-nurturing technique used by Chinese medicine practitioners onto the challenges facing species conservation. Highlighting our own intricate interconnections with, and dependence upon, other living beings, *Mending the Web of Life* provides the "faces" for species conservation efforts. It argues passionately for seeking replacements of those species whose basic survival is threatened by their use in Chinese medicine.

Mending the Web of Life reasons that maintaining balance and harmony in ecosystems is as important as it is in a human body. The book makes the case that illness prevention, a principal that has long been cherished in the Chinese medicine tradition, should also be applied to biodiversity preservation and species protection.

Mending the Web of Life is a pioneering effort at bridging the gap between two seemingly divergent disciplines and communities—Chinese medicine and species conservation. It embodies the authors' collective desire to preserve the ecosystems on which the Chinese medicinal practice depends for survival.

Healthy ecosystems will help maintain the integrity and sustainability of TCM for generations to come. At the same time, the active participation of Chinese medicine practitioners in conservation endeavors will help them succeed while projecting an image of this ancient healing method as an advanced philosophy, worthy of the world to embrace—cruelty-free, environmentally friendly, and ethically responsible.

Grace Ge Gabriel
International Fund for Animal Welfare
Beijing, China

Acknowledgements

Many people and organizations contributed time, expertise, and resources to make this book possible. First, I would like to thank the National Fish and Wildlife Foundation for awarding the original grant, as well as attorney Jim Turner for a significant "in-kind" donation that released monies to begin the project. I am also tremendously indebted to the International Fund for Animal Welfare (IFAW), whose generous matching funds enabled us to complete this work. Both Grace Ge Gabriel and Jennifer Sheetz of IFAW provided extraordinary support along the way.

As with any complex, long-term project, there are those visionaries who begin the work by imparting their expertise before moving on to other endeavors. Heena Patel and Barbara Mitchell laid the foundation for a national dialogue in our profession on the issue of species conservation. My thanks and respect go to them.

This book resulted from a multidisciplinary educational approach to conservation. I am indebted to a number of non-governmental environmental organizations that contributed information on the various species profiled here. Most notably, Rebecca Respess with WildAid, Grace Ge Gabriel with International Fund for Animal Welfare, Linda Krueger and Andrea Heydlauff with Wildlife Conservation Society, Rhema Bjorkland and Sarah Foster with Project Seahorse, and Sandra Altherr with Pro Wildlife all generously prepared and reviewed the species data in this book. Their dedication and commitment to collaboratively communicating a meaningful conservation message to our community were deeply gratifying.

Thanks go to Michael McGuffin who was willing to take issue with and respect the subject matter in a way that helped focus the work. His partnership here has been appreciated. Thanks also go to James Kinney and Bill Schoenbart for assistance in copy editing, and to Hannah Stevens who steadfastly went the extra mile with the survey analysis. I am also grateful to IFAW, WCS, Robert Blancehtte, Eric Burkhart, Steven Foster, and Jean Giblette for permission to use their photographs.

I would also like to thank Andrew Gamble who demonstrated how a great teacher is continually learning. He was courageous enough to question the validity of traditional practices as they have been influenced by conservation imperatives and provided an opportunity for discussion on these issues in his classes. By his example, he has taught others to do the same.

And most of all, thanks to Mary Maruca who helped to conceive the book and provided support and inspiration along the way. As an editor, she has the uncanny ability to make changes that speak so eloquently from the very souls of all the species. We started as partners and have become close friends. For her, every word was a labor of love for the Earth.

I also would like to express my gratitude to a number of busy practitioners, authors, and teachers of Chinese medicine who provided practice-based information by responding to questions posed in an additional survey. Furthermore, they took time out to exchange and clarify ideas during several conference calls. Special thanks go to Andrew Ellis, Bob Flaws, Andrew Gamble, Ted Kaptchuk, Dagmar Ehling, and Ping Ping Zhang for their assistance. Also, I would like to acknowledge Ulrich Beyendorff, Li Jin, George Kitchie, Xiemei Lin, Xiaoyu Liu, Cathy McNease, Chuan Qin, Yiwen Su, and Zong Lan Xu for the information provided by their extra surveys.

I would also like to thank the 301 practitioners who filled out the first and broadest survey, which forms the heart of the practical herbal data included in this book. The time and commitment they gave inspired me during many of the long hours working on this project. These practitioners listed below provided the basis for species substitutions. Many wrote unsolicited comments expressing their support for these efforts. Others expressed their surprise at the number of endangered species in the survey and their lack of knowledge on this issue. There were many days (and nights) when I thought about all those comments, knowing that this book, however difficult to complete, would be worth it. Thank you all for your commitment, support and patience in the creation of this mutual work.

However, before I list practitioners, I would also like to express my gratitude for all of the animals and plants, and the Creator of all the incredible diversity we share on Earth. Darwin's "endless forms most beautiful" bestow their abundant gifts on us every day, offering us life, health, sustenance, inspiration; indeed—every needful thing.

Anderson, Cynthia
Ballentine, Anne
Barak, Anna
Bellis, Paul
Albertson, Kathie
Berks, Alex
Beyendorff, Ulrich
Bilton, Karen
Blair, Jennifer
Bloom, Phyllis
Blossom, Scott
Blunk, Rachel
Blunk, Scott
Boccino, Joan
Bock, David
Bonte, Andrenia
Bowler, Polina
Brameier, Ann
Brancato, Mark
Broder, Julie
Brown, Dee
Brown, Tamara
Burke, Colleen
Burke, Robert
Butler, Christopher
Cachia, Eric M.
Callihan, Marty
Cardinale, Chet
Cedar, JoAnne
Chain, Stephanie
Chalek, Mitchell
Chan, Adelle
Chang, Huei Mindy
Chao, Rose
Chasens, Steve
Chaudoir, Curry
Chen, Zhaoyang
Chen, Zhong
Chiasonn, Judy
Chiu, Yu-Wen
Choe, Jay
Ciao, Jing
Ciarcia, Carmen
Clark, Bryn
Cook, Amanda
Corbett, Nicole
Costello, Mark
Coughlin, Edward
Cronin, Keiko

Cuddy, Madir
Cui, Shugui
Cuneen, Peter
Czuckra, Susanna
Dagouret, Regina
Davida, Leah
Davis, Robert
Day, Heidi
DeBraal, Karen
DeMollts, Alexander
Devina, John
Dietz, Leada
Ding, Jihong
Dodson, Karen
Donnelly, John W.
Dovey, Michael
Doyle, Jacquelin
Eddy, Walter
Ehling, Dagmar
Evans, Scott
Fang, John
Fiedler, Ann
Fischer, Alan
Flaws, Bob
Ford, Charles
Fradkin, Mark
Frame, Jennifer
Franklin, Laura
Frosolone, Sue
Gabinelle, Regina
Gae, Jingyun
Gamble, Andrew
Gardner, Bridget
Gianarelli, Stephanie
Gilbert, Nan
Glick, Soma
Goldsmith, Ellen
Goldstein, Joshua
Goodwin, Frances
Gordon, Steven
Griffin, Adam
Grimes, Claudia
Grossberg, Dan
Grossman, Glenn
Gruber, Linda
Grymonnt, Taylore
Guan, Pingfei
Guo, Shaoqing
Han, Seung Hoon

Harvey, Brenton
He, Xuxin
Heller, Moshe
Henderson, Drew
Hermes, JoEllen Donahue
Hershey, Ron
Hiatt, Kathleen
Hong, Harry
Huang, Pao-Chin R.
Insung, Park
Jackson, Christina
Jacobs, Thad
Jarsky, Steven
Jeon, David H.
Jeong, Jae
Jin, Li
Jou, Lily
Jurata, Sheryl
Kang, Wanhink
Kaptchuk, Ted
Kauffman, Laura
Kaufman, Steven
Kellerman, Kathleen
Kent, Diane
Kim, Karen
Kim, Kimmy
Kim, Paul
Kinchen, Anne
Kirks, Susan E.
Kitchie, George
Kou, Mengke
Kuchinski, Lynn
Lahans, Tai
Lan Xu, Zong
Langer, Carol
Larmansingh, Rajput
Latham, Keith
LeCroy, Carol
Lee, Amy
Lee, Cathy
Lee, Hye Kyung
Lee, Lance
Lee, Lorna
Lepore, Gina
Lerner, David
Lewis, Dan-ning
Li, Mingxia
Li, Shen-Yi
Li, Xiaobin

Li, Xu
Lian, Nityano
Lindblad, Anne
Lipten, Gregory
LiQuin, Yang
Liu, Helen
Liu, Jade
Liu, Xuemei
Lu, Yuanming
Lynch, Patricia
Madison, James
Maghen, Deborah
Mangum, Jody
Marsder, Steve
Marshall, Anita
Max, Michael
Mc Gill, Reenah
McAdams, Martha
McCarron, Michael
McCrea, Tish
McElwain, David
McIntosh, Theresa
McLean, Bonnie
McNease, Cathy
Meadows, Mary
Michelitsch, Edward
Miller, Rebecca
Mince-Ennis, John
Mitchell, Craig
Mo, Zunli
Mogan, M.
Mok, Anne
Moon, Jae
Moriguchi, Miki
Murray, Maya
Music, Judith
Naimon, David
Netherland, Judith
Nicolson, Lisa
Norberg, Lyna
Nystrom, Amy
Oi Wu, Andrew
Olson, Kristina
Ou Li, Xiaoyu
Pabers, Christina
Pacik, Deborah
Paine, Carole
Paio, Yingai
Parolisi, Margie

Parson, Angela
Paten, Sabine
Pearl, James
Pendleton, Gray, Marsha
Perkins, Anne M.
Pettis, William
Pi, Wen Chiang
Pickup, Pam
Pirog, John
Pitman, Shelley
Potyk, Lisojeanne
Price, Dana
Quale, Kamala
Raes, Barbara
Raz, Anat
Redman, Laruel
Regli, Robert
Roberts, Lucy
Roberts, Ralph
Roesch, Barbara
Rosen, Ross
Rosenfarb, Andy
Roth, Julie
Royce, Wesley
Ryan, Mary Kay
Salinas, Michele
Schaefer, Cari
Scheuerman, Elizabeth
Schneider, Laurie
Schulte-Groecking, Heike
Scott, Justine
Sellers, Bettina
Shapiro, Phyllis
Sheir, Warren
Shinney, Robert
Siena, Dustin
Siokos, Susan
Smith, Lorraine
Snyder, Stephen
Spencer, Susan
Stape, Jill
Steinway, Frederick
Stephens, Eric
Su, Yong-Zhuang
Sweeney, P
Takei, Quinn
Tandias, Aman
Tear, Stephen
Thie, Julia

Thompson, Madhuma
Tian, Wen
Tibeau, Mark
Tierra, Lesley
Toker-Rojany, Rina
Tseng, Shuli
Ullmer, Patricia
Uno, M.
Uveges, Kristen
VanCott-Fein, Brett
Varis, Gila B.
Voss, Joe
Vouhardt, Isabeau
Walz, Jennifer
Wang, Min
Wang, Renee Xiaofan
Wang, Wendy
Wang, Yi
Watson, Ruth
Wayne, Michael
Wehinskey, Erika
Weinapple, Jane
Weinberg, Neil
Weissbuch, Brian Kie
Weissler, Patti
Williams, Galen
Wing, Judith
Wisgirda, Kristin
Wong, Ping
Wu, Andrew
Wu, Ping
Xiao, Kejian
Yagoobian, Fariba
Yang, Liqun
Yang, Xiu Juan
Yu, Wendy
Zang, Kris
Zdravkovic, Robin
Zeng, Donghong
Zhang, Minghua
Zhang, Pingping
Zhang, Yue
Zheng, Li
Zilavy, Pamela

Part I

Qi Bo replied...

*The power of individuated existence (te) is the presence of Heaven
   within my being.
Energy (qi) to become form is the presence of Earth within my being.
When power and energy stream and surge through one another, living
   beings arise....*

Chapter 1

PROLOGUE: "PRIMORDIAL" BEGINNINGS

Elizabeth Call

What could possess someone to write a book on conservation of Chinese medicinal plant and animal species? Well, I'll try to tell the short version, because the longer one began before I even heard of Chinese medicine. The shorter version begins not so long ago, when I first began to study acupuncture.

In those days, I, like so many others, recognized the potential application of the principles of Chinese medicine to numerous other professional fields. I could easily understand that everything is part of the Tao, or at least that everything responds to the principles inherent in it. I realized that Chinese medicine held the keys to a more profound understanding of nature. Indeed, as Qi Bo teaches in the *Ling Shu*, when the power of heaven and earth stream and surge through one another, living beings come forth. And in sharing these common origins, all living beings are interconnected and their life sacred.

When I first began to study acupuncture, the theories of Tao, Qi, Yin/Yang, Five Phases, Meridians, and Organs fascinated me. I could understand how these theories demonstrated the various ways in which everything in the body is connected. Chinese medicine did not separate organ systems from each other, from the individual, or from the environment. This gave me a model that reinforced my own pre-existing sense of the connections within and among all life. Through acupuncture practice, I found an outlet to express and to use this sense of connection in my life work. The concepts and theories of Chinese medicine became inscribed upon my heart.

After graduating from acupuncture school, I started studying Chinese herbs. Those classes felt less connected for me, just plain memorization, which I found far more difficult than I expected. Deep down, I felt no connection to studying the healing properties of these wonder-

3

ful plants and animals without knowing anything about them in their own right.

Essentially, I knew them as substances to "drain dampness" or "extinguish wind," rather than understanding how they came to be part of the "ten thousand things," how they emerged from the void to fill their unique place on Earth. The pictures I saw of the animals and plants in the texts rendered them flat and lifeless, far different from the animals and plants I observed in nature. Rather than connecting to these forms of life that supplied my medicine, I felt the disconnection of knowing the medical data and not the spirit—Heaven's presence so to speak—the essence of the plants and animals that provided health. Though I knew that learning is sometimes uninspired, I had always enjoyed the hard work of memorizing acupuncture information, because I felt connected to the "tools" —the acupuncture points—which I studied within the context of live human beings. It was different studying Chinese herbs. I persisted nonetheless.

When we began to study tiger bone, I remembered somewhere in the depths of my consciousness a vague niggling memory about tigers being endangered. This memory refused to go away, and I started to question the rationale for even studying such a substance. Then, I recalled studying the use of rhinoceros horn and bear bile earlier in the course. This made me wonder whether herb programs and texts were ignoring the foundation of the medicine – the animals and plants that make up the materia medica – in favor of the clinical distance that a "profession" confers. Part of me could acknowledge that perhaps these were the sensibilities of someone new to the medicine who had all the enthusiasm of a novice without the "sophistication" of "professional distance." Did I care too much? But these musings seemed right to me, and I continued to pursue such thoughts.

Specifically, I was struck by the fact that none of the texts referenced the endangerment of tigers and rhinos—or that their use was illegal. In addition, the use of bears and seahorses for medicinal purposes had just started receiving media attention, all of it negative. Some of my fellow students also expressed similar concerns.

Serendipitously, about that time, Heena Patel, an environmentalist who had worked on endangered species issues with the Chinese medicine community in Los Angeles, got in touch with me. Through her, I began working with the U.S. Fish and Wildlife Service, which found itself in the process of developing an outreach program on conservation issues for the Chinese medicine community. This was based on recommendations from CITES Tenth Conference of the Parties (CoP10) held in Zimbabwe in 1997.*

The direction of this new effort was inclusive. The group felt that conservation initiatives would be more effective if those to whom they were addressed had an opportunity to comment and actively participate. In previous years, I learned, some environmental groups took a more confrontational approach to conservation issues in Asia, excluding from the initial planning those whose practices they had wished to alter. Rather than continue to support separation between conservationists and practitioners, this new effort sought to build bridges of understanding and cooperation—to invite participation from all who had a stake in the discussion and its outcome.

At that point, I decided to devote my time to understanding the conservation issues surrounding our use of plant and animal medicines. I also chose to help make the needs of endangered species more visible in the Chinese medicine community. To this end, I started to work with and learn from the conservationists collaborating with the U. S. Fish and Wildlife Service.

At first I collaborated with conservationists to work locally with the professional community, raising awareness on biodiversity issues. I spoke on these subjects to several New York State acupuncture associations. As interest grew, we became involved at the national level, making presentations on endangered species protection and biodiversity at two meetings of the National Acupuncture and Oriental Medicine Alliance. I also wrote articles that appeared in national and local professional publications. As interest and support increased, it became apparent that a book would expand the availability of in-depth information to a larger audience.

This book is born from that need. It aims to provide students and practitioners with species-specific information, to give conservation efforts a "face" for our community, and offers readers a context for making informed decisions regarding the use of endangered species. During the book's creation, we polled the Chinese medicine community, so that their knowledge and expertise regarding the use of replacements could be represented here.

---

* Resolution Conf.10.19 (Rev. CoP12) Traditional Medicine, available at: www.cites. org/eng/res/10/10-19.shtml

In short, this project reached out for its inspiration to the heart and soul of the Chinese medicine community here in the United States, which, like its sister communities around the world, is an inheritor of the knowledge from which the medicine first arose. We believed that if the community could help find answers, it would respond by helping to rebuild the connections its ancestors recognized when they first learned and then refined the power of Chinese medicine to heal.

We also dared hope (and continue to do so), that this book could be used as a reference text in herbal medicine programs to educate new generations who, from the beginning, would then instill conservation into their own work and the training of those who come after them. Thus, the cycle of connections among all things that live and breathe in the breath of Heaven would continue. It is our conviction that relationships can be rebuilt among the plants, the animals, and the people who come to them for healing.

In other words, we felt that a conservation account for Chinese medicine needed to be written, and that the silence concerning the plight of endangered species needed to be broken, so that their stories might pour forth. Whatever your personal beliefs about conservation, endangered species, sustainable use, replacements, and all the other ten thousand issues related to these topics, we believe you will agree that the animals, the plants and their future on the Earth are compelling and worth knowing.

Author Henry Beston once described animals: "They are not brethren, they are not underlings, they are other nations, caught with ourselves in the net of life and time, fellow prisoners of a splendor and the travail of the earth." Perhaps once we understand animals and plants in their own right—as their own nations, to use Beston's term—we will begin to look differently at medicinal "substances." Hopefully, this will bring renewed respect, profound love, and commitment to the creatures and plants that comprise our materia medica—literally, our "roots."

Chapter 2
CONSERVATION FRAMEWORK: "ANATOMY OF A LOOM"

Elizabeth Call

Before any of us can decide how we really feel about new information, we need a frame of reference. Lacking this, we are something like a weaver without a loom, having no framework to support concepts and actions. One of the hardest things for me about researching this book was the learning curve it required before I could begin to use and understand the nuances of language specific to conservation.

Like every profession, conservation has terms and definitions pertinent to its activities—words common to its practice that help us understand why some actions are taken and others are not. Complicating this terminology is the international status of conservation efforts and the network of nations whose rules and regulations influence trade and, thereby, consumption.

A global conservation awareness is critical to the practice of Chinese medicine, because the raw materials necessary for our herbal remedies come primarily from the natural resources of other nations. So, to have some context for the conservation initiatives proposed in future chapters, an understanding of basic terms and an acquaintance with the responsibilities of various conservation organizations that influence species trade are useful to this discussion.

The definitions and descriptions that follow, offer only a brief overview of what is as complex and detailed a terminology as that used in Chinese medicine. I hope this brief summary provides sufficient information to understand certain forces that influence availability, cost, and, ultimately, the survival or extinction of the plants and animals that we use for healing. The following terms will be described:
- Chinese Medicine
- Identification and Nomenclature
- Sustainable Use

- Convention on International Trade in Endangered Species of Wild Flora and Fauna (CITES)
- World Conservation Union (IUCN)

....

CHINESE MEDICINE

I chose to use the term "Chinese medicine" throughout these chapters rather than the often used descriptor, "Oriental medicine". People in Japan, Korea and throughout Asia use the term "Chinese medicine" in their own language when referring to herbal usage based on the Chinese materia medica and the theories of Chinese medical practice. Although these countries and cultures have adapted Chinese medicine to their unique needs and sensibilities, they acknowledge the roots and source of this information by keeping "Chinese" as part of the phrase describing the medicine—something I also wanted to recognize. I purposely avoided referring to "Traditional Chinese Medicine," because this phrase connotes a stagnant quality to the practice rather than the dynamic, changing and evolving traits that are characteristic of Chinese medicine.

....

IDENTIFICATION AND NOMENCLATURE

It is important to note that the Pin Yin name of a medicinal substance may also include more than one species in a genus or in a different family. Knowing the difference is clinically relevant because sometimes an herb may be given to a patient labeled, for example as "*ban xia,*" which could be pinellia or typhonium. One of these plants may be more appropriate than another, but as long as the Latin binomial name is not given, it would be very difficult if not impossible to determine which plant may have been used (Leonard, 2003). This system has worked for centuries by acknowledging automatic substitutions that have a long tradition in Chinese medicine and allows for replacements based on local availability.

However, beyond the clinical confusion and possible tragedy caused by "sloppy herbal nomenclature" (Leonard, 2003), inaccurate labeling has had a huge impact on the conservation of endangered species used in Chinese medicine. A case in point is *e jiao*. No one knows exactly which species it comes from. We know it is fairly inexpensive, so we assume that it comes from domestic donkeys. But does it really? As we shall see it could also come from 3 wild species and some of their sub-species. Similar situations exist for bears, seahorses, turtles–the list goes on. How can trade and populations of these animals be effectively monitored under such conditions? Since we do not know, we should exercise caution by avoiding entirely, the use of these and other endangered species. It is important to keep these issues in mind as you read the species profiles for both animals and plants later in the text. Unfortunately, even if our profession were to demand stringent labeling, it would be far too late for many of the animal species covered here. However, if *e jiao* could be verified as being replaced by domestic cattle for example, and labeled as such, that would make good conservation sense.

....

SUSTAINABLE USE

The term "sustainable use" may be heard in almost any discussion involving conservation theories. Indeed, volumes have been written attempting to define the term and illustrate its practical application. I found it helpful, as I began to understand the meaning of this phrase, to survey the ways in which two major dictionaries defined *sustain*. Two examples are "to support, hold, or bear up from below; to keep up or keep going, as an action or process" (Random House); and "...to prolong; to support the life of" (Chambers Concise).

Using these definitions as a foundation for my understanding, I learned that the most straightforward use of the term refers to consuming resources in ways that support their continued accessibility for future generations. The definitions also suggest that resources should be managed and used in ways that support, prolong and uphold them for long-term use.

Opinions differ on what actually constitutes the sustainable use of resources. A fascinating overview of authors' differing definitions of "sustainability" is provided by the University of Reading website (www.ecifm.rdg.ac.uk/definitions.htm). Below are four quotes from that site, which capture core concepts germane to the sustainable use of species employed by Chinese medicine practitioners. Each quote is followed with a brief exploration of the concepts it presents that are fundamental to our understanding of the term.

1. Regulation and Enforcement

[Sustainable use is the] *Exploration into a tangled conceptual jungle where watchful eyes lurk at every bend.* O'Riorden (1985)

This quote suggests that regulatory forces are the "watchful eyes lurk(ing) at every bend." Indeed, a discussion of regulation and enforcement generally goes hand-in-hand with all references to sustainable use. Regulation is part of the framework that helps validate conservation programs. When regulations are not implemented appropriately, conservation initiatives are worth little more that the paper on which they were written.

International efforts to regulate wildlife trade presume several things (Oldfield, 2003):

- That sufficient desire and resources exist in range states (states where resources originate) to enforce trade regulations.

- That regulatory design recognizes and supports species' reproductive processes, and takes into consideration the complex forces driving trade in that species.

- That law enforcement efforts make the enforcement of wildlife trade provisions a priority, and that enforcement officers have the expertise and knowledge to inspect paperwork and shipments.

- That the penalties for illegal trade act as a deterrent.

However, these requirements do not always come together when trade regulations are developed to aid a particular species (Oldfield, 2003). When they do, a species can be more or less "sustainably" used. When they don't, a species may face rapid decline.

2. Valuation of Natural Resources

Lack of precise definition of the term 'sustainable development' is not all bad. It has allowed a considerable consensus to evolve in support of the idea that it is both morally and economically wrong to treat the world as a business liquidation (Daly, 1991).

Sustainable development is concerned with the development of a society where the costs of development are not transferred to future generations, or at least an attempt is made to compensate for such costs (Pearce, 1993).

Daly's statement suggests that wildlife resources are often treated as a "business liquidation" – "everything must go." Though such behavior often occurs when regulation is inconsistently applied, his statement also refers to another underlying attitude, particularly in developed nations, that natural resources are and should remain very cheap; their actual value is not reflected in the prices we pay. Indeed, some individuals erroneously promote the idea that wildlife and natural resources are limitless commodities (Arnold, 1996) and, therefore, as Pearce suggests, they "transfer the cost of development to future generations" through the after-effects of pollution, loss of biodiversity, and diminishment of ecosystem services. Some considerations to keep in mind when determining the actual value of wildlife and natural resources are these:

- The ecosystem services that natural areas provide to all of us, when they remain free of human disturbance. Wetlands, for example, filter toxins, cleanse water, and provide a buffer area for flood waters, certainly valuable ecosystem services in a world that is increasingly polluted and more prone to flooding due to global warming. If wetlands are drained for shopping malls, office parks and housing developments or destroyed for some other use, we all lose their ecosystem services, and the plants and animals that make their home in them disappear as well.

- That the needs of people in financially poor, but biodiversity-rich countries should be considered, with appropriate compensation for consuming their abundant resources. Often the poorest people are the most dependent on income from their wildlife resources (Oldfield, 2003), a recognition that is bringing fair trade issues to public consciousness.

- That the "side effects" from destructive industries need to be reflected in the price paid for their products. For example, in the U.S., conventional farming uses high amounts of herbicides, fungicides and pesticides to treat large areas planted with only one plant type (called a monoculture). The low cost of foods (and herbs) grown in this manner results from government subsidies paid to farmers. It does not reflect the substantial price all of us end up paying for the loss of biodiversity and the attendant health issues that occur due to water, soil, and air pollution, which impact human, animal, and plant systems.

3. Carrying Capacity

Sustainable development, sustainable growth, and sustainable use have been used interchangeably, as if their meanings were the same. They are not. Sustainable growth is a contradiction in terms; nothing physical can grow indefinitely. Sustainable use is only applicable to renewable resources. Sustainable development is used in this strategy to mean: improving the quality of human life whilst living within the carrying capacity of the ecosystems (IUCN, UNEP and WWF, 1991).

This statement recognizes that any given ecosystem will have what is known as "carrying capacity"—the amount of change the system can endure and still retain its inherent integrity or identity. This statement also suggests that, to preserve biodiversity, we must learn to live within the limits of our ecosystem. Unfortunately, humans find this harder and harder to achieve as our numbers increase, placing more demands on global trade in natural resources from distant ecosystems. One biologist (Eldridge, 1998) observes that:

- The immediate "side effects" of biodiversity loss may not be felt soon enough to help with policy changes, or forces driving species extinction may occur in a place removed from the actual site of loss, making it difficult to press for change.

- The loss of ecosystem services or biodiversity in one part of the world is not noticed in another part of the world, at least in the short term.

- The consequences of destroying an ecosystem or a species are not experienced until after the ecosystem/species is gone.

- The long-term effects of over-harvesting or poor land use policies are not taken into consideration, because they occur at locations distant from where most of us live our lives.

- And finally, global inequalities of people in poor countries have less bearing on our choices to use natural resources, because, again, these people live far away (Oldfield, 2003).

These factors—regulation, law enforcement, valuation, and carrying capacity—play a role in the sustainability of medicinal resources. The use of medicinal plants and animals is a worldwide activity, cutting across cultures and countries. How these factors are implemented around the world are often at the heart of conflicts between the needs of wildlife and the needs of humans.

Ultimately, sustainable use and development depend on our values, our relationship to nature (both local and global) and, particularly for us in the developed countries of the West, our ability to live with less and to grasp the far-reaching consequences of our daily choices. As conservationist and author Edward Abbey observed, "Unlimited growth is the ideology of a cancer cell."

....

CONVENTION ON TRADE IN ENDANGERED SPECIES OF WILD FLORA AND FAUNA (CITES)

The idea of an international treaty that could help ensure the survival of wild species in global trade first came under discussion in the 1960s. Countries came to an agreement on the importance of conservation because "...wild fauna and flora in their many beautiful and varied forms are an irreplaceable part of the natural systems of the earth which must be protected for this and the generations to come."* After various efforts to develop a treaty, CITES entered into force on July 1, 1975.

CITES is defined in this way:

- *CITES is an international agreement between Governments. Its aim is to ensure that international trade in specimens of wild animals and plants does not threaten their survival.*

- *Because the trade in wild animals and plants crosses borders between countries, the effort to regulate it requires international cooperation to safeguard certain species from over-exploitation. CITES was conceived in the spirit of such cooperation. Today, it accords varying degrees of protection to more than 30,000 species of animals and plants, whether they are traded as live specimens, fur coats, or dried herbs.*

- *CITES is an international agreement to which States (countries) adhere voluntarily. States that have agreed to be bound by the Convention ('joined' CITES) are known as Parties.*

- *Although CITES is legally binding on the Parties – in other words they have to implement the Convention – it does not take the place of national laws. Rather it provides a framework to be respected by each Party, which has to adopt its own domestic legislation to make sure that CITES is implemented at the national level.*

---

* Text of the Convention, www.cites.org

- *Not one species protected by CITES has become extinct as a result of trade since the Convention entered into force and, for many years, CITES has been among the largest conservation agreements in existence, with now 169 Parties.**

Each species subject to CITES regulation is monitored; all import, export, re-export, and introduction of species identified in international trade by member countries has to be authorized through a system of permits. Each party to CITES must have a Management Authority to administer this system and a Scientific Authority to advise on the consequences of trade to the survival of the species. Therefore, while CITES lists protected species and expects parties to implement the Convention, it does not specify exactly *how* each country implements the treaty, only that it must accomplish the agreed-upon results. CITES leaves internal domestic legislation to individual countries, though it may sometimes bring international pressure to bear on specific countries for wildlife trade abuses.

There are three Appendices which denote the level of protection a species regulated under CITES should receive:

- *Appendix I includes species threatened with extinction. Commercial trade in these species is prohibited.*

- *Appendix II includes species not necessarily threatened with extinction, but those for which trade among nations is regulated to ensure species survival as well as the species' continued availability in trade.*

- *Appendix III contains species protected in at least one country, which has asked other CITES Parties for assistance in controlling the trade.*

Trade in CITES-listed species is monitored in accordance with decisions made by member countries at triennial Conference of the Parties (CoP). Enforcement of CITES depends primarily on the law enforcement capacity of individual member countries, as well as the support that Interpol and other enforcement organizations may provide for the prosecution of international wildlife crime.

Where the line is drawn for the ability of a species to be traded catalyzes the debate over what constitutes "sustainable use". As practitioners, we advise our patients to prevent disease before it starts. This philosophy is a hallmark of Chinese Medicine. Can we apply this precautionary approach for maintaining human health to the health of ecosystems? In

---

* As of March 2006, www.cites.org

other words, do we hastily trade a species and wait to find out the ecological consequences, or do we err on the side of caution to avoid trade in a CITES-listed species for which data is insufficient?

....

The World Conservation Union (IUCN)

Begun in 1948, the World Conservation Union, officially known as the International Union for the Conservation of Nature and Natural Resources or IUCN, "...brings together 111 government agencies, more than 800 non-governmental organizations, and some 10,000 scientists and experts from 181 countries in a unique worldwide partnership."* These groups and individuals volunteer their services to IUCN's six global commissions. The organization calls this their "Green Web" of partnerships that has "generated environmental conventions, global standards, scientific knowledge and innovative leadership."

This "Green Web" offers "partnerships, knowledge, innovations and action," providing people and institutions the support they need to conserve ecosystems, protect threatened or endangered species, and promote sustainable use of resources, among other things. IUCN also monitors the "state of the world's species in the IUCN Red List," and provides policy advice and technical support to the CITES Secretariat. Thus, CITES monitors trade, and IUCN, through its Species Survival Commission (SSC), monitors the species.

The IUCN Red List provides the world "with the most objective, scientifically-based information on the current status of globally threatened biodiversity." IUCN promotes the Red List as a foundation for making "informed decisions about preserving biodiversity from local to global levels." The Red List profoundly influences decisions made by CITES regarding a given species.

The IUCN Species Survival Commission Red List Program has the following objectives:

- *To assess, in the long term, the status of a selected set of species;*
- *To establish a baseline from which to monitor the status of species;*
- *To provide a global context for the establishment of conservation priorities at the local level; and*

---

* As of March 2006, www.iucn.org

- *To monitor, on a continuing basis, the status of a representative selection of a species (as biodiversity indicators) to cover all the major ecosystems of the world*

To carry out its objectives, the IUCN Red List goes by a set of "Operating Principles," which further clarifies the goals of the Red List as follows:

- *The Red List should be available to all potential users;*
- *The process of undertaking status assessments of species should be clear and transparent;*
- *The listings of species should be based on correct use of the categories and criteria and should be open to challenge and correction, based on the categories and criteria, when necessary;*
- *All status assessments of species should be correctly documented and supported by the best scientific information available;*
- *The Red List should exist as an electronic version on the World Wide Web to be updated once a year;*
- *To publish an analysis of the findings of the Red List approximately every five years; and*
- *The information on the web should be interactive, providing a mechanism to allow people (through appropriate procedures) to provide information for consideration when updating the list.*

In keeping with the preceding principles, anyone can do a search of all the species discussed in this book. In fact, I suggest that those who study, teach and recommend herbs should use the search capabilities of the Red List to help put their work into perspective.

....

PUTTING IT ALL TOGETHER

As we can see, issues surrounding the trade in species are at the heart of the work involving both CITES and IUCN, with these organizations applying their interpretation of "sustainable use" to species conservation. Both organizations profoundly influence each other and bring their authority to bear on the global economics associated with the consumption of thousands of species. So, with this terminology as the framework for subsequent discussions, let us turn our attention to the role Chinese medicine plays in the dance of biodiversity and the web of life.

---

* www.redlist.org

SOURCES:

Arnold R (1996) Overcoming Ideology. In *A Wolf in the Garden*, Rowman & Littlefield Publishers, Inc., Maryland VA.

Convention on International Trade in Endangered Species of Wild Fauna and Flora. As of 2006 available at www.cites.org.

Eldredge N (1998) *Life in the Balance: Humanity and the Biodiversity Crisis.* Princeton University Press, Princeton NJ.

Leonard DB and Newman R (2003) Everything You Know Is Wrong. *Acupuncture Today, 4: 8.*

Oldfield S (2003) Introduction In *The Trade in Wildlife: Regulation for Conservation.* S. Oldfield (ed.). Earthscan Publications Ltd., London, UK/Sterling VA.

University of Reading, Environmental Challenges in Farm Management. Agriculture Policy and Development: Definitions. As of 2006 available at: http://www.ecifm.rdg.ac.uk/definitions.htm.

World Conservation Union. As of 2006 available at: http://www.iucn.org/en/about.

World Conservation Union. As of 2004, available at: http://www.redlist.org/info/programme.

Part II

Thus, the origins of life are the essential yin and yang.
When these two essences collide and couple this is the expression of life
  force or spirit.
That which follows the comings and goings of the spirit is called the hun
  (yang aspect).
That which accompanies the exits and entrances of the essence is called
  the po (yin aspect).

Chapter 3

Introduction:
Chinese Medicine and the Web of Life

Elizabeth Call

During my tenure as Dean of Clinical Training at Tri-State College of Acupuncture, I had the opportunity to interview numerous prospective students. I found that most of them desired to learn and practice Chinese medicine because they sought an alternate way to reach out to other human beings in need, using a different philosophy and skills than those we in the West have come to know as "medicine."

The desires of those students echoed my own aspirations when I first came to study Chinese medicine, and I suspect they are consistent for the majority of students and practitioners in the West. While we appreciate the wondrous technological advances modern Western medicine provides, from specific in-depth diagnostics to high-tech procedures that save a life on the brink, we also have experienced some frustration with the limits of such technology.

Practitioners of Chinese medicine appreciate the "holistic" approach, which provides individualized treatment and can acknowledge and incorporate aspects of a patient's body, mind, and spirit. After many years of clinical practice and concern for the environment, I, like others (Jarrett, 1998), am convinced that aspects of our holistic paradigm can be extended beyond their clinical applications to species conservation. Indeed as you shall see, some aspects of the philosophy of Chinese medicine could be used by conservationists to more effectively carry out their work of rebuilding healthy populations of plants and animals.

The Differences Between "Yin" (East) and "Yang" (West)

The science and philosophy that form the basis of Chinese medicine differ greatly from that of Western science. Yet these systems at opposite

21

ends of the spectrum can complement one another in efforts to support species conservation. Each discipline has its own strengths and weaknesses. From our clinical experience, we know that sometimes a patient needs both Eastern and Western medicine treatments to achieve the best effect.

I believe this also holds true for conservation. To best appreciate the assistance that both Eastern and Western modes of thought could bring to complex issues associated with global conservation, let us first consider their differences.

In general, Western science excels in the *quantitative, structural* analysis of objects (Jarrett, 1998). This contribution of its investigative technologies has alerted us to species decline and helped us assess data, reinforcing the significance of biodiversity to environmental and human health. Western science gives us facts about an individual species, while Chinese science excels at studying and assessing the *qualitative* and *functional* relationships *between* things (Jarrett, 1998). Applied to conservation, Chinese philosophy would focus more on the *functional relationship* of a species to its environment and the *quality* of that environment, rather than the individualized physical structures that comprise the species or the environment in which it lives.

Further, Western science generates an extraordinary amount of detailed information, fueling the creation of specialized fields of study, such as biology. It excels at discovering vast storehouses of facts and statistics that apply to very specific areas. However, it has no paradigm for integrating and understanding how these facts relate back to the "higher order" (Jarrett, 1998). Nor does it have a model for integrating the statistics and facts *between* specialized fields of study.

These are areas in which Chinese medicine can excel, thanks to our understanding of Yin/Yang and Five Phase theories. These principal theories help practitioners integrate signs and symptoms gathered from a patient into a larger understanding of that patient's life. They help define relationships among signs, symptoms, and the environment—both social and natural—in which the patient lives. As such, they may be helpful additions to the healing modalities used by conservationists to influence the well being of the global environment. Indeed, what are conservationists but healers of a slightly different order? Their patients may not be humans, but perhaps more critically, they are the plants and animals with whom we share the surface of the Earth. As may be expected, however, the paradigms available to Eastern and Western scientists differ vastly, particularly in the ways they view the role of humans in relationship to the natural order.

....

THE MECHANISTIC WORLDVIEW

René Descartes, a profound thinker living in the seventeenth century, radically influenced development of the scientific method as it is practiced today. Descartes believed he could understand a phenomenon *only* if he used rational thought and consciously avoided applying information derived from any one of his five senses. His statement, "I think, therefore I am" sent waves of change through his generation as old paradigms fell, and new ones took their place. Indeed, his observations created enduring reverberations for future generations of thinkers. His declaration suggested that humans existed apart from their environment. Because we think—exercise rationality—we are defined as living beings. Because Descartes could not conceive of thought as an attribute of plants and animals, he did not consider them to be alive in the same way we are. Instead, he regarded the universe as a machine comprised of increasingly smaller parts. This and similar concepts inherent in Cartesian thought laid the foundation for our modern mechanistic view of life.

Western culture teaches that science gathers information and finds "truth" through laboratory research, accompanied by specific experiments. The common belief is that scientists research something out of curiosity and in the spirit of pure exploration, which has been frequently shown to be a myth (Channel, 2004). Mechanistic philosophy has so thoroughly permeated science that scientists are starting to put forth a perception that the universe can best be understood in terms of "…information and computation, concepts that arise from the artificial world of technology…" (Channel, 2004). This extends into the modern era Descartes' idea of the world as a machine. In fact, observers of science and scientists themselves report that "science" is more like "applied technology" since much scientific research is influenced and supported by industry, which suppresses research results and ideas that question the status quo (Channel, 2004; Campbell, 2006). In addition, "science" promulgates the belief that it is capable of "fixing" anything and aims to manipulate natural processes either to improve on their original configurations or to intervene in such a way that demonstrates little trust in the forces that sustain life.

In short, the Cartesian worldview presumes that anyone seeking "truth" will not only ignore their five senses but the very thing that infuses us with life: our spirit. Therefore, "applied technology" suggests we cannot come to "truth" if we listen to our hearts and minds simultaneously, connecting on a deep level with a subject, whether it is a plant, an animal or a human. Such actions could limit our access to "truth" and undermine the validity of our observations. We are expected to be objective—to not get personally involved.

THE INTEGRATED WORLDVIEW

In general, Chinese medicine takes a more organic view of nature, holding that physical, cognitive, and spiritual reality are one (Jarrett, 1998). It proposes that the universe is not a machine or a computer, but rather that it expresses an essential directive force that permeates all life and unifies it into an inextricable web. Humans are understood to be a representation of nature's unity, rather than a separate fragment. Within this context, humans are not isolated from nature or its influences. We learned early in our studies of Chinese medicine that the bodies of humans incorporate all the forces of nature—dampness, dryness, heat, cold or wind, for example—and that treatment balances these forces within the patient. In fact, we were taught that to really understand various influences and their action within our patients, we must also be keen observers of the same forces in nature (Flaws, 1989).

The process that infuses Chinese medicine seeks to work with nature, complement body processes, and reconnect and integrate the physiological and psychological possibilities within the entire being (Jarrett, 1998). Most Chinese medicine practitioners actively use their five senses in patient evaluation. Every student knows "The Four Exams," which rely on looking, asking, listening/smelling, and touching. The organic approach of Chinese medicine fosters the use of intuition, integrated with critical thinking, academic knowledge, and practical experience.

Unfortunately, a split from nature also has occurred in Chinese medicine, the philosophy of which is applied only in clinical practice. For example, some Chinese doctors justify their use of endangered animals, because they insist that people are more important than animals (Parry-Jones, Vincent, 1998). This position ignores the contributions of nature to *people* and wedges people and nature in conflicting opposition. So, while these individuals do not consider humans to be isolated from nature, they place humans in an elevated position (much like in the West), which maintains their distance from the web of life.

Both Eastern and Western attitudes toward people and nature suggest the separation of Yin and Yang—an energetic trajectory that leads to ill health or death in humans and portends the same when applied to wildlife species.

....

THE IMPORTANCE OF BIODIVERSITY

People around the Earth depend on more than 40,000 species of animals, plants, fungi, and microbes each and every day for the necessities of life (Eldredge, 1998). In fact, the global commerce in wildlife and their by-products is estimated to be 159 billion dollars a year (Cook, et. al., 2002). The great quantity and diversity of nature provides us with shelter, food, medicine, and all our comforts, as well as the ecosystem services that influence the quality of our air, water, food, and medicine. Nature's diversity also provides important esthetic benefits. The loss of species on our Earth is so extensive that we are now in the midst of the "Sixth Extinction," and it threatens to rival the five previous mass extinctions the Earth has seen.

The troubling thing about the Sixth Extinction is that species are being lost forever before we even know they exist (Eldredge, 1998). Most biologists accept E. O. Wilson's estimate of 27,000 species becoming extinct every year. That translates to three species lost every hour (Eldredge, 1998).

On the other hand, we are reminded rather sardonically that some *"... species are bucking the trend towards extinction. In 1953 there were about 2.5 billion people; today there are 6 billion. Ensuring other species keep their living space is not sentimental. It is the only way we shall survive. Extinction, whatever Steven Spielberg says, really is forever. The web is unraveling"* (Kirby, 2005).

So what does the potential extinction of species, which may or may not be used in medicine, mean to the healing arts? It is significant to note that more than half—57 percent—of the top 150 brand name western medical drugs prescribed for the first nine months of 1993 "contained at least one compound now or once derived or patterned after compounds derived from biological diversity" (Grifo, 1997). Out of Earth's approximately 250,000 plant species, however, no more than 5 percent have been studied to evaluate their therapeutic potential. Nevertheless, scientists estimate that we may be losing one plant species per day (Center for Biodiversity and Conservation, 1997).

Loss of biodiversity not only jeopardizes the supply of raw materials with which to develop new drugs—such as the cancer drug taxol, which comes from the yew tree—it also creates conditions supporting fewer models for medical research (Center for Biodiversity and Conservation, 1997). For example, scientists working to address the increased resistance of bacteria to common antibiotics are studying the secretions of certain amphibians (Grifo, 1997). This model for addressing resistance would be unavailable if there were no amphibians, a group that has suffered significant species loss during the past 10 years.

In fact, loss of biodiversity affects all systems of medicine, potentially limiting their ability to respond to new diseases and develop new treatments. Because traditional medicine systems rely exclusively on products from nature, it follows that losing biodiversity would also affect these systems.

In recent years, the link between Chinese medicine and the loss of certain species has become more apparent. Certainly, the most obvious losses are those within the animal kingdom. However, many wild plants are also over-harvested for use in all traditions of herbal medicine. For centuries, Chinese medicine has used substances derived from a variety of animals and plants. Traditionally, these substances were obtained from wild species, and for centuries their use was relatively sustainable. That is no longer the case, with millions more people on the planet and a sharp increase worldwide in the use of traditional medicines. The following statistics help put the demands placed on medicinal species into perspective.

China has about 30,000 species of vascular plants, comprising about 10 percent of the world's total plant species (Raven, 2001). Approximately 10,000 to 12,000 of these species have a history of medicinal use. Indeed, in the late 1990s, an encyclopedia on Traditional Chinese Medicine published in Shanghai listed 9,000 medicinal species (Raven, 2001; Hui, 2001).

Only about 15 percent of medicinal plants come from cultivated sources. This fact suggests significant concern over China's ability to sustain the use of wild plants in the future as demand increases in world markets (Raven, 2001). Indeed, the prospect for survival of many species of flora and fauna in China is fairly grim: "Approximately one out of every four species of plants and animals in China is of concern regarding its conservation status…." (Raven, 2001).

We cannot over-estimate the impact the global market has on medicinal species when we consider statistics from the World Health Organization (WHO). The WHO reports that up to 80 percent of Africans use traditional medicine for primary health care. In China, 30 to 50 percent of all medicinal consumption comes from traditional Chinese medicine. In Germany, 90 percent of the population at some point has used a natural remedy. In the United Kingdom, approximately 230 million U.S. dollars are spent annually on alternative medicine (WHO, 2003). In the United States consumers spend approximately $4 billion each year on herbal remedies (*Nutrition Business Journal*, 2004).

Although the human requirement for resources is not new, the quantities now needed are beyond imagining. Cultivation meets some of this need, but wild species continue to be used in astounding quantities, making sustainable consumption more difficult, but certainly that much more important.

While loss of habitat contributes to the decline of medicinal species and threatens their long-term survival, unsustainable harvesting plays a significant role. This is particularly the case in those regions where biodiversity is especially rich, and people are also the poorest members of the world's community. Here, the people and their resources are preyed upon by powerful and affluent forces.

Perhaps the most sobering fact is that these effects are not localized, as was once the case. A few vanishing plants and animals in one bioregion may not be considered cause for alarm, but when extinction threatens plants and animals everywhere on Earth as it does now, the need for action becomes critical. In order to stem the tide, each person, community, profession, industry, and nation must take action to support biodiversity in every way possible.

Thus, it follows that the profession of Chinese medicine has a large part to play in the survival of the species referenced in its materia medica, as well as in the preservation of its medicine for future generations.

....

Insulating Ourselves From Nature

Because we no longer use resources restricted to our local ecosystems (Eldredge, 1998), we humans have become less connected to the natural world and less cognizant of its importance in our everyday lives. This is especially true for practitioners of Chinese medicine outside of China, who are not able to see the medicinal plants they use growing wild in open areas or being cultivated on the farm in the next township. Roots, leaves, grasses, and tubers simply show up on our doorsteps courtesy of parcel post, bearing little or no resemblance to the living plants from which they came.

In the West, we do not have a system in place that encourages us to question where these plants come from. For us, they simply *are*—bulk herbs or prepared medicine products to restore health, but unconnected to their origins in an ecosystem. By living outside the ecosystems that provide our medicine, we know little of the supply chain through which these medicinals reach us, a condition making it more difficult to initiate significant change for conservation.

On the other hand, because of the magnitude of global trade and our dependency on natural resources from all over the world, humans are becoming an increasingly interconnected species. However, we have yet to extend this idea of interconnection to the global ecosystems that are the foundation for this tremendous diversity (Eldredge, 1998).

....

EMBRACING NATURE

As we have been taught, Chinese medicine evolved partly through the influence of Taoism, a philosophy that recognizes the interconnectedness and interdependence of all life forms. Indeed, as a practice, we acknowledge that the relationship *between* "things" is as important as the "thing" itself. The theories of Yin and Yang and the Five Phases demonstrate this relationship. Although some Westerners continue to dismiss these concepts, the idea that all "things" are interconnected is not as unfamiliar as it once was, thanks, in part, to the work of Western-trained scientist and philosopher James Lovelock.

Lovelock explains the functioning of Earth processes in terms of the Gaia hypothesis (Lovelock, 1995). This hypothesis regards the Earth as a self-regulating organism with the ability to maintain conditions optimum for its well-being, dependent on the symbiotic relationship between all life forms on the Earth and the Earth itself. Lovelock's research demonstrates that a deeply connected relationship exists among all levels of life—even the growth of the smallest plankton in the oceans has an impact on whether or not cloud cover develops, rains fall, and fish feed.

Lovelock brings scientific methodology to a view of the living planet that is Taoist in its essence. He confirms through scientific exploration what the first Taoists recognized by observing the passage of seasons and the response of living things to these cycles.

Therefore, in our tendency to draw hard and fast lines between ecosystems and species, and the impact of human activity on them, we sometimes overlook the intricately interwoven ways in which we are all connected beyond the economics of world trade. Now, more than ever, we need, as Lovelock said, "…to formulate a new, or perhaps revive a very ancient, concept of the relationship between the Earth and its biosphere."

We need to rely less on human systems and human understanding and place a greater value on Gaia, the Biosphere, the Tao, whatever we choose to call it. However, we must do more to remove humans from the center of our worldview and put the magnificent Earth in that place (Lavigne, 2004). This will encourage the creation of human systems that adapt to and are harmonious with nature. When we force ecosystems and species to fit into economic arrangements that do not or will not take their needs into account, we end up pushing them beyond their ability to regenerate.

The Chinese language gives us some guidance. The character "脉" (Mai) signifying nature's web of life also includes in its meaning the meridian system. This is our own web of life, which supports the sound functioning of our bodies, suggesting perhaps that the intricate, harmonious systems that make up a healthy "web" for us provide the same function for all of nature.

....

The Saga of The Saiga

Every student and practitioner of Chinese medicine has memorized the use of *ling yang jiao*— saiga antelope horn. Most of us probably recall the picture of this odd looking antelope with its bulging nose and side-placed eye staring at us dolefully from our materia medicas. What we did not learn was that, in the early 1990s, the saiga antelope numbered well over a million animals in the steppes of central Asia, and that today, the population has crashed to a frightening 30,000—a fall of *97 percent* (Pearce 2003). In a perverse twist that underscores the interconnectedness of things, the devastation of the saiga is intimately tied with the fate of the rhinoceros.

The late 1980s spelled disaster for African rhinoceroses as their numbers plummeted, due in large part to poaching for Chinese medicine use. In a desperate effort to save rhinoceroses, World Wildlife Fund (WWF) supported research to find an effective replacement for rhino horn at the Chinese University of Hong Kong (Ellis, 2004).

This research showed saiga horn to be an effective substitute. The results were published in the *Journal of Ethnopharmacology*. In 1991, WWF started to encourage Chinese medicine practitioners to replace rhino horn with saiga horn. In 1992, the UN Environment Programme enlisted a prominent WWF ecologist to convince pharmacies throughout Asia to substitute saiga horn for rhino horn. By 1998, to the surprise and dismay of conservationists, the saiga population had dropped to 600,000, reduced to almost half its 1993 size (Pearce, 2003). With the Chinese medicine community supporting the direction of WWF, and the legal and inevitably illegal supply chains for saiga antelope in place, the central Asian saiga populations continued to fall to their present-day size of approximately 30,000, most of which are females (Pearce, 2003).

How could this have happened, especially with experts, researchers, and scientists confirming the results? To answer this question, we may remember that science does not have a paradigm to integrate its findings "to the higher order" of understanding. Thus, it lacked a blueprint to properly integrate the facts that researchers uncovered. Without such a paradigm, conservationists were unable to take into account the unique characteristics of the saiga antelope, the ecosystem in which it lives, and how it is acted upon by the local humans, as well as the political situation of the countries providing habitat for the saiga. In short, the "scientific facts" were evaluated in a vacuum and not integrated into the higher order.

The Higher Order

Call it sour grapes or maybe "hindsight is 20/20," but the "saga of the saiga" demonstrates that conservationists and scientists could incorporate aspects of the Chinese medicine paradigm. We could share awareness of patterns that might enable them to project future actions onto a template, giving them a larger, more expansive view. In addition, using models from Chinese medicine will help conservationists in their work in Asia, since people from different cultures tend to be more responsive to changes explained within their own contextual understanding. This in turn helps them feel ownership for the solutions.

Almost every practitioner of Chinese medicine uses some aspect of the Five Phase (or Five Element) theory to analyze information gained from a patient. Five Phase theory helps us understand how symptoms are inter-related and whether or not the organs or meridians are working together. It is a model for balancing the interactions and dynamics among the major forces in the body. As we recall, the phases generate and control one another, helping us integrate information "to the higher order."

Five Phase theory, when applied to conservation, is not a literal one-to-one correspondence as it is in Chinese medicine. However, the intention of the model fits nicely into a conservation framework. It can be used to balance the forces that impact the environment and as a safeguard to prevent the decline of species. What we might call the "Five Phases of Conservation" as applied to the saiga might look like this:

Phase One, the species: Each species has unique behavioral and physical characteristics that are considered when administrators make policy changes. In this case, the tendency for saiga antelopes to startle easily and, when frightened, huddle together without running—the "wagon circle" effect (Ellis, 2004)—would have been information considered by a practitioner when interviewing or collecting research information about the species. A Five Phase assessment might have noted that only the male antelope sports horns. This detail would have alerted us to the easy targets the animals would become if they stood still and huddled together as a defense mechanism. Another important detail that might have influenced outcomes is the animals' lifespan. The saiga live only 3 or 4 years, making it crucial to constantly maintain the appropriate ratio of males to females to ensure reproduction for the long-term health of the herd (Ellis, 2004).

Saiga antelope males usually have a harem of 12-30 females—a polygynous system. In a curiously unscientific anthropomorphisation of male saiga behavior, scientists presumed that in such systems males will mate with all available females. In this case, however, as saiga numbers later demonstrated, a point comes where the males cannot keep up (Roach, 2003). It became apparent that males do not mate successfully if they have too many females in their harem. The breaking point falls somewhere between 36 and 106 females (Milner-Gulland, et. al. 2003; Roach, 2003). So, as poachers easily used motorcycles to surround the herd and kill the males with high-powered weapons, the numbers of females per harem increased, but the mating did not. Thus, the population of the herd could not renew itself.

Phase Two, the ecosystem in which the species lives: Each ecosystem has its defining characteristics that need to be weighed to ensure that outside pressure does not jeopardize its balance. Saiga antelopes live in remote desert environments, which increased the ease with which the animals could be slaughtered. No trees impeded poachers, who had easy access to the area. Also, the saigas' range is vast, making it nearly impossible for countries with these species to protect herds and enforce regulations against poaching.

Phase Three, the local community: This includes how local people relate to and use a species and the value they place on it as part of the ecosystem in which they live. In this Phase, we recognize how critical the local community becomes to the survival of a species. Humans and animals have to live together—a basic tenet of conservation—if both are to survive. The value of this phase is the opportunity for the local community to exercise self determination in their resource stewardship. This might include outside groups championing local initiatives and assisting them in realizing their vision.

Phase Four, national and international laws: The abilities of a nation and the international community to conserve shared resources in ways that ensure their sustainability reflect our collective faith in the future. Laws are the tools through which society promotes the continuation of biodiversity and the successful regeneration of life.

Generally speaking, rules and regulations have been promulgated with the conservation of saiga antelope in mind. Hunting bans were put in effect when saiga numbers dropped. Fear of their possible extinction prompted CITES Parties to list saiga on Apprendix II. Currently the government of Mongolia is working with local shepherds to conserve the species. National census data has been collected to monitor the animals' biological status. However, the vulnerability in this phase occurs at the enforcement level, which often lacks capacity to keep poachers at bay.

Phase Five, global civil society: This phase includes individuals from the grass roots level to professional organizations, corporations and everyone else in between. These individuals and groups conduct activities as diverse as research, advocacy and education, financial and programmatic support for maintaining the healthy balance in and among ecosystems. This phase encourages everyone to be good stewards to all living beings wherever they are—next door or half a world away. The wild fauna and flora in their varied forms are the catalysts that help us find our rightful place on the Earth we share.

Therefore, an integrated assessment would take into consideration and weigh carefully, the information gathered from each of the Five Phases. If vulnerabilities appeared in any of the phases, the practitioner would prescribe accordingly. In the case of the saiga, the greatest vulnerabilities appeared to be at the species, community and national level. Failure to see the implications of these details and to prescribe changes based on reviewing significant details within the larger context helped undermine the species and send it down the slippery slope towards disappearance in the wild.

As Chinese medicine so sensibly teaches, it is always much easier to maintain health by wise and prudent living, rather than try to rescue a desperately ill patient. The rescue is also more costly and may have unforeseen residual effects. Analyzing the status of species within their environments, using Five Phase theory, might provide another tool to help ensure that the web of life in the glorious diversity of nature remains a part of our lives and our medicine for generations to come. To bring the concept into full circle, we can recall that in the early Chinese Five Phase theory, there were four phases with the Earth in the center!

....

THE DANCE OF YIN (EAST) AND YANG (WEST)

Chinese medicine practitioners have the ability to model for conservationists the art of bringing our five senses, hearts, and philosophy to species conservation, just as we would to any patient who walks through our clinic door. Western science has given us compelling reasons to engage in species conservation. In truth, extinctions will affect everyone, regardless of paradigm, culture, ethnicity, or country, making it imperative for us to bring our differing skills together to solve environmental problems. This will enable us to leave behind a world we would be proud to pass on to our children.

Chinese medicine and western science could draw on the effective components of their paradigms to benefit species conservation. Such a hybrid might contain elements of "deep ecology," which advocates that humans and nature are one, that we approach nature with humility, and that all of nature has intrinsic worth (Pepper, 1996). However, this new East/West Paradigm would also rely on scientific understanding to increase the artfulness with which conservation initiatives are applied, something that deep ecology does not tend to do (Pepper 1996). The East/West Paradigm would demonstrate the advantages of deep ecology and environmental science by incorporating the best aspects of both. It would also improve on them, thanks to its ability to integrate information to the higher order as noted above. In addition, it would apply techniques particular to Chinese medicine—the ability to evaluate situations, events, and phenomena on an individualized basis.

Applying Five Phase theory effectively does require tangible practice. It also necessitates recognition that the theory offers more than inspiration and guidance—that it actually can be put to practical use in the conservation arena. Consider, for example, the tendency of environmentalists to focus conservation efforts on individual species. Instead of recognizing the role of a species within its ecosystem and in relationship to plants and animals co-existing with it, they tend to spotlight animals with charismatic public appeal in order to attract public support. This may or may not be good conservation. From the Taoist perspective, true conservation is initiated by recognizing the role of the species within the context of their community. Unfortunately, although Taoism recognizes that humans are a reflection of the Earth, it does not acknowledge their need to actively contribute to the Earth's well-being. Indeed, the recognition that human beings should attend to the health of our planet is more representative of Western conservation practices.

....

WHAT DOES THIS MEAN FROM THE FIVE PHASE PERSPECTIVE?

What we need is an integrated agenda that allows groups with mutual interests to unite on issues for the common good. The development of this book provides such a model. Conceived as a cooperative effort among Chinese medicine practitioners and conservationists, it has been a collaborative enterprise in the best sense. We hope that such collaboration is only the beginning—not only for the benefits it will engender for the medicine, but also for the plants and animals, and, ultimately, we hope, for the web of life.

As practitioners, we necessarily focus on the health of our patients. But we also need to keep an eye on the health of the planet, the foundation of our existence. To that end, this book not only provides information about individual species whose trade is regulated, it also examines replacements, law enforcement concerns, cultivation issues, and possible trends. These themes form the essence of this book and the paradigm for change it offers.

....

WHAT IS OUR COMMITMENT?

Chinese medicine is proud of its significant history and relatively unbroken tradition. We often allude to our 2,000-year-plus past to help policy makers and patients alike respect our work. Our actions now will lay the foundation for the continuation of certain medicinal species for the next 2,000 years.

Are we up to the challenge? Do we have a commitment to the future? Are we willing to participate in partnerships? Does our profession have the strength of character to acknowledge the problem and be receptive to outside influence? Can our profession in turn influence and challenge other disciplines, particularly environmental scientists, biologists and policy makers, to start looking at the relationship *among* animals, plants, their environment and people, and the economies humans have created? Can we take the lead and draw on the wisdom of our five senses and the passion of the human heart to study, use and restore the creatures and plants that live on our Earth?

It takes time, energy, and commitment to change the future, but it is a future we can be proud to have helped shape. If we want to leave behind for others at least what we have enjoyed ourselves—and hopefully more—we need to identify practices that can protect biodiversity and take whatever actions we can, now, to accomplish this goal.

Conservationists and practitioners of Chinese medicine have much to offer each other. We have common ground from which we can work together to share our respective philosophies and information. In this way, we can improve the survival of medicinal species. By working collaboratively, we seek to inspire the students and practitioners of Chinese medicine, for whom this book is written, to use their whole being—heart, emotions, and mind—in projecting the future they are shaping now for generations of practitioners and patients yet to come.

SOURCES

Anonymous (1991) Rhino remedy. *New Scientist* vol.129 issue: 1759-09, pp. 15.

Anonymous (2004) Annual Industry Overview 2005. *Nutrition Business Journal.* Vol. X, No. 5/6, May/June 2005, pp. 9.

Campbell TC (2006) *The China Study: Startling Implications for Diet, Weight Loss and Long-Term Health.* Benbella Books, Dallas TX.

Center for Biodiversity and Conservation, (1997) *Biodiversity and Human Health: A Guide for Policymakers.* American Museum of Natural History, New York.

Channel D (2004) The Computer at Nature's Core. *Wired Magazine.* issue 12.02.

Cook D, Roberts M and Lowther J (2002) The International Wildlife Trade and Organized Crime: A review of the evidence and the role of the UK. Regional Research, University of Wolverhamptom, June 23, 2002.

Colin T (1991) Can we end rhino poaching? *New Scientist* 132: 1789-05, pp. 34.

Eldredge N (1998) *Life in the Balance: Humanity and the Biodiversity Crisis.* Princeton University Press, Princeton NJ.

Ellis R (2004) *No Turning Back: The Life and Death of Animal Species.* HarperCollins, New York NY.

Flaws B (1989) Lecture notes. Tri-State Institute of Traditional Chinese Acupuncture, Stamford CT.

Grifo F and Rosenthal J (eds.) (1997) *Biodiversity and Human Health.* Island Press, Washington D.C.

Hui Y (2001) Approaching Traditional Chinese Medicine: Inheritance and Exploration. In *Drug Discovery and Traditional Chinese Medicine: Science, Regulation and Globalization.* Y Lin (ed.) Kluwer Academic Publishers, Boston MA.

Jarrett L (1998) *Nourishing Destiny: The Inner Tradition of Chinese Medicine.* Spirit Path Press, Stockbridge MA.

Kirby A, Biodiversity: The sixth great wave. BBC News, UK Edition. As of 2004 available at: http://news.bbe.co.uk/1/hi/sci/tech/3667300.stm

Lavigne D (2004) Reinventing Wildlife Conservation for the 21st Century. IFAW Forum, 2004.

Raven P (2001) Floras, Plant Conservation and China's Future. In *Drug Discovery and Traditional Chinese Medicine: Science, Regulation and Globalization.* Y Lin (ed.) Kluwer Academic Publishers, Boston MA.

Lovelock J (1995) *Gaia: A New Look at Life on Earth.* Oxford University Press, Oxford, England.

Milner-Gulland EJ, Bukreeva OM, Coulson T, Luschchekina AA, Kholodova MV, Bekenov AB and Grachev IA (2003) Reproductive collapse in saiga antelope harems. *Nature,* vol. 422, 13 March, pp. 135.

Novacek MJ, ed. (2001) *The Biodiversity Crisis.* American Museum of Natural History, New York NY.

Pearce F (2003) Going the way of the dodo? *New Scientist* vol.177 issue 2382, pp. 4.

Parry-Jones R and Vincent A (1998) Can we tame wild medicine? *New Scientist* 157: 2115-03, pp. 26.

Pepper D (1996) *Modern Environmentalism: An Introduction.* Routledge, New York NY.

Roach J (2003) Rare Antelope Species on Brink of Extinction. *National Geographic:* April 25, 2003.

Sharma C (2003-2004) Enforcement Mechanisms for Endangered Species Protection in Hong Kong: A Legal Perspective. *Vermont Journal of Environmental Law,* vol. 5.

U.S. Fish and Wildlife Service, International Affairs Factsheets. As of 2006 available at: www.fws.gov/international/factshet.html

World Health Organization (2003) Available at: http://www.who.int/mediacentre/factsheets/fs134/en/

Chapter 4
ANIMAL SPECIES PROFILES: THE "WEFT"

Elizabeth Call

Since its inception, CITES has highlighted the use of animals in Chinese medicine. This emphasis has led to divergent opinions that have sometimes separated conservationists and practitioners, particularly in Asia. While each animal species has unique conservation needs, however, they share the fact that our profession has had difficulty establishing criteria that balances the clinical need to use an animal substance with conservation protocols to ensure the continued viability of the species. Given the conservation status of many of the creatures that our profession has historically relied upon for medicine, animal use as presented in the *materia medica* is an important topic for us to examine carefully and discuss openly.

The impact of Chinese medicine (indeed all traditional medicine systems) on wildlife has raised questions concerning the efficacy of healing methodologies based on history and tradition rather than scientific inquiry. While practitioners challenge themselves to remain true to the original spirit and intent of our medicine, awareness of larger issues and the ability to remain flexible—to adapt to new influences—keep every tradition strong in the face of change. Indeed, Chinese medicine has evolved from such principles.

Through the centuries, Chinese medicine has met many challenges and has survived and adjusted to political and social change. Today, though many advances have been made, the practice still encounters challenges, one of which is its use of animal species.

The issue is a complex one. Can we simultaneously balance the needs of humans and animals? Can we determine how and when to use these species so that we reduce our impact on them or find appropriate substitutes for them? Should we continue to reference them in our texts and literature? Does teaching and referencing the use of endangered species expose us to accusations of complicity in species' destruction, even though some of these animals are legally unavailable? Indeed, does such implicit encouragement suggest that, at the least, we may be disregarding international concern for animal conservation or implying advocacy of illegal trade?

Such views of our actions may appear especially true for CITES Appendix I species, such as tigers and rhinos, whose commercial trade is prohibited. Failure to initiate and follow through with discussions of animal-based medicines, and advocate substitutes may make us vulnerable to accusations of indifference at the very least and of collusion at the most extreme. Ultimately, this undermines the value of our medicine, since our client base, the public, usually does not have time to sort through the issues and, generally, is easily influenced by others' opinions of our successes and failures.

While many practitioners would not risk their time, money and licensure to illegally obtain a particular species—especially those animals whose trade is regulated—a small minority do purchase species illegally. For example, bile from bear farms in China comes from a species listed on Appendix I with an allowance for trade because the use is considered to be "sustainable". At the same time, it is possible and legal in many areas to obtain parts from North American bears, many of which have an Appendix II listing. In the United States, individual state regulations for the sale of bear parts vary widely, allowing poachers to exploit inconsistent laws, making it difficult to detect the difference between legal and illegal bear gallbladders. Individuals taking such risks to procure illegal animal products invite legal action, as well as capture public attention. In so doing, they open our profession to accusations of irresponsibility and other negative perceptions.

To effectively reflect on the use of animal products in Chinese medicine, it is important to understand this in the context of recent events. Throughout the 1980s and 1990s, prepared formulas claiming to contain tiger and rhino parts on their labels were still referenced in the literature (Fratkin, 1986; Naser, 1990). They were also openly sold, despite the animals' listing on CITES Appendix I since 1975. By the mid 1990s, however, practitioners theorized that, most likely, these formulas contained neither tiger bone nor rhino horn; however, they failed to express concern about the misleading labels, or even acknowledge the possibility that these products might contain illegal species.

Because of growing interest in traditional medicines in the United States and concerns expressed from conservation organizations, the U.S. Fish and Wildlife Service began testing prepared formulas that claimed to contain tiger bone or rhino horn, which are CITES Appendix I species. Finding either substance in these products would have constituted an illegal action on the part of importers.

Eventually, what the agency found was that the formulas, wines and plasters did *not*, in fact, show evidence of either calcium or keratin, markers for the presence of tiger bone or rhino horn respectively. Instead, many contained high levels of heavy metals as well as pharmaceuticals—items neither listed on the labels nor found in consistent concentrations throughout similar product batches. In addition, they found that other prepared formulas claiming to contain CITES Appendix II animal products on the label suffered from similar adulteration. Around this time, the California Department of Health Services also began testing prepared formulas. These results also confirmed the presence of adulterants in a significant number of these products (Ko, 1997-98).

Resulting health concerns enabled conservationists and the media to call for the Food and Drug Administration (FDA) to regulate Chinese herbs (Bolze, 1998). If we look back over the past decade, we can see that such regulation has begun. Indeed, the adulterant issue may have served to heighten FDA concern and scrutiny of Chinese herbs, leading to a ban of several species.

With continued pressure from conservationists, who asserted that products claiming to contain rhino horn and tiger bone perpetuated the use of these species and provided a cover for illegal trade, the United States passed the "Rhinoceros and Tiger Conservation Act of 1998." This act amended the 1994 version in order to "prohibit the sale, importation, and exportation of products intended for human consumption or application containing, or *labeled or advertised* (italics added) as containing, any substance derived from any species of rhinoceros or tiger." To echo federal legislation and show concern for wildlife at the local level, the New York City Council passed a bill that could convict and fine violators "for buying or selling products labeled or advertised as containing endangered species – without a showing of proof" (Lombardi, 2004).

MAINTAINING REFERENCES

Therefore, one dilemma our profession faces now is not whether we should use any endangered animals such as those listed on CITES Appendix I—we already know the answer to that—but whether we should continue to maintain references to these and other endangered animal species in our literature and to teach their use to new generations of students. Some assert that keeping these animal references in the literature helps maintain the historical continuity of our medical tradition, but others believe that this detracts from long-term conservation efforts and are particularly uneasy with references to animals whose use is illegal. It is interesting to note that despite the "Rhinoceros and Tiger Conservation Act of 1998" making it illegal to sell or import products labeled or advertised as containing rhino horn or tiger bone, literature in our profession continues to reference these products (Fratkin, 2001). Such allusions send mixed messages about our profession's collective concern for these species and our resolve in sustaining the law.

It is instructive to note that, while both tigers and rhinoceroses have been listed on CITES Appendix I since 1975, two tiger subspecies have gone extinct since the 1960s. Although extinction involves many factors, we must also acknowledge the role of the written word in some outcomes—consider texts used in China, the United States and elsewhere that perpetuate a perception of a need and use for these species. After all is said and done, the "paper trail" we are leaving continues to implicate our profession.

Let us face the facts:

- The future survival of both tigers and rhinoceroses in the wild is grim.

- Using tiger bone and rhino horn is illegal and very risky to procure.

- Tiger bone and rhino horn are expensive. In the early 1990s, for example, powdered horn cost approximately US $60,000 per kilo on the black market. The average dose for powdered horn in decoctions is 2-6 grams, but in some cases can be as much as 9 grams (Chen, 2004). Therefore, using a 6 gram dose, the rhino horn in each decoction would cost approximately $360! Cost alone makes the argument for using this substance a rather difficult sell to the average patient and mocks any claim of cost effectiveness and universal access in health care.

- There are other choices and options for practitioners and patients to exercise if they have a need to address the symptoms treated by tiger bone or rhino horn.

....

Consistent Criteria

Fortunately, our profession is beginning to see the need for more information on CITES species. First steps in this direction can be seen in two recently published *materia medicas*, the *Chinese Herbal Medicine Materia Medica* (Bensky, et. al., 2004) and *Chinese Herbal Medicine and Pharmacology* (Chen, et. al., 2004). Both texts acknowledge CITES and make recommendations on the use of endangered species. However, the endangered species data in both texts provides little consistency regarding how much and what kind of information is given for species with a CITES Appendix I or II* listing. Below is a table comparing and contrasting these books in their presentation of animal species with CITES listings.

Species	Chinese Herbal Medicine Materia Medica	Chinese Herbal Medicine and Pharmacology
Tiger bone	In a separate chapter called "Obsolete Substances"	In its regular place with a disclaimer.
CITES Listing?	No	Yes
Provided Substitute?	No	Yes
Rhinoceros horn	Deleted from text with a brief note on CITES status.	In its regular place with a disclaimer.
CITES Listing?	Yes	Yes
Provided Substitute?	Yes	Yes

Bear gallbladder	In a separate chapter called "Obsolete Substances"	In its regular place with a disclaimer.
CITES Listing?	Yes	Yes
Provided Substitute?	Yes	Yes
Pangolin	In a separate chapter called "Obsolete Substances"	In its regular place.
CITES Listing?	Yes	No
Provided Substitute?	Yes	No
Saiga horn	In its regular place	In its regular place.
CITES Listing?	Yes	No
Provided Substitute?	Yes, but substitutes given are also endangered.	No
Seahorse/Pipe Fish	In its regular place.	In its regular place
CITES Listing?	Yes	No
Provided Substitute?	No	No
Musk Deer	In its regular place.	In its regular place.
CITES Listing?	Yes	No
Substitute Provided?	Yes	No
Turtle	In its regular place.	In its regular place.
CITES Listing?	Yes for Gui Ban. No for Bie Jia.	No
Substitute Provided?	Yes, but substitutes given are also endangered.	No

* The *Chinese Herbal Medicine Materia Medica* (Bensky, et. al., 2004) does note plants that are on CITES Appendix II; *Chinese Herbal Medicine and Pharmacology* (Chen, et. al., 2004) does not.

To understand and effectively address the use of animal species, practitioners need access to the same level of consistency concerning

CITES listings and conservation information as they do with clinical knowledge. As this is currently lacking, it is essential for our profession to establish consistent criteria and consensus on the issue, something this book attempts to address.

If the Chinese medicine professional literature chooses to maintain references to animals, particularly CITES Appendix I species, we must recognize the strength of the written word in creating the impression that these species are crucial to the medicine. Because of these references, we could be seen as encouraging use, stimulating demand and becoming an indirect accomplice to poaching. For example, the government of India admitted to losing 122 tigers in a five year period commencing in 1999. In the same period, 211 cases of seized tiger parts were reported, including the biggest seizure by Chinese Customs in 2003 involving 32 tigers (IFAW 2006). According to conservationists, the Indian Customs authorities "multiply known offences by ten to estimate the size of an illegal trade" (WPSI, 2005).

Ironically, while the historical precedence of tigers as medicine persists, poaching continues. I take cold comfort in recognizing that soon, *any* reference in the *materia medica* to these species may be as archaic as wild tigers themselves could be before long. Is this what we aspire to? It is ironic that Chinese medicine holds many keys to disease prevention and encourages a balanced lifestyle; yet pushes species to the very edge of extinction.

A Questionable "Harvest"

A second dilemma for consideration is the issue of farming wild animals for their products. While farming wild animals can be seen as one way of trying to reconcile biodiversity *and* human health, it has its own problems and requires us to look at the relationship between wild and cultivated life forms and the relative values we place on each.

Conservation concerns about farming an endangered species mainly revolve around the impact that farming can have on the wild populations of a creature whose survival in the wild is grim. Such concerns arose at the 1992 CITES Conference of the Parties in Kyoto, Japan, where representatives from China proposed tiger farming as a means to alleviate pressure on wild tiger populations and supply tiger bone for medicinal use (Meacham, 1997).

Confident of international approval, facilities to farm tigers emerged before CITES endorsed the plan. Once the idea to trade the parts from these tigers was presented, the opposition from the international community was so intense that the delegates withdrew their proposal (Meacham, 1997). Nevertheless tiger farming persisted, lying in wait for political winds to shift. Indeed, as tiger numbers on the farms have increased, so has the political pressure in China to trade tiger parts again. The promoters of this trade make the argument that tiger parts are necessary ingredients in Chinese medicine. On a more encouraging note however, the use of tiger bone is being questioned more and more by Chinese medicine practitioners due to the availability of replacements (see Chapter 8) and their concern for the environment.

Conservationists feel that tiger farms place a price on the head of all wild tigers and encourage poaching (Meacham, 1997). They cite problems with crocodile farming in Thailand as an example of what could happen if tiger farming were allowed. It has been well documented that crocodile skins from all over the world were being laundered through Thailand, making international conservation efforts for the species more difficult. There are no longer wild crocodiles in Thailand, since farming provided an easy cover for domestically poached crocodiles (Meacham, 1997).

Bear farming represents another challenge for our profession. There are those who regard bear farming as nothing more than a way to supply the demand for bear bile, while "conserving" wild bear populations. However, opponents of bear farming assert that it is a superficial answer to a more multi-faceted problem. Like their tiger and crocodile counterparts, bear farms provide opportunities for laundering bear parts, creating more complex law enforcement problems in the long run. In addition, conservationists believe that by supplying a relatively cheap form of bile, these farms perpetuate the public's misconception that endangered species ingredients are irreplaceable, which continues to fuel poaching of wild bears and the illegal trade in their parts. As previously mentioned, because of inconsistencies among U.S. state laws that regulate bear hunting and the sale of bear parts, individuals intent on obtaining and selling gallbladders illegally, often go undetected. A large population of North American black bears tempts some people to take advantage of legal loopholes to supply the demand for gallbladders. The situation has become so alarming, that the Bear Protection Act was proposed and later passed by the Senate in 2002. Had it been enacted (passed in *both* the

House and the Senate), the bill would have made it illegal to sell bear parts across state borders.

Another strike against farming bears are the conditions under which they are compelled to exist. Confined to small metal cages that restrict movement, the bears often self-stimulate by banging their heads against the cages, thus causing head wounds. The metal catheters surgically implanted to extract bile create infections. Some bears are fitted with metal vests to prevent them from pulling out the devices when the pain becomes too much to tolerate. Fortunately, articles on the inhumane aspects of bear farming have been circulated to the professional community by Mayway (Robinson, Lau, 2004), a company that has discontinued selling products containing bear bile, replacing it with pig bile from pigs previously slaughtered for consumption.

....

Global Medicine

The third dilemma we face is the need to reassess the clinical value of animals on Appendix II that are still approved for trade under CITES. In initiating such a discussion, it may be helpful to acknowledge the global nature of our economy and its influence on health care.

Author Bob Flaws believes that "…a universal New Medicine (is) being shaped out of a combination of modern Western medicine, TCM, and other healing traditions from around the world. These may include bodywork systems, various psychotherapies, clinical nutrition and ecology, homeopathy and homotoxicoloy, Ayurvedic, Tibetan, and Unani medicines, and indigenous folk remedies and modalities from around the world."

This speaks to the fact that all forms of traditional medicine are in the process of expanding their *materia medicas* and their treatment options. While Flaws' vision is not yet a reality, portions of it are visible in the trend among herbalists who not only borrow from one or more traditions, (Tierra, 1988; Foster, 1992) but also include vitamin and mineral supplements in their practices (Flaws, 1991).

Looking for new plants and their uses is a long standing practice in China. Expansion of the *materia medica* has historical precedent, as various organizations there engage actively in discovering and researching plants for possible use (Foster, 1992). An increasing number of practitioners in the West also use both Chinese and Western herbs, as well as supplements. Helping these practitioners are texts that demonstrate how to combine Chinese and Western herbs.

With this in mind, it might be beneficial to conceive the traditional *materia medica* in a more fluid way. Actively seeking substitutions for endangered species from within Chinese medicine and other traditions might be one way to help ensure species conservation. By doing so, we could create a "beautiful mosaic" of herbs and treatment options from different cultures and sources.

In addition to the plant options from other traditions, and a plethora of medicines, treatments, drugs and supplements available today, practitioners in the West have more medicinal choices than their ancient predecessors and, thus, no reason to consider rhino horn (or its animal-based replacements) to manage vomiting of blood, convulsions, delirium, purpura, and unremitting high fever. Generally such emergent symptoms can successfully be treated by Western allopathic medicine. Indeed, these symptoms would require immediate Western medical attention and, probably, hospitalization.

Likewise, practitioners have numerous remedies to control less serious symptoms. For example, the treatment of hemorrhoids need not include bear bile products. Acupuncture and other herbs, plus diet and lifestyle considerations, can greatly improve or eliminate this condition.

When a patient presents with symptoms where a formula containing a CITES Appendix I or II species might be considered, practitioners have several choices. They can substitute the herb in question or refer the patient out for other types of treatments. Such actions would benefit both patients and biodiversity, without compromising either our medicine or our professional standing.

Chinese medicine can and should easily accommodate flexibility in treatment options, while seeking out alternatives to endangered species. If we do not, we may find ourselves as dogmatic as we have accused Western medicine practitioners of being—an outcome that would be especially ironic at a time when Western practitioners are beginning to acknowledge the usefulness of alternative approaches to health care.

....

Reassessing Animal Use

When we reflect on the use of animal products we should consider the following:

1. When a patient has symptoms that indicate the use of an endangered species, Western medicine may be the treatment of choice. If referral to Western medical treatment is not warranted, a substitution can be chosen from within the Chinese materia medica. In this case, practitioners should be trained to identify replacements and use them effectively (see survey results). Practitioners can also choose an herb from another tradition, if they understand how it will work within their chosen Chinese medical formula.

2. We can reconsider the role our "tradition" plays in finding the balance between human needs and animal needs. Can we effectively look outside our tradition for other non-endangered substances that could accomplish the same end? Sometimes clinical choices result from a habit steeped in tradition, rather than a factual consideration of whether a particular substance offers the only clinical choice.

3. We can acknowledge animal welfare issues in making decisions regarding our use of the *materia medica*. The major issues involve whether or not to use farmed species and how farming practices might impact wild populations of a species. In addition, we need to consider how the animals are treated. These points can and should play a role in influencing the contents of our *materia medica,* as well as our personal decisions about whether or not we should use a farmed species.

4. As Chinese medicine practitioners in the West, we can focus our energies on maintaining and optimizing health. This leaves us free to focus our practice on prevention, health enhancement and the everyday sort of ills and chronic complains that Western medicine does not tend to treat very well.

I believe it is important to include animal welfare issues in the development of policies for the medicinal use of CITES-listed species. As you read the species profiles that follow, consider them within the global context of our medicine, of animal welfare and of patient needs.

Fortunately, thanks to the medical breakthroughs of the past decades, no one will die because products containing endangered species are unavailable. While animal-based medicines may treat serious symptoms and a case could be made that Western medicine may not be available in rural villages when such illnesses appear, the cost of Appendix II (and I) animal substances generally exceed the purchasing power of poorer people. In reality, such issues present themselves more as a case for fair health care distribution than traditional use. While traditional people need to maintain the continuity of their medical practices, they also need access to global medicine in order to treat ailments that have become global in scope.

Chinese medicine is indeed a global medicine. To help guarantee species conservation, we have every reason to hope that, as Chinese medicine adapts to other cultures and practitioner environments, it will retain the flexibility that has characterized it for millennia, and that it will also evolve positively in the face of change. The animals need this to happen and so do we—the practitioners and the companies who serve as stewards for the future of each plant and animal used, and the patients who benefit from this powerful form of health care.

Sources:

Bensky D and Gamble A (eds.). (1993) *Chinese Herbal Medicine Materia Medica. Revised Edition.* Eastland Press, Seattle WA.

Bensky D, Clavey S and Ströger E (eds.). (2004) *Chinese Herbal Medicine Materia Medica, 3rd Edition.* Eastland Press, Seattle WA.

Bolze D et.al. (1998) The Availability of Tiger-Based Traditional Chinese Medicine Products and Public Awareness About the Threats to the Tiger in New York City's Chinese Communities. Wildlife Conservation Society, NYC.

Chen J and Chen T (2004) *Chinese Medical Herbology and Pharmacology.* Art of Medicine Press, City of Industry CA.

Ellis A (1997) Personal communication.

Ellis R (2004) *No Turning Back: The Life and Death of Animal Species.* HarperCollins, New York NY.

Environmental Investigation Agency (1997) Report on the Availability of Tiger Parts in New York's Canal Street Area, Washington, D.C.

Flaws B (1991) *Something Old, Something New.* Blue Poppy Press, Boulder CO.

Foster S (1992) *Herbal Emmissaries: Bringing Chinese Herbs to the West.* Healing Arts Press, Rochester VT.

Fratkin J (1986) *Chinese Herbal Patent Formulas.* Shya Publications, Boulder CO.

Fratkin J (2001) *Chinese Herbal Patent Medicines: The Clinical Desk Reference.* Shya Publications, Boulder CO.

Gaski A (1997) While Supplies Last: The Sale of Tiger and Other Endangered Species Medicines in North America. Traffic North America.

IFAW (2006). Wild Tigers in Crisis. *Between the Conferences of the Parties.* Issue 6, International Fund for Animal Welfare.

Ko R and Au A (1998) *Compendium of Asian Patent Medicines 1997-1998*. California Department of Health Services.

Lau Y (2004) The Suffering on Bear Bile Farms. *Mayway Mailer*, vol.5:1. San Francisco CA.

Lombardi F (2004) New York City Council Bill Targets Illegal Trading in Endangered Species. *Daily News*, New York. 11/23/04.

Meacham C J (1997) *How the Tiger Lost Its Stripes*. Harcourt Brace & Company, New York NY.

Naser M (1990) *Outline Guide to Chinese Herbal Patent Medicines in Pill Form*. Boston Chinese Medicine, Boston MA.

Robinson J (2004) The Suffering of Bears – Part 2. *Mayway Mailer*, vol.5:2. San Francisco CA.

Tierra M (1988) *Planetary Herbology*. Lotus Press, Santa Fe NM.

Wildlife Protection Society of India. As of 2005, available at: www.wpsi-india.org

Asian Tortoises and Freshwater Turtles

Sandra Altherr
PRO WILDLIFE, Germany

Testudinis Plastrum/ Trioycis Carapax	Guī Bǎn/Biē Jiǎ	Listed by family, since individual species used are so numerous. For individual species see table at the end. TESTUDINIDAE BATAGURIDAE PLATYSTERNIDAE TRIONYCHIDAE CARETTOCHELYIDAE CHELIDAE

Today's turtles and tortoises trace their evolutionary history back 230 million years. During this time, they have diversified to inhabit a wide range of habitats—from the sea turtles of the world's tropical and temperate oceans to the wide assortment of species native to terrestrial and freshwater habitats in all the continents except Antarctica. Tortoises and freshwater turtles represent the tremendous adaptability of nature, living in hot and dry deserts, cool mountain streams, brackish tidal zones, and numerous types of forested, grassland, and rock-strewn habitats.

For the last few decades, Asia's tortoises and freshwater turtles have faced extreme pressure from human collecting. In many cases, this pressure far surpasses habitat destruction and other human threats as the primary factor threatening their extinction in the wild. The primary cause of such vulnerability is the human demand for traditional medicine and food.

....

Distribution

Despite its relatively small landmass, Southeast Asia holds the world's richest diversity of terrestrial turtles. With at least 100 species of tortoises and freshwater turtles, it provides habitat for more than 25 percent of the world's species. In addition, the number of newly described species of turtles in Asia continues to grow.

Unfortunately, researchers now believe that a small number of Asian turtle species already may be extinct in the wild due to over-collection for the medicinal and food trades. In addition, a growing number of species are now considered critically endangered for the same reasons. Many species that were widespread just 20 years ago are now considered rare.

BIOLOGY

Turtles are easily distinguished from other reptiles by their shell, which generally protects them from most predators, excluding humans. Although tortoises and freshwater turtles (also called terrapins in many parts of the world) share such physical features as egg production and lack of teeth, the feature that continues to fascinate humans and makes turtles perennially valuable to our society is their shells. Virtually all turtles have bony plates forming part of the shell—the only exceptions are leatherback sea turtles (*Dermochelys coriacea*), pig-nosed turtles (*Carettochelys insculpta*), and softshell turtles (Trionychidae). The top of a turtle's shell is called the carapace; the bottom shell is the plastron. Nevertheless, in spite of their leathery exterior, softshell turtles also have found themselves coveted by humans as food. The same is true for their terrestrial and freshwater relatives.

Through time, tortoises and freshwater turtles developed numerous reproductive strategies to help them survive. As late maturing, long-lived creatures, they have a low reproductive rate, characterized by infrequent egg laying and small clutch sizes. High adult survivorship, combined with this strategy of small infrequent clutches, helps ensure that populations do not expand beyond their environment's ability to sustain them.

However, low reproductive rates combined with extensive collection can have serious consequences on these species. Removing adult specimens from the wild has the potential to threaten long-term survival of tortoises, as well as freshwater and land turtle populations.

The exception is sea turtles. These creatures have a high reproduction rate to compensate for high egg and juvenile mortality. Nevertheless, extensive human exploitation has also endangered many sea turtle species.

....

THREATS

Two types of trade threaten Asian chelonian. Large-scale trade for food and medicinal preparations involves several million tortoises and freshwater turtles annually. A smaller but increasing number of turtles are also exported as pets, which can have a serious effect on species whose wild populations already may have been critically depleted. Additionally, habitat loss and other human disturbances continue to impact turtle populations in many parts of Asia.

Tortoises and freshwater turtles have been used by humans for centuries. They are still favored as food and medicine in many Asian countries, particularly as affluence increases in Asia. Virtually all species of Asian freshwater turtles and tortoises can be found in markets across Asia.

In 1989, when Chinese currency became convertible on world markets, the Chinese middle class gained world access to turtles. The tremendous demand that surfaced in China and neighboring countries was met by an equally large supply of imported tortoises and freshwater turtles. International trade routes developed, while existing trade routes expanded. These carried the supply of live turtles from as far away as Pakistan in the west, and New Guinea in the southwest.

At present, a minimum of 12 to 20 million freshwater turtles and tortoises are consumed in Asia each year. Captive bred or farmed turtles comprise an increasing proportion of available specimens also. However, the demand for wild-collected tortoise and freshwater turtle specimens remains high. This portion of the trade now depends on wild populations that are severely depleted.

The trade in tortoises and freshwater turtles constitutes a large proportion of the trans-border wildlife trade between certain Asian countries, with China importing, often illegally, large numbers of specimens through Indonesia, Malaysia, Myanmar, Singapore, and Vietnam. These countries source many of the specimens they export from neighboring countries, also often illegally. Specimens originate from Bangladesh, Cambodia, China, India, Indonesia, Lao PDR, Malaysia, Myanmar, Nepal, Pakistan, Papua New Guinea, Thailand, Vietnam and the United States. An increasing number of specimens from North America and Chinese species appear to be farmed in China to supply the trade.

The overall situation for tortoises and freshwater turtles in Asia is bleak. Following a regional conference on turtle conservation in Cambodia in 1999, the turtle and tortoise experts of IUCN reviewed the status of Asia's tortoise and freshwater turtle species. In their year 2000 review of almost 90 species, the IUCN Red List re-classified 66 species to a more serious category of threat. Compared to the 1996 list, more than two-thirds of the evaluated species are declining in the wild. At present, 18 species are classified as *critically endangered*, 27 as *endangered* and 21 as *vulnerable*. At least one species was believed to be extinct at the time the review was conducted (*Cuora yunnanensis*), although uncertainty continues over the potential extinction of other similar species.

The situation of China's turtle fauna documents the seriousness of the problem. All of China's native turtle species are directly affected by escalating commercial demands. As a result, most populations have declined precipitously, while a large number have completely collapsed.

The Red Data Book of China – Amphibia and Reptilia classifies 15 native turtle species as *endangered*, four as *critically endangered*, and two as *probably extinct in the wild*. These 21 species represent 70 percent of the 30 native tortoises and freshwater turtles. However, this publication also has not been updated since 1998, during which time the condition of several species has declined further.

....

Conservation Strategies and Research

Immediate action and international cooperation are necessary to avoid extinction of increased numbers of Asian tortoise and freshwater turtle species. A sustainable level of trade needs to be determined, then monitored and regulated to help ensure protections for these creatures. In addition, existing trade restrictions and prohibitions need to be enforced by national authorities. The cooperation of traditional medicine practitioners and consumers, as well as the food market and pet traders, is essential in achieving this goal.

Some steps already have been taken by national governments and the international community to address species decline. CITES has added 33 Asian freshwater turtle species to Appendix II at COP 10, 11, and 12. All Asian land tortoises are already listed on Appendix II, and all sea turtles on Appendix I. Also, a number of importing and exporting countries in Asia have taken steps to improve enforcement, update existing laws and regulations governing the trade, and work with CITES to improve the trade's management.

Chinese CITES authorities also hosted a workshop in Yunnan Province (Kunming; March 2002) on these issues, organized by the CITES Secretariat. The Asian countries attending this meeting agreed that all of their freshwater turtles should be CITES-protected. They also agreed on a host of implementation, enforcement, and cooperative measures for trade control. Tools for law enforcement authorities, such as species identification guides, have been produced in Chinese, Lao, Vietnamese, Khmer, English, French, and Spanish.

Increased efforts to farm turtles have been discussed as a way to partially satisfy consumer demand while relieving pressure on wild populations. However, farming may pose other ecological risks, such as disease transmission and establishment of non-native populations. Plans to increase this form of production should be carefully analyzed and discussed.

In addition to such policies and management-based actions, other strategies are needed to advance conservation initiatives surrounding the use of turtle species for food and medicine. Collaborating on conservation initiatives with practitioners and developing public education and outreach activities offer valuable opportunities to help conserve these species. As part of this effort, it is also helpful to understand the environment in which decisions are made by the public regarding food and medicines. For example, soft shell turtles are among the most sought after food species because of the palatability of their meat. Certain Chinese box turtles of the *Cuora* genus are prized for their reported cancer-curing properties, promoted in popular culture as a result of advertising. The collection of turtle eggs also has a long tradition in many Asian cultures.

According to Chinese mythology, the turtle, together with the tiger, dragon, and phoenix, is one of four divine animals present at the creation of the world. Each animal is associated with a season and a compass point. The turtle represents winter and the north—the reason why turtles are regarded as "hot food," to be eaten in winter to strengthen the body.

While the flesh of turtles is consumed as "hot food," other turtle parts and organs, such as plastrons, carapaces, bile, and blood, along with manufactured products are sold for traditional medicine. The shell, made into a jelly by prolonged boiling in water with herbal and other ingredients, is especially valued. In China, the use of turtle shells in traditional medicine is an ancient tradition. Today, turtle shell is still a common ingredient in traditional Chinese formulas, and can be found in more than 100 preparations.

Traditional Chinese medicinal prescriptions often mention certain native species, like the Chinese Three-keeled Pond Turtle (*Chinemys reevesii)* and the Chinese Softshell Turtle (*Pelodiscus sinensis).* However, systematic groupings that reference turtles in Asian medicine systems tend to vary greatly from those used in western zoology. According to Chang, "There are five or six general types, based on considerations of local and medicinal effects. Manufacturers and dealers of Chinese medicine may even market the shells of an assortment of species as just plain 'turtle shell' (Chang, 1996ab)."

Some species, such as the Three-striped Box Turtle (*Cuora trifasciata)* and the Gold-headed Box Turtle (*Cuora aurocapitata),* are especially sought as medicine. These species are highly prized, with the former now achieving prices of several thousand dollars per specimen. *Cuora trifasciata* is reported to cure cancer, and it is sometimes prescribed to treat male erectile dysfunction and pneumonia.

With the collapse of Asian wild turtle populations, traditional medicine practitioners and consumers are increasingly confronted with the question of substitutes for turtle products, including the use of farmed or other specimens. Although turtles have been used in medical preparations for centuries, some Chinese medicine practitioners argue that turtle ingredients are not essential for traditional prescriptions.

According to scientists of the Research Institute for Traditional Medicine in Sichuan, the carapace of both softshell and hardshell turtles (Biejia) can be replaced by plants. And the President of the Association of Chinese Medicine and Philosophy, Lo Yan-Wo, commented on the use of turtle shell and jelly in medicines as follows: "The herbs used in the jelly are the most important ingredients, not turtles. Herbs are very cheap, but by adding turtle, they [the jelly manufacturers] can charge much more."

Therefore, the conservation measures for Asian turtles should not be limited to conservation laws and their enforcement. They should include the development of ecologically harmless substitutes for turtle parts, as well as measures that increase consumer acceptance for such substitutes. In this context, practitioners of traditional Chinese medicine have a special responsibility. They are critical partners in the development of effective turtle conservation strategies.

SOURCES

Altherr S (2001) The Relevance of the Use of Wild Animals in Traditional Chinese Medicine to the Conservation of Animal Species. Chin Med 2001, Societas Mediciane Sinensis, No. 4: pp.143-151.

Chang CJ (1996a) Worshipped and Cursed – The Turtle's Place in Chinese Culture. *Sinorama* July 1996.

Chang CJ (1996b) From Panaceas to Pollutants – Turtle shells' Checkered History. *Sinorama*, July 1996.

Chinese Turtle Network website. As of March 2006, available at: http://www.zhangjian.ebigchina.com/

Compton J (2000) An overview of Asian turtle trade. In *Asian Turtle Trade – Proceedings of a workshop on conservation and trade of freshwater turtles and tortoises in Asia.* Phnom Penh, Cambodia, 1st to 4th December 1999, P.P. van Dijk, B.L. Stuart, and A.G.J. Rhodin (eds.): pp. 24-29.

IUCN/SSC TFTSG (2000) Recommended changes to 1996 IUCN Red List Status of Asian Turtle Species. IUCN Species Survival Commission, Tortoises and Freshwater Turtles Group. In *Asian Turtle Trade – Proceedings of a workshop on conservation and trade of freshwater turtles and tortoises in Asia.* Phnom Penh, Cambodia, 1st to 4th December 1999, P.P. van Dijk, B.L. Stuart, and A.G.J. Rhodin (eds.): pp. 156-164.

Jenkins MD (1995) Tortoises and freshwater turtles: The trade in Southeast Asia. TRAFFIC Southeast Asia.

Klemens MW (2000) From information to action – developing more effective strategies to conserve turtles. In *Turtle Conservation*, M. Klemens (ed.). Smithsonian Inst. Press, Washington: pp. 239-258.

Lau M, Chan B, Crow P and Ades G (2000) Trade and conservation of turtles and tortoises in the Hong Kong Administrative Region, People's Republic of China. In *Asian Turtle Trade – Proceedings of a workshop on conservation and trade of freshwater turtles and tortoises in Asia*. Phnom Penh, Cambodia, 1st to 4th December 1999, P.P. van Dijk, B.L. Stuart, and A.G.J. Rhodin (eds.): pp. 39-44.

Lau MW, Ades G, Goodyer N and Zou F (1995) Wildlife trade in southern China including Hong Kong and Macao. Kadoorie Farm & Botanical Garden Cooperation.

NEPA (1998) China Red Data Book of Endangered Animals – Amphibia and Reptilia. Science Press, S. Wang (ed.). Beijing, Hong Kong, New York.

Obst FJ (1992) Turtles and Tortoises. In *Reptiles and Amphibians*, H.G. Cogger and R.G. Zweifel (eds.). Weldon Owen Inc., San Francisco: pp. 108-125.

Pro Wildlife (2000) The decline of Asian turtles – Food markets, habitat destruction and pet trade drove Asia's freshwater turtles and tortoises to extinction. Munich, Germany.

Rhodin A (2002) Conservation and trade of freshwater turtles and tortoises in Asia: Review of status and threats using IUCN Red List and CITES criteria with proposed recommendations for CITES listing changes. Chelonian Research Foundation.

Thorbjarnarson J, Lagueux C, Bolze D, Klemens M and Meylan A (2000) Human use of turtles – a worldwide perspective. In *Turtle Conservation*, M. Klemens (ed.), Smithsonian Inst. Press, Washington DC: pp. 33-84.

Van Dijk PP (2000) The status of turtles in Asia. In *Asian Turtle Trade – Proceedings of a workshop on conservation and trade of freshwater turtles and tortoises in Asia*. Phnom Penh, Cambodia, 1st to 4th December 1999, P.P. van Dijk, B.L. Stuart, and A.G.J. Rhodin (eds.): pp. 15-23.

Zhang L and Zhang F (2001) Some Considerations about the Substitution of Chinese Medical Remedies in Prescriptions. Chin Med 2001, Societas Mediciane Sinensis, No. 4, pp.152-155.

Zhou E (compiler) (1998) China Red Data Book of Endangered Animals – Amphibia and Reptilia. Science Press. S. Wang (ed.). Beijing, Hong Kong, New York.

Table 1. Status, trend and international protection of populations of Asian freshwater turtles and tortoises. (?) = status unclear

SPECIES	Distribution	IUCN RED LIST 1996	IUCN RED LIST 2000	POPULATION TREND	CITES
TESTUDINIDAE					
Geochelone elegans Indian Star Tortoise	India, Sri Lanka, Pakistan	not listed	Lower risk	Decrease	App. II (1977)
Geochelone platynota Burmese Star Tortoise	Myanmar	Critically Endangered	Critically Endangered		App. II (1977)
Indotestudo elongate Elongated Tortoise	Bangladesh, Cambodia, China (?), India, Laos, Malaysia, Myanmar, Nepal, Thailand, Vietnam	Vulnerable	Endangered	Decrease	App. II (1977)
Indotestudo forstenii Sulawesi Tortoise	Indonesia	Vulnerable	Endangered	Decrease	App. II (1977)
Indotestudo travancorica Travancore Tortoise	India	Vulnerable	Vulnerable		App. II (1977)
Manouria emys Asian Brown Tortoise	Bangladesh, Cambodia, China (?), India, Indonesia, Malaysia, Myanmar, Thailand	Vulnerable	Endangered	Decrease	App. II (1977)

Manouria impressa Impressed Tortoise	Cambodia, China, Laos, Malaysia, Myanmar, Thailand, Vietnam	Vulnerable	Vulnerable		App. II (1977)
Testudo horsfieldii Central Asian Tortoise	China, Central Asia	Vulnerable	Not evaluated		App. II (1977)
BATAGURIDAE					
Batagur baska River Terrapin	Bangladesh, Cambodia, India, Indonesia, Malaysia, Myanmar (?), Singapore (?), Thailand (?), Vietnam (?)	Endangered	Critically Endangered	Decrease	App. I (1975)
Callagur borneoensis Painted Terrapin	Bhutan, Indonesia, Malaysia, Thailand?	Critically Endangered	Critically Endangered		App. II (1997)
Chinemys megalocephala Chinese Broad-Headed Pond Turtle	China	not listed	Endangered	Decrease	
Chinemys nigricans Chinese Red-necked Pond Turtle	China	Data Deficient	Endangered	Decrease	
Chinemys reeversii Chinese Three-keeled Pond Turtle	China, Japan, Taiwan	not listed	Endangered	Decrease	

Species	Distribution				
Cuora amboinensis South Asian Box Turtle	Bangladesh, Cambodia, India, Indonesia, Laos, Malaysia, Myanmar, Singapore, Thailand, Vietnam	Lower Risk	Vulnerable	Decrease	App. II (2000)
Cuora aurocapitata Golden-headed Box Turtle	China	Data Deficient	Critically Endangered	Decrease	App. II (2000)
Cuora flavomarginata Black-bellied Box Turtle	China, Japan, Taiwan	Vulnerable	Endangered	Decrease	App. II (2000)
Cuora galbinifrons Indochinese Box Turtle	Cambodia (?), China, Laos, Vietnam	Lower Risk	Critically Endangered	Decrease	App. II (2000)
Cuora mccordi McCord's Box Turtle	China	Data Deficient	Critically Endangered	Decrease	App. II (2000)
Cuora pani Pan's Box Turtle	China	Data Deficient	Critically Endangered	Decrease	App. II (2000)
Cuora trifasciata Three-striped Box Turtle	China, Laos, Vietnam	Endangered	Critically Endangered	Decrease	App. II
Cuora yunnanensis Yunnan Box Turtle	China	Data Deficient	Extinct		App. II (2000)
Cuora zhoui Zhou's Box Turtle	China	Data Deficient	Critically Endangered	Decrease	App. II (2000)

Species	Distribution				
Cyclemys dentata Asian Leaf Turtle	Bangladesh, Brunei Darussalam, Cambodia, China (?), India, Indonesia, Laos, Malaysia, Myanmar, Nepal, Singapore, Thailand, Vietnam	not listed	Lower Risk	Decrease	
Geoclemys hamiltonii Spotted Pond Turtle	Bangladesh, Indonesia, Nepal (?), Pakistan	Lower Risk	Vulnerable	Decrease	App. I (1975)
Geoemyda japonica	Japan	Endangered	Endangered		
Geoemyda silvatica	India	Endangered	Endangered		
Geoemyda spengleri Black-breasted Leaf Turtle; Spiny Turtle	China, Vietnam	not listed	Endangered	Decrease	
Hardella thurji Crowned River Turtle	Bangladesh, India, Nepal. Pakistan	Lower Risk	Vulnerable	Decrease	
Heosemys depressa Arakan Forest Turtle	Myanmar	Critically Endangered	Critically Endangered	Decrease	App. II (2002)
Heosemys grandis Giant Asian Pond Turtle	Cambodia, Laos, Malaysia, Myanmar, Thailand, Vietnam	Lower Risk	Vulnerable	Decrease	App. II (2002)

Species	Distribution			Trend	CITES
Heosemys leytensis Philippine Pond Turtle	Philippines	Endangered	Critically Endangered	Decrease	App. II (2002)
Heosemys spinosa Spiny Turtle	Brunei Darussalam, Indonesia, Malaysia, Myanmar, Philippines, Singapore, Thailand	Vulnerable	Endangered	Decrease	App. II (2002)
Hieremys annandalei Yellow-headed Temple Turtle	Cambodia, Malaysia, Myanmar, Thailand, Vietnam	Vulnerable	Endangered	Decrease	App. II (2002)
Kachuga dhongoka Three-striped Roof Turtle	Bangladesh, India, Nepal (?)	Lower Risk	Endangered	Decrease	App. II (2002)
Kachuga kachuga Red-crowned Roof Turtle	Bangladesh, India, Nepal	Endangered	Critically Endangered	Decrease	App. II (2002)
Kachuga smithii Brown Roof Turtle	Bangladesh, India, Pakistan	not listed	Lower Risk	Decrease	App. II (2002)
Kachuga sylhetensis Assam Roof Turtle	Bangladesh, India	Data Deficient	Endangered	Decrease	App. II (2002)
Kachuga tecta Indian Roof Turtle	Bangladesh, India, Nepal, Pakistan	not listed	Lower Risk	Decrease	App. I (2002)
Kachuga tentoria Indian Tent Turtle	Bangladesh, India	not listed	Lower Risk	Decrease	App. II (2002)

Species	Range				CITES
Kachuga trivittata Burmese Roof Turtle	Myanmar	Endangered	Endangered		App. II (2002)
Leucocephalon yuwonoi Sulawesi Forest Turtle	Indonesia	Critically Endangered	Data Deficient	Decrease	App. II (2002)
Malayemys subtrijuga Malayan Snail-eating Turtle	Cambodia, Indonesia, Laos, Malaysia, Thailand, Vietnam	Vulnerable	not listed	Decrease	
Mauremys annamensis Annam Pond Turtle	Vietnam	Critically Endangered	Lower Risk	Decrease	App. II (2002)
Mauremys iversoni Iverson's Pond Turtle	China	Data Deficient	Data Deficient		
Mauremys japonica Japanese Freshwater Turtle	Japan	Lower Risk	not listed	Decrease	
Mauremys mutica Chinese Freshwater Turtle	China, Japan, Taiwan, Vietnam	Endangered	not listed	Decrease	App. II (2002)
Mauremys pritchardi Lashio Pond Turtle	China, Myanmar (?)	Data Deficient	Data Deficient		
Melanochelys tricarinata	Bangladesh, India, Nepal	Vulnerable	Vulnerable		App. I (1975)
Melanochelys trijuga Indian Black Turtle	Bangladesh, India, Maldives, Myanmar, Nepal, Sri Lanka	Lower Risk	Data Deficient	Decrease	

Species	Range				
Morenia ocellata Burmese Eyed Turtle	Myanmar	Lower Risk	Vulnerable	Decrease	App. I (1975)
Morenia petersi Indian Eyed Turtle	Bangladesh, India	Lower Risk	Vulnerable	Decrease	
Notochelys platynota Malayan Flat-shelled Turtle	Brunei Darussalam, Indonesia, Malaysia, Myanmar (?), Singapore, Thailand	Data Deficient	Vulnerable	Decrease	
Ocadia glyphistoma Notched-tomium Stripe-necked Turtle	China	Data Deficient	Data Deficient		
Ocadia philippeni Philippen's Stripe-necked Turtle	China	Data Deficient	Data Deficient		
Ocadia sinensis Chinese Stripe-necked Turtle	China, Thailand, Vietnam	Lower Risk	Endangered	Decrease	
Orlitia borneensis Malayan Giant Turtle	Indonesia, Malaysia	Lower Risk	Endangered	Decrease	App. II (2002)
Pyxidea mouhotii Keeled Box Turtle	China, India, Laos, Myanmar, Vietnam	not listed	Endangered	Decrease	App. II (2002)
Sacalia bealei Eye-spotted Turtle	China	Vulnerable	Endangered	Decrease	
Sacalia pseudocellata False Eye-spotted Turtle	China	Data Deficient	Data Deficient		

Species	Distribution				
Sacalia quadriocellata Four-Eyed Turtle	China, Laos, Vietnam	Vulnerable	Endangered	Decrease	
Siebenrockiella crassicollis Black Marsh Turtle	Cambodia, Indonesia, Malaysia, Myanmar, Singapore, Thailand, Vietnam	not listed	Vulnerable	Decrease	App. II (2002)
PLATYSTERNIDAE					
Platysternon megacephalum Big-headed Turtle	China, Laos, Myanmar, Thailand, Vietnam	Data Deficient	Endangered	Decrease	App. II (2002)
TRIONYCHIDAE					
Amyda cartilaginea Asiatic Softshell Turtle	Brunei Darussalam, Cambodia, India, Indonesia, Laos, Malaysia, Myanmar, Singapore, Thailand, Vietnam	Vulnerable	Vulnerable		
Aspideretes gangeticus Indian Softshell Turtle	Bangladesh, India, Pakistan	not listed	Vulnerable	Decrease	App. I (1975)
Aspideretes hurum Peacock Softshell Turtle	Bangladesh, India	not listed	Vulnerable	Decrease	App. I (1975)

Aspideretes leithii	India	Lower Risk	Vulnerable	Decrease	App. I (1975)
Aspideretes nigricans	Bangladesh	Critically Endangered	Critically Endangered		App. II (2002)
Chitra chitra Southeast Asian Narrow-headed Softshell Turtle	Indonesia, Malaysia (?), Thailand	Critically Endangered	Critically Endangered		App. II (2002)
Chitra indica (Indian) Narrow-headed Softshell Turtle	Bangladesh, India, Myanmar, Pakistan	Vulnerable	Endangered	Decrease	App. II (2002)
Dogania subplana Malayan Softshell Turtle	Indonesia, Malaysia, Myanmar, Singapore, Thailand	not listed	Lower Risk	Decrease	
Lissemys punctata Indian Flapshell Turtle	Bangladesh, India, Myanmar, Pakistan, Nepal, Sri Lanka	not listed	Lower Risk	Decrease	App. II (1995)
Lissemys scutata Burmese Flapshell Turtle	Myanmar, Thailand (?)	Data Deficient	Data Deficient		
Nilssonia formosa Burmese Peacock Softshell Turtle	Myanmar	Vulnerable	Endangered	Decrease	
Palea steindachneri Wattle-necked Softshell Turtle	China, Vietnam	Lower Risk	Endangered	Decrease	
Pelochelys bibroni New Guinea Giant Softshell Turtle	Indonesia, Papua New Guinea	Vulnerable	Vulnerable		App. II (2002)

		Vulnerable	Endangered	Decrease	App. II (2002)
Pelochelys cantorii Asian Giant Softshell Turtle	Bangladesh, Cambodia, China, India, Indonesia, Laos (?), Malaysia, Myanmar, Philippines, Papua New Guinea, Thailand, Vietnam	Vulnerable	Endangered	Decrease	
Pelodiscus sinensis Chinese Softshell Turtle	China, Japan, Taiwan, Vietnam; farmed in Thailand	not listed	Vulnerable	Decrease	
Rafetus swinhoei Swinhoe's Softshell Turtle	China, Vietnam (?)	not listed	Critically Endangered	Decrease	
CARETTOCHELYIDAE					
Carettochelys insculpta Pig-nose Turtle	Australia, Indonesia, Papua New Guinea	Vulnerable	Vulnerable		
CHELIDAE					
Chelodina mccordi Roti Island Snake-necked Turtle	Indonesia	Vulnerable	Critically Endangered	Decrease	
Chelodina novaeguineae New Guinea Long-necked Turtle	Australia, Indonesia, Papua New Guinea	not listed	Lower Risk	Decrease	

Chelodina parkeri Parker's Long-necked Turtle	Indonesia, Papua New Guinea	Vulnerable	Vulnerable	
Chelodina pritchardi Pritchard's Snake-necked Turtle	Papua New Guinea	Vulnerable	Endangered	Decrease
Chelodina reimanni	Indonesia, Papua New Guinea (?)	Data Deficient	Lower Risk	Decrease
Chelodina siebenrocki	Indonesia, Papua New Guinea	not listed	Lower Risk	Decrease
Elseya branderhorstii	Indonesia	not listed	Vulnerable	Decrease
Elseya noveaguineae New Guinea Snapping Turtle	Indonesia, Papua New Guinea	not listed	Lower Risk	Decrease
Emydura subglobosa Red-bellied Short-necked Turtle	Indonesia, Papua New Guinea	not listed	Lower Risk	Decrease

ASIATIC WILD ASS

Andrea Heydlauff
Wildlife Conservation Society, USA

Gelatinum Corii Asini	Ē Jiāo	Equus hemionus, hemionus. E. h. luteus, E. h. khulan, E. h. onager, E. h. khur Equus Asinus Linneus*

Mentioned in the Old Testament's Book of Job and in the writings of the Italian explorer Marco Polo, the Asiatic wild ass *(Equus hemionus)* is one of the world's seven equid species. Tens of thousands of years ago, this animal roamed from the plains of Mongolia across Eurasia, as far west as what is now Germany.

Unlike some other members of the horse family, the Asiatic wild ass proved impossible to tame or domesticate. But while its speed and stamina may have helped it stay "wild," both the range of the species and its numbers have shrunk through the centuries. Hunted for its meat and increasingly confined to smaller areas, the Asiatic wild ass exists today as five geographically isolated subspecies, all of which appear on the IUCN Red List of Threatened Species. They also receive some level of protection under CITES. One subspecies, the Syrian wild ass (*E. h. hemippus)* became extinct in 1927.

The skin of the Asiatic wild ass is used in traditional Chinese medicine to tonify blood, typically in a hardened gelatin form. It is believed to benefit nails, as well as serve as a general female tonic to help gynecological problems.

....

DISTRIBUTION

In the thirteenth century, herds of Asiatic wild ass thrived in Persia, the Middle East, Arabia, Turkestan, and the Gobi Desert. Today, southern

---

* The Ē Jiāo coming from China does not list which species it was made from. Some surmise that because of the low cost, Ē Jiāo might be from domestic cattle.

Mongolia is home to the largest population, one that accounts for more than 80 percent of the individual animals that now make up the species.

The Mongolian population includes two of the five surviving subspecies, the Mongolian khulan (*E. h. hemionus*) and the Gobi khulan (*E. h. luteus*), both of which are considered "vulnerable" by the IUCN. The Gobi khulan may also exist across the frontier in the Chinese province of Xinjiang. The khulan (*E. h. khulan*) and the onager (*E. h. onager*) —both classified as "critically endangered" by the IUCN—may actually represent one species. The former are found in Turkmenistan and Kazakhstan, while the latter inhabit northern Iran and the Badkhyz Reserve in Turkmenistan.

A fifth subspecies, the Indian wild ass or khur (*E. h. khur*), is considered "endangered" by the IUCN. Khur once spanned the arid zone of northwest India (including present-day Pakistan); populations extended west toward Syria and throughout much of central Asia. In recent years, khur have been confined to the Little Rann of Kutch in Gujarat, India, where the population has steadily increased since the area was declared a sanctuary for the animal. As a result, khur have been sighted dispersing toward the Great Rann of Kutch on the Gurarat/Rajasthan border, the Pakistan border to the north, the Dhandhuka-Dholera highway in the south, and toward Malia in the west.

....

BIOLOGY

Asiatic wild ass weigh about 200 to 260 kilograms, exceeding on average the size of both the African wild ass and its descendant, the domestic donkey. These animals breed seasonally; gestation lasts for 11 months, and births (typically one foal) peak between April and September. Asiatic wild ass vary in color geographically and seasonally. Breeding stallions, in particular, turn reddish brown in summer. The upper parts of the animal may appear reddish, tawny, yellowish, or gray. Most typically have a broad white-bordered stripe running down their backs, as well as a transverse stripe across the shoulders.

When grass is available, Asiatic wild ass feed as grazers. In dry seasons, however, they browse on woody plants. They have been seen eating seedpods and breaking up woody vegetation with their hooves to reach succulent forbs growing at the base. In Mongolia, the animals will eat snow as a substitute for water. They have been known to dig holes as deep as 60 centimeters to gain access to water from dry riverbeds.

The fastest of the horse species, the Asiatic wild ass can clock speeds up to 70 kilometers per hour in brief spurts. They can run as fast as 50 kilometers per hour for sustained periods. Known for their strength and stamina, they often travel long distances to find favorable feeding grounds in the winter and watering sites in the long, hot summer.

Group behavior differs slightly among the different subspecies. In some cases, males defend territories or form all-male groups. Territorial stallions will defend their "turf" year round or seasonally if a seasonal harem is formed. The social behavior of the khulan resembles that of feral horses; these animals form small family groups consisting of individual males, several females, and their foals. Stallions have been observed protecting females and foals from predators.

Scientists have suggested that differences in social behavior and structure among subspecies may depend on climatic seasonality, vegetation cover, and hunting pressures. More research is needed to analyze the different factors affecting wild ass populations and their interactions.

....

THREATS

Poaching appears to be the greatest threat to the Asiatic wild ass. Environmental factors, such as drought or disease and the continued fragmentation of the animal's habitat, may also jeopardize its long-term survival.

In Iran, the Persian onager is struggling to survive. In order of importance, threats include poaching, loss of habitat due to overgrazing by domestic livestock, competition for water, and removal of shrubs (an alternative food source to grass). Although the animals are hunted primarily for their meat, some reports suggest that poaching may have occurred at times for medicinal use.

In India, human activities that threaten the khur include canal building and the dismantling of protected areas, such as the Wild Ass Sanctuary. An increase in salt mining and livestock grazing, especially within reserves, is also having a negative effect.

Over the past few years, poaching for meat has caused a massive decline in the khulan population. The only naturally occurring population of this subspecies inhabits a reserve in Turkmenistan. During the summer months, however, the animals migrate out of the protected area to find water, exposing themselves to poachers.

In certain areas in Mongolia, herdsmen and their livestock compete with the khulan for available forage. The number of cattle being grazed has increased over the past decade, intensifying this conflict. Poaching for meat and hides is also a concern for this subspecies.

At this time, international trade in Asiatic wild ass subspecies is not a major threat. Reports from TRAFFIC (the trade monitoring arm of the IUCN and World Wildlife Fund) show no trophy imports over the past decade. Live animals may, however, be moving between zoos and private reserves in "non-origin" countries. Products listing Asiatic wild ass as an ingredient are present in the medicinal trade, but more studies are needed to determine whether and how this traffic is affecting subspecies in individual countries and on a global scale.

Although trade is not at present considered a factor in species decline, global commerce in Asiatic wild ass is regulated under the CITES treaty because of the animal's increasingly imperiled status in the wild. The Mongolian and Gobi khulans and the khur are listed on CITES Appendix I (which essentially bans commercial trade), while the onager and khulan appear on Appendix II.

....

CONSERVATION STRATEGIES AND RESEARCH

Efforts to stave off extinction for the Asiatic wild ass have been underway since the middle decades of the last century. The drastic decline in khulan populations in the 1940s, for example, prompted the former Soviet Union to spearhead the formation of a reserve to protect the last 200 khulan in Turkmenistan. This population increased to 5,000 individuals by 1995, but numbers fell to 650 as poaching for meat accelerated. The few remaining animals were moved to other sites in Turkmenistan and Kazakhstan to increase khulan populations in different locations.

The Gobi khulan is a protected species in China, where it appears in the "First Category" of the list of "State Key Protected Wildlife." The government has established four reserves for the animal, covering a total of 1,548,840 hectares in Gansu, Inner Mongolia, and Xinjiang.

A khulan-onager cross was introduced into the Negev highlands in Israel in 1982, and numbers have increased to date. Studies have examined habitat use and changes in species diversity and vegetation density. Biologists are using the results to devise management plans for the population.

Ongoing conservation strategies are focusing on preserving and increasing populations of onagers in Iran and khur in India and setting up conservation areas for Asiatic wild ass in Mongolia and China. Aerial surveys conducted in 2001 in the latter two countries show that populations are increasing.

Specific local conservation projects include efforts to maintain the Wild Ass Sanctuary in the Little Rann of Kutch; attempts to protect the khulan population in the Badkhys Reserve from poachers; studies to clarify taxonomy of the subspecies to aid in effective management; work to reduce livestock/wildlife conflict in areas where rangeland is under significant grazing pressure; and monitoring and evaluating reintroduced populations in Turkmenistan.

Numerous research studies are underway to fill the many gaps in our knowledge of the Asiatic wild ass. In Mongolia, studies on the status, distribution, ecology, and social structure of the khulan in Gobi have recently been completed. In India, research is being conducted to document the status, ecology, and social structure of the khur in the Little Rann of Kutch. Surveys are being conducted in Iran, while studies and monitoring continue to track the introduced populations in Israel.

SOURCES

Duncan P (1992) *Zebras, Asses, and Horses: An Action Plan for the Conservation of Wild Equids.* IUCN/SSC Equid Specialist Group. IUCN, Gland, Switzerland.

Feh C, Boldsukh T and Tourenq C (1994) Are family groups in equids a response to cooperatively hunting predators? The case of Mongolian khulans. (*Equus hemionus luteus* Matschie). Rev. Ecol (Terre Vie), 49: pp. 11-20.

Feh C, Munkhtuya B, Enkhbold S and Sukhbaatar T (2001) Ecology and social structure of the Gobi khulan in the Gobi B National Park. *Biological Conservation* 101: pp. 51-61.

Harper F (1945) Extinct and vanishing mammals of the old world. Special Publication of the American Committee for International Wildlife Protection, 12: 849 pp.

MacFadden B (1992) *Fossil Horses: Systematics, Paleobiology and Evolution of the Family Equidae.* Cambridge University Press, Cambridge.

Moehlman PD (ed). (2002) *Equids: Zebras, Asses, and Horses: Status Survey and Conservation Action Plan.* IUCN/SCC Equid Specialist Group, IUCN, Gland Switzerland and Cambridge.

Reading R, Mix HM, Lhagvasuren B, Feh C, Kane DP, Dulamtseren S and Enkhbold S (2001) Status and distribution of khulan (*Equus hemionus*) in Mongolia. *Journal of Zoology* 254: pp. 381-389.

Ryder O and Chemnick L (1990) Chromosomal and molecular evolution in Asiatic Wild Asses. *Genetica*, 83: pp. 67-72.

Shah NV (1993) Ecology of Wild Ass (*Equus hemionus khur*) in Little Rann of Kutch. PhD thesis, M.S. University of Baroda.

Shah NV (1998) Mammalian diversity in Little Rann of Kutch, Gujurat, India. Report, Gujarat Ecological and Education Foundation, Gandhinagar, Gujarat.

Walker EP (1999) *Walker's Mammals of the World.* 6th Edition, Vol 2. Johns Hopkins University Press, Baltimore, MD: pp. 1013-1015.

Wang S (1998) *China Red Data Book of Endangered Animals - Mammalia.* Science Press, Beijing, PRC: pp. 215-219.

Grace Ge Gabriel
International Fund for Animal Welfare, USA

Vesica Fellea Ursi	Xióng Dǎn	Ursus thibetanus, Ursus arctos, Ursus americanus, Ursus maritimus, Melursus ursinus, Ailuropoda melanoleuca, Tremarctos ornatus, Helarctos malayanus

Throughout history, humans have been fascinated by bears (*Ursidae* spp.). To the ancient Greeks and Romans, the bear was a figure of motherly compassion, a belief based on the unique care a mother bear gives her cubs. Many native North American cultures respected the bear as a powerful and magical spirit.

Bears continue to play a role in our society today. For many of us, this influence begins in childhood when we clutch our first teddy bear, hear the story of Goldilocks and the three bears, or read the adventures of such beloved characters as Winnie-the-Pooh or Paddington Bear. We laugh at the antics of Yogi Bear and heed Smokey the Bear's warnings about preventing forest fires. In the night sky, two of our best-known constellations are named after bears: Ursa Major and Ursa Minor. The enduring popularity of bears in the names of sports teams shows that we continue to revere this animal for its strength and courage.

....

DISTRIBUTION

Eight species of bears live in more than 65 countries: American black bear (*Ursus americanus*), Asiatic black bear (*Ursus thibetanus*), brown bear (*Ursus arctos*), giant panda (*Ailuropoda melanoleuca*), polar bear (*Ursus maritimus*), sloth bear (*Melursus ursinus*), spectacled bear (*Tremarctos ornatus*), and sun bear (*Helarctos malayanus*). Bears are found on every continent except Antarctica, Africa, and Australia. (Despite its name, the koala bear is a marsupial, not a bear). A diverse group of large mammals, bears occupy a variety of habitats from tropical rainforests to arctic ice fields.

....

BIOLOGY

Bears range in size from the polar bear, weighing up to 680 kg (1500 lbs), to the sun bear, weighing just 27 to 66 kg (60-145 lbs). Bulky and muscular, bears rely on their strength rather than their speed to obtain food.

Most bears are generalist omnivores. They feed primarily on berries and nuts, but also consume meat, fish, insects, buds, tubers, and leaves. Some bears, such as the polar bear and the giant panda, are more specialized feeders. Polar bears subsist almost exclusively on meat, preying on seals, young walruses, beluga whales, and narwhals. The giant panda, on the other hand, is primarily herbivorous, feeding on bamboo and eating very little meat.

All bear species rely heavily on their powerful sense of smell, color vision, and good memory to help them forage and hunt for food. Many bears are active at night. A specially adapted reflective membrane in their eyes captures ambient light and acts like night vision goggles to help them see in the dark. Forward facing eyes also help with depth perception.

Each of the eight bear species has unique adaptations that help it survive in its particular habitat. The giant panda, for example, has a modified wrist bone forming a "pseudo-thumb" that the animal uses to grasp bamboo stalks. Polar bears have large, oar-like front paws and a streamlined body, making them powerful swimmers. Spectacled, black, and sun bears have curved, hook-like claws for climbing trees, and the brown bear has long, straight claws for digging up vegetation. The sloth bear has long, curved claws to open nests of insect prey and large, protrusible lips for sucking up termites and ants.

Many, but not all, bears hibernate to conserve energy during the winter, when food resources are scarce and foraging becomes difficult. Bears living in warmer climates closer to the equator tend either not to hibernate or to do so for shorter periods; bears closer to the polar regions hibernate longer. Before hibernation, bears build up fat stores to provide enough energy to carry them through lean months without food and water. Their body temperature also drops a few degrees, producing a significant decline in heart and respiratory rates. By the end of hibernation, bears have been known to lose as much as 40 percent of their total body weight.

Most bears lead solitary lives, except when they are mating or living in family groups. Many bears will also congregate in areas of optimal foraging habitat, or, in the case of polar bears, when they are fasting.

Males and females mature sexually between three and five years of age. Breeding may last a few days to a few weeks. Gestation averages six to eight months, with some species experiencing delayed implantation. Cubs of black, brown, and polar bears are born in a den during the winter. Sun bears are thought to give birth throughout the year, but little is known about the reproductive cycles of other bear species. Litter size varies between species and depends on the size of the mother, availability of food, and geography. Cubs usually weigh 300 to 600 grams (10 to 21 oz) at birth. They stay with the mother from one to three years, until she drives them away. While bear longevity varies between individuals and species, most bears in the wild have an average life span of 20 to 30 years.

....

Threats

Like most large mammals, bears around the world are being affected by human activities that cause increased mortality. These activities include legal and illegal hunting, as well as habitat loss and degradation from the expansion of human settlements, logging, and road building. Certain species, such as the polar bear, are likely to be severely impacted by climatic warming and increased pollution.

People hunt bears for a variety of reasons, depending on the species and location. Some bears are legally hunted for sport, while others are poached for food or used in traditional medicines. Still others are killed because they are considered to be pests, or because they are perceived to be a threat to humans.

Bears also suffer when they are kept in captivity, either as pets or for use in entertainment. In some countries, bear cubs are taken from the wild and raised to fight with dogs in exhibitions of bear baiting. Because bears can walk upright, they are often made to "dance," ride bicycles, and perform other unnatural behaviors for human entertainment. Concerns exist over the level of care that bears receive in zoos and circuses.

The trade in bear bile and gallbladders, which are used for traditional medicine, tonics, and other health-related purposes, directly impacts several bear species. Populations of Asiatic black bear, sun bear, and brown bears in Asia, in particular, are severely affected by the trade in bear products. Parts from American black bear and other brown bear populations can also be found in the medicinal trade.

Bear gallbladder, sold under the pharmaceutical name of Vesica Fellea Ursi, is believed to have entered the Chinese pharmacopoeia approximately three thousand years ago. It is used to remove heat from the liver, relieve convulsions and spasms, improve vision, and clear toxic materials. Bear bile is the liquid or dried powder extracted from the gallbladder. Bear bile may be sold as dried bile powder or incorporated into products such as eye drops, hemorrhoid cream, wine, tea, and power drinks.

Asiatic black bears are favored for medicinal purposes, and products from Asiatic black bears are readily available in many Asian countries. In China, the commercial demand for bear bile has resulted in the creation of large-scale bear farms, where animals are held in small cages, and their bile collected through a tube that has been surgically inserted into their bile ducts. As many as 9,000 bears are thought to be kept on such farms; many of these animals were caught and removed from the wild.

Although it is legal to hunt American black bears in North America, brown bears in North America, Europe and Russia, and polar bears in North America, Greenland and Russia, the gallbladders from these animals are often illegally sold to supply the bear bile and gallbladder markets in Asia. Brown bears and sun bears are also smuggled alive across borders, and their gallbladders are sold in Asian markets.

Many bear species are threatened because the lack of available scientific information inhibits clear management decision for these populations. Inadequate enforcement of laws that protect bears and conserve their habitats continues to undermine the survival of many species.

....

CONSERVATION STRATEGIES AND RESEARCH

The threats and challenges facing bears are diverse, and successful strategies for bear conservation require broad approaches that include a range of tactics. These approaches include instituting and enforcing international agreements to protect bears; improving knowledge and understanding of bears through scientific research; and encouraging local initiatives to educate the public (particularly consumers of bear products) about threats to bears. Conservationists are working to strengthen existing laws and their enforcement to protect bears and control the trade in bear products. They are also working to improve bear research and management and increase public awareness of the plight of bears around the world.

Laws and enforcement measures: CITES provides a global mechanism for bear protection. The Asiatic black bear, giant panda, sun bear, sloth bear, spectacled bear, and populations of brown bear in Bhutan, China, and Mongolia are all listed on the treaty's Appendix I, meaning international trade in their products is prohibited. Polar bears and the remaining brown bear populations are listed on Appendix II, which controls trade through the use of permits. Although populations of American black bear are more abundant, this species is also listed on Appendix II to address the "look alike" issue explained below.

Like many international treaties with broad oversight responsibilities, CITES is not strictly enforced in many countries. Although more than 160 nations have ratified the treaty, some still have not passed domestic legislation to fully implement and enforce it. In many of these countries, effective enforcement is hindered by a lack of laws that would allow violators to be prosecuted based on product label claims and advertisements. Furthermore, financial incentives are often too great, and penalties too weak, to deter illegal trade in bear products.

Because some countries allow legal markets for bear products from certain species, the "look alike" problem makes it difficult to control the commercial trade in bear products. Dried bear gallbladders and bile products look identical, whether they were taken from a legally hunted bear, a farmed bear, or an illegally killed bear of a threatened species. As a result, neither consumers nor law enforcement officers can easily determine whether a bear product was derived from a legal or illegal source. In addition, bear products from illegally killed species are often found in the market labeled as coming from a legal source. The legal trade in bear parts in some countries thus provides a cover for the illegal trade in the parts of other bear species. These legal markets encourage the poaching of bears of all species and further threaten bear populations worldwide.

To effectively control the trade of bear parts from CITES Appendix I species, measures are needed to close legal loopholes—a huge challenge, considering the range of countries in which bears are found and the diverse national authorities under which they are managed. Some conservation groups have recommended a global ban on the import, export, and domestic sale of bear parts and derivatives, as well as products that contain or are labeled as containing bear parts. However, the multitude of legal authorities for bear management among nations may make this a long-term rather than an immediate goal.

Management plans and habitat preservation projects: Successful bear conservation requires good management plans. These plans must be based on sound biological and environmental knowledge, enjoy governmental and political support, recognize legal and economic dynamics, and promote public understanding of the need to preserve biodiversity and assure the survival of bears. The current lack of scientific data on biology, population size, distribution, and habitats prevents the establishment of conservation plans for most Asian bear species. Survey projects to develop basic knowledge of bear habitat requirements, population status, and mortality are urgently needed.

The lack of biological data, however, should not be an excuse for inaction. To address the predominant threats to bears, projects are also needed that consider the legal, social, political, and cultural pressures shaping human interactions with bears. The IUCN/Bear Specialist group has suggested, "Subtle changes in this behavioral landscape may be all that is required to reduce illegal kills, limit human activity in bear habitat, and increase stewardship for bears while long term solutions are sought." (IUCN 1998)

Specific actions required to protect bears include:

- Undertaking biological research, monitoring and surveys on all bear species for which information is lacking, particularly research conducted in the wild to identify threats to bears and form the basis for regional management plans.

- Initiating projects that document the impact of trade, both legal and illegal, on all bear species to determine levels of sustainability for the global trade in bear parts and products.

- Conducting herbal research and identification of plants with efficacy similar to that of bear bile in accordance with the principles of traditional Chinese medicine (TCM).

- Conducting educational projects that increase appreciation of the cultural, traditional, and spiritual attitudes toward bears, with the hope that increased awareness will encourage bear conservation.

Consumer awareness: With Asia's increasing wealth and the expanding popularity of Chinese medicine, bears face a worldwide threat due to demand for their parts and products. The hundreds of "farms" in China producing bear bile have created a two-tiered market for bear products. Consumers in the first tier purchase the less expensive bile from captive bears and encourage the capture of more wild bears for the farms. Those in the second tier demand the more expensive, harder-to-obtain gallbladders from wild bears. Demand from both groups of consumers results in declining wild Asian bear populations and increased hunting pressure on bear populations elsewhere.

Discussions among government agencies, Chinese medicine communities, consumer groups, and conservation organizations are vital to reduce the trade in bear products and ensure the survival of these magnificent animals. Consumer attitude polls and market surveys, conducted in many Asian countries and in Asian communities in the West, show that bear parts or products often are used in TCM without knowledge of the devastating impact this use has on bear populations. The public knows little about the illegal trade in bear products, the inhumane methods used to "farm" bear bile and, most importantly, the availability of alternatives to bear products.

Attitude surveys in two urban centers in China showed that 70 percent of the Chinese public would not have used bear bile products if they had understood the level of cruelty involved in bear farming. The surveys also indicated that more than 86 percent of respondents did not want to relax regulations to allow international export of bear bile products, although only slightly more than half were aware of the existence of any international wildlife trade controls (such as those imposed by CITES).

Although bear gallbladder has a long history of usage in Chinese medicine, a report by the Chinese Association of Medicine and Philosophy and Earth Care Society (Hong Kong) identified at least 54 herbal alternatives to bear bile for its various medicinal applications. Practitioners surveyed in China also indicated that, for treating diseases that require medicine to expel heat and relieve convulsions, doctors have effectively replaced bear bile with herbs that promote blood circulation and remove blood stasis.

From a global perspective, CITES resolution (Conf. 10.8) called for working with traditional medicine communities to reduce demand for bear parts and derivatives. This resolution promotes research on, and the use of, alternatives that do not endanger wild species and promotes increasing public awareness and industry knowledge of bear conservation. Focusing worldwide attention on the conservation of these animals gives hope that bears will continue to be part of the Earth's biodiversity for many generations to come.

Sources

Association of Chinese Medicine and Philosophy and EarthCare Society (Hong Kong) (1994) The Herbal Alternative to Bear Bile in Chinese Medicine. Report commissioned by the International Fund for Animal Welfare.

Bensky D and Gamble A (eds.). (1993) *Chinese Herbal Medicine Materia Medica*, Revised Edition. Eastland Press, Seattle WA,.

CITES (1999) Issues relating to species—Bears. Forty-first meeting of the Standing Committee, Geneva (Switzerland), 8-12 February 1999.

CITES (2002) Resolution Conf. 10.8 (Rev. CoP12) Conservation of and Trade in Bears.

Emanoil M (1994) Asiatic Black Bear. In *Encyclopedia of Endangered Species.* IUCN and Gale Environmental Library, Detroit MI.

Gabriel GG (1999) A Bitter Medicine: Use of Bear Bile in China. In Proceedings of the 3rd International Symposium on the Trade in Bear Parts, 26-28 October, 1999, Seoul,   Korea. D. Williamson and M.J. Phipps (eds.) 2001. TRAFFIC East Asia, Ministry of Environment of ROK, IUCN/Bear Specialist Group.

Garshelis DL, Joshi AR, Smith JL and Rice CG (1998) Sloth Bear Conservation Action Plan. In *IUCN SSC Status Survey and Conservation Action Plan: Bear.* C. Servheen, H. Herrero, B. Peyton and the IUCN/SSC Bear and Polar Bear Specialist Groups (eds). IUCN, Gland, Switzerland.

IFAW (1998) Animal Welfare Attitude Poll in Beijing and Shanghai. International Fund for Animal Welfare.

Investigative Network and the Humane Society of the United States/ Humane Society International (1996) *From Forest to Pharmacy—The Global Underground Trade in Bear Parts.* HSUS/HSI 1996.

IUCN (1998) Global Status and Management of the Polar Bear. In *IUCN SSC Status Survey and Conservation Action Plan: Bear.* C. Servheen, H. Herrero, B. Peyton and the IUCN/SSC Bear and Polar Bear Specialist Groups (eds.). IUCN, Gland, Switzerland

Macdonald D (2001) *The New Encyclopedia of Mammals*. Oxford University Press, Oxford.

Nowak RM (1991) *Walker's Mammals of the World*. Vol. 2. Johns Hopkins University Press, Baltimore MD..

Parker SP (1990) Asiatic Black Bear. In *Grizmek's Encyclopedia of Mammals*.

Peyton B, Servheen C and Herrero S (1998) An overview of bear conservation planning and implementation. In *IUCN SSC Status Survey and Conservation Action Plan: Bear*. C. Servheen, H. Herrero, B. Peyton and the IUCN/SSC Bear and Polar Bear Specialist Groups (eds.). IUCN, Gland, Switzerland

Phillips T and Wilson P (2002) *The Bear Bile Business*. World Society for the Protection of Animals.

Reid DG and Gong J (1998) Giant Panda Conservation Action Plan. In IUCN SSC Status Survey and Conservation Action Plan: Bears. C. Servheen, H. Herrero, B. Peyton and the IUCN/SSC Bear and Polar Bear Specialist Groups (eds.). IUCN, Gland, Switzerland

Roberts A (2001) A Case for a Uniform Global Ban on the Trade in Bear Parts and Derivatives. In Proceedings of the 3rd International Symposium on the Trade in Bear Parts, 26-28 October, 1999, Seoul, Korea. D. Williamson and M.J. Phipps (eds.) 2001. TRAFFIC East Asia, Ministry of Environment of ROK, IUCN/Bear Specialist Group.

Servheen C (2001) The Status of the Bears of the World with Emphasis on Asia. In Proceedings of the 3rd International Symposium on the Trade in Bear Parts, 26-28 October, 1999, Seoul, Korea. D. Williamson and M.J. Phipps (eds.) 2001. TRAFFIC East Asia, Ministry of Environment of ROK, IUCN/Bear Specialist Group.

Servheen C (1999) Bear Conservation Around the World. Friends of the National Zoo, Smithsonian National Zoological Park.

Stirling I (ed.). (1993) *Bears, Majestic Creatures of the Wild*. Rodale Press, Emmaus, PA.

Table 1. Bear Status by Species

Species	Biological Characteristics	Distribution	Population	CITES Status
American black bears (Ursus americanus)	Medium size with uniform black to brown fur with brown muzzle.	Forested areas in Canada, the United States, and Mexico.	About 600,000	Appendix II
Asiatic black bears (Ursus thibetanus)	Medium size. Black fur with white "V" on chest. Long hair ruff around neck.	Forested areas in East Asia, Southeast Asia, & Central Asia countries.	China: < 20,000 India: unknown Japan: 10,000-15,000 Russia: <5,000 Taiwan: unknown Vietnam: unknown	Appendix I
Brown bears (Ursus arctos)	Large size with uniform light to dark brown fur. Distinctive hump over front shoulders, with a slightly flat face.	Densely forested areas in Northern Hemisphere, from United States and Canada to Northern Japan, Russia, Northern and Central Asian countries. Smaller populations in Europe (Greece, Italy, and Spain).	About 125,000	Appendix II (except Bhutan, China, and Mongolia populations; Appendix I)

Giant panda (Ailuropoda melanoleuca)	Medium size with distinct pelage. Ears, eye patches, muzzle, limbs, and shoulders are black; the rest all white.	Six separate mountain ranges in southwest China.	About 1,000	Appendix I
Polar bear (Ursus maritimus)	Largest bear. White fur, often stained yellowish.	Coastal habitat in five nations: Greenland, Norway, Russia, Canada, and the United States, as well as on the Arctic Sea.	Estimated 22,000 to 27,000	Appendix II
Sloth bear (Melursus ursinus)	Black, with distinctive long, shaggy coat. White "U" shaped marking on chest.	India, Sri Lanka, Nepal, Bhutan, and Bangladesh.	No good estimates available, but thought to be 10,000 – 25,000	Appendix I
Spectacled bear (Tremarctos ornatus)	Medium size. Black coat with white biblike marking on chin, neck, or chest and white markings around eyes.	Fragmented small populations in the Andes Mountains in Venezuela, Columbia, Peru, Ecuador and Bolivia.	Estimated 18,000	Appendix I
Sun bear (Helarctos malayanus)	Smallest bear, with short black or dark brown fur and yellow 'U' shaped crescent on the chest.	Dense tropical forests in Southeast Asian countries and in parts of India and Southern China.	Unknown	Appendix I

MUSK DEER

Andrea Heydlauff
Wildlife Conservation Society, USA

Moschus	Shè Xiāng	Moschus moschiferus, Moschus beresovskii, Moschus chrysogaster, Moschus fuscus, Moschus sifanicus, Moschus anhuiensis

Musk deer (*Moschus* spp.) are a group of species native to at least 15 different countries in East, Southeast, and South Asia. Scientists estimate that the total musk deer population numbers between 400,000 and 800,000 individuals. The animal's range, however, involves so many different countries that a more precise count is difficult to obtain.

Musk deer are the source of natural musk, a strong-smelling substance obtained from the scent gland of the male. Musk can be found in many traditional medicines used to treat ailments involving the heart, nerves, and lungs. In the past, natural musk was also widely used in perfumes; synthetic musk now meets most of the demand in this market.

....

DISTRIBUTION

To date, the taxonomy of musk deer remains debatable; at present, four or more species are recognized, all of which have been listed since 1979 in CITES. Siberian musk deer (*Moschus moschiferus*) are found in China, Mongolia, North and South Korea, Russia, Kazakhstan, and Kyrgyzstan. The forest musk deer (*Moschus berezovskii*) lives in China and Vietnam. Himalayan musk deer (*Moschus chrysogaster*) are found in Afghanistan, China, India, Nepal, and Pakistan, while the black musk deer (*Moschus fuscus*) occurs in Bhutan, China, India, Myanmar, and Nepal. Two additional species, the Alpine musk deer (*Moschus sifanicus*) and the Anhui musk deer (*Moshcus anhuiensis*), may exist only in China.

....

BIOLOGY

As a species, musk deer fall phylogenetically between deer and antelope. Musk deer lack horns, antlers, and facial glands but possess long upper canine teeth that look like saber-shaped tusks. Both males and females have a gallbladder, but only males have caudal and musk glands. These identifiers distinguish them from antelope and deer.

A musk deer stands approximately 50 to 80 centimeters (20 to 31 inches) high at the shoulder. Its body is covered with thick, bristly hairs that protect it in harsh climates. Musk deer are not herd animals. Musk deer are shy, timid and primarily solitary (UNEP/WCMC 2006).

They prefer dense cover during the day, but will venture into open areas at night. Musk deer are mainly browsers that eat woody plant leaves, flowers, forbs, and shrubs.

Both males and females communicate chiefly through smell, including urination, defecation, and, in the case of males, through secretions from the musk and caudal glands. The musk gland is found beneath the skin of the abdomen. Males can secrete musk in their urine and will scent mark by rubbing the tail region against bushes. Musk is synthesized before each rut.

During the breeding season, females actively seek out males with well-developed musk and caudal glands. Musk secretion might play an important role in reproduction, possibly stimulating the estrous cycle in females. Beginning at the age of 12 to 18 months, musk is secreted into the sac where it takes approximately 30 days to mature, changing from a creamy, white, unscented fluid to a potent, dark-red granular substance. Musk deer reach sexual maturity by the age of 18 months, and females can reproduce in their first year (Shrestha 1993, 1998, Walker 1999).

....

THREATS

Although habitat loss caused by deforestation is a threat to the long-term survival of musk deer species, continued demand for natural musk has already caused the rapid decline of musk deer populations. As a result, musk deer now face the possibility of extinction throughout most of their range (TRAFFIC 2002, Zhang 2003).

Musk deer are illegally hunted for their musk gland or "pod." The major traders and consumers of musk products for medicinal purposes, which make up approximately 90 percent of the international musk trade, are in East Asia and Southeast Asia (Homes 1999). Most natural musk is used in indigenous systems of medicine, mainly in China, India, Nepal, and Japan (Shrestha 1998). Secretions from the gland can be found in at least 300 manufactured East Asian medicines; a limited amount of musk is used in the homeopathic industry in Europe (Homes 1999). Musk also is used in the perfume market.

All six species of musk deer live in China, making that country the major source of musk deer medicinal products (Zhang 2003). In China alone, the estimated annual demand for musk averages between 500 and 1,000 kilograms (1,100 – 2,200 lbs.) — an amount equivalent to the pods from approximately 100,000 musk deer.

On average, 3,000 male musk deer in Mongolia and 20,000 in Russia are harvested illegally every year by local people seeking to alleviate their poverty with income from the illegal musk trade (TRAFFIC 2002). The hunting and trapping techniques used typically result in the killing of three to five animals for every male musk deer that has a gland of sufficient size (Homes 1999). Scientists estimate that 18 to 52 percent of the Himalayan musk deer population is harvested annually to supply the medicinal market (Green 1986, Shrestha 1998).

Musk continues to be one of the world's most valuable commodities. Retail prices in the United States and Japan range between US $30 to $50 per gram, a price higher than gold (US $10 per gram). Due to its high cost, the use of musk has declined in the perfume industry, where it has largely been replaced by synthetic musk (Homes 1999).

....

CONSERVATION STRATEGIES AND RESEARCH

Musk deer populations in Afghanistan, Bhutan, India, Myanmar, Nepal, and Pakistan are listed on Appendix I of CITES. These animals, and products made from them, are thus banned from global commercial trade.

All other populations of musk deer fall under CITES Appendix II, which requires the country of origin or re-export to issue permits authorizing international trade (Holmes 1999). Musk deer are also protected under national legislation in Bhutan (where poachers may be shot on sight), China, India, North Korea, Mongolia, Myanmar, Nepal, and

Vietnam. Despite these protections, most musk deer populations remain in jeopardy (Homes 1998).

Although musk deer are usually killed so their musk glands can be removed, musk can be harvested from male deer without harming the animal (Shrestha 1998). In the 1950s, China launched efforts to establish musk deer farms to meet the demand for musk. These farms, however, have not been able to produce enough musk to satisfy market needs (Zhang 2003), and questions remain about the viability of such operations, as well as the role they play in the reduction of wild populations.

Musk deer are difficult to breed in captivity due to their shy nature, their solitary lifestyle, and their susceptibility to disease (Sheng 1998, Yang et al. 2003). Differing opinions exist about China's success in farming musk deer (Yang et al. 2003). The question arises as to whether farming results in a conservation gain for the species or merely a financial gain for the farmers. Most examples currently available suggest that musk deer farming is a lose-lose situation. The Anhui Musk Deer Breeding Center, established in the 1970s, reportedly had 101 musk deer at its peak, but disease and mismanagement reduced the survival rate, leaving only 50 individuals by 1980. From 1980 to 1981, 43 additional musk deer were captured, and hybrids were obtained by cross breeding offspring, but the project continued to flounder. By 1986, no musk deer remained.

Other institutions and organizations have tried to raise musk deer during the past decades. However, no successful models appear to have resulted from these efforts (Wang, 1998).

China has outlawed selling and hunting wild musk deer and has set aside 10 musk deer conservation areas. But creating protected areas for the giant panda has indirectly had a more beneficial effect on musk deer conservation, since pandas and forest musk deer share similar ranges (Holmes 1998, Zhang 2003).

Some conservationists looking for ways to safeguard musk deer species have proposed that countries importing musk be required to provide financial or technical support to help range countries monitor and protect musk deer populations (Holmes 1999). Increased public awareness of the threat to musk deer species may help reduce the use of natural musk in medicines and perfumes (Homes 1999).

Other measures that would help conserve musk deer include labeling products containing musk in both the medicinal and perfume trade (Yang et al. 2003), establishing protected zones throughout the species range, and restricting the unsustainable harvest of timber in forests where musk deer are found (Yang et al. 2003, Zhang 2003). Finally, laws regulating the live capture of musk deer and sale of their parts and products must be enforced. Further steps need to be taken to eliminate illegal trade (Zhang 2003).

Additional research is also needed. Few studies have been conducted on musk deer conservation, and knowledge of these species is less than comprehensive. Many questions have been posed and areas identified where information is lacking. Education is also needed to promote the use of plant alternatives and synthetic musk as replacements for natural musk.

SOURCES

Homes V (1999) *On The Scent: Conserving Musk Deer—The Uses of Musk and Europe's Role in its Trade.* TRAFFIC Europe Report. As of March 2006 available at: www.traffic.org/musk/

Shrestha MN (1993) Musk deer husbandry and possibility of farming in Nepal. The Bulletin of Veterinary Science: Animal Husbandry 21 (23): pp. 34-37.

Shrestha MN (1998) Animal welfare in the musk deer. *Applied Animal Behaviour Science* 59: pp. 245-250.

Tierra M, Comparing the Liver According to Traditional Chinese and Western Scientific Physiology. As of March 2006 available at: http://planetherbs.com/articles/Liver-%20Chinese%20and%20We stern%20scientific%20Physiology.html

TRAFFIC, WWF (2002) The Challenge of Conserving Musk Deer (*Moschus* spp.). TRAFFIC and WWF briefing. As of March 2006 available at: www.traffic.org/cop12/muskdeer.pdf

UNEP/WCMC. As of March 2006 available at:

http://www.unep-wcmc.org/index.html?http://www.unep-wcmc.org/ species/data/species_sheets/smuskdee.htm~main

Walker EP (1999) *Walker's Mammals of the World*, 6th Edition, Vol 2. Johns Hopkins University Press, Baltimore MD.

Wang S (1998) *China Red Data Book of Endangered Animals - Mammalia.* Science Press, Beijing, PRC: pp. 231-245.

Yang Q, Meng Z, Xia L, and Feng Z (2003) Conservation status and causes of decline of musk deer (*Moschus* spp.) in China. *Biological Conservation* 109 (3): pp. 333-342.

Zhang E (2003) Musk deer case study (*Moschus* spp.). Wildlife Conservation Society.

Pangolins

Michael Spencer
WildAid

Squama Manis	Chuān Shān Jiǎ	Manis carssicaudata, Manis pentadactyla, Manis javania, Manis tetradactyla, Manis tricuspis, Manis temmenki, Manis gigantea

Sometimes known as scaly anteaters, pangolins (*Manis* spp.) have hard and scaly body armor that gives them a reptilian appearance, although they are mammals. Described by the American poet Marianne Moore as a "near artichoke" on whose body "scale lap[s] scale with spruce-cone regularity," these small, shy, nocturnal animals feed almost exclusively on ants and termites. When threatened, they roll themselves into a ball, leaving would-be predators to contend with a sphere of hard, protective scales.

Pangolins were long thought to belong to the same family as armadillos and anteaters. While they may have co-evolved with these species along a parallel track, they are now believed to be more closely related to carnivores such as civets and mongooses. Fossil species with clearly defined scales that date to the Eocene have been uncovered in Europe.

Worldwide, seven species of pangolin are included in the single family *Manidae,* all from the warmer parts of Asia and Africa. In Nepal, pangolins are called "salak" or "kaynana," referring to the color of their scales. The animal's Malayan name means "to roll," describing its defensive posture. The word "pangolin" itself is thought to be of French origin; it too refers to the animal's practice of rolling into a ball to protect itself.

Destruction of the pangolin's natural habitat and hunting the animal for medicine or food have left all three of the Asian species and one of the African species on the brink of extinction. The Pangolin Species Specialist Group reports that these threats have made "these strangely scaled mammals one of the most endangered groups in the world."

DISTRIBUTION

Pangolins were originally found in abundance in the tropical and subtropical regions of Asia and Africa. They inhabit forests, thick bush, and savannah country where ant and termite nests abound.

The Indian pangolin (*Manis crassicaudata*), as its name implies, may be found in India and Sri Lanka. The Chinese pangolin (*Manis pentadactyla)* ranges through Nepal and the Assam region of India into China. A burrowing species, the Chinese pangolin lives underground. The Malayan pangolin (*Manis javanica*) is found in Malaysia, Indonesia (Borneo, Java, Sumatra), Myanmar, and Thailand where it is a tree-dweller, sleeping during the day in the forks of trees.

The four species found in Africa are the long tailed pangolin (*Manis tetradactyla*), small-scaled or white-billed pangolin (*Manis tricuspis*), Cape pangolin (*Manis temmenki*), and giant pangolin (*Manis gigantea*).

BIOLOGY

Pangolins have elongated, tapering bodies, the outer surfaces of which are covered with overlapping scales. This scaly armor, an unusual feature in mammals, is their most distinctive characteristic. Only one species, the Chinese pangolin, possesses hair as well as scales. Scale colors range from brown to olive or yellow, and the skin is gray with a blue or pink tinge in some areas. When alarmed, pangolins can raise their scales; those on the tail are particularly sharp. The stomach and portions of the face, such as the nose, are unscaled. All their limbs have five claws.

Depending on species and age, pangolins vary in length from 60 to 160 centimeters (23 to 62 inches) and weigh anywhere from 4 to 33 kilograms (8.8 to 72.7 pounds). Long-tailed and small scaled pangolins have prehensile tails and live in trees. The Cape and giant pangolin dig burrows, although they can also climb trees. These animals' tails are usually as long as their head and body combined.

Unlike most mammals, pangolins have no teeth. To compensate, their lower jaw works as a small blade-like bone. Pangolins also swallow stones that further help grind their food. The tongue, which is about 5 millimeters (0.1 inch) thick and can be extended about 25 centimeters

(9.8 inches) in the adult, is an essential tool for gathering food. When not in use, the tongue is rolled in a pouch inside the pangolin's throat. Its root passes down through the animal's chest cavity and into the pelvis.

Unless alarmed, pangolins move slowly and deliberately. When they walk on their hind legs, the tail provides a brace for balance. When on all four limbs, they curl their front feet inward to walk on the knuckles, thus protecting their claws.

Although the pangolin's scales and claws make it look unapproachable, the animal is generally timid. When frightened, its main defensive mechanism is its ability to roll itself into a tight ball, its armored limbs and tail protecting soft underparts. Once the animal is in this rolled-up position, its sharp-edged scales make it difficult for predators to attack. This behavior, however, makes pangolins vulnerable to their most deadly predator - humans. Hunters merely pick up the coiled pangolin and put it in a sack. They also dig or smoke the animals out of their burrows.

Pangolins have been observed escaping from danger by rolling down a steep slope. When threatened, they also lash out with their tails, which are covered with sharp-edged scales, and spray a foul-smelling liquid from their anal glands. Pangolins can run at a speed of about three miles per hour.

The pangolin's diet consists mainly of ants and termites, but it will eat other soft-bodied insects and larvae on occasion. The search for food is constant; water is also a necessity.

Pangolins have relatively poor vision and hearing, so they probably locate their prey by scent. Balanced with the help of their heavy tail, they use the long claws on their forefeet to tear apart ant and termite mounds. They use their long, sticky tongue to flick in and out of the passageways in search of food. They protect themselves from ants by closing their nostrils and ear openings, as well as their thick eyelids. Because pangolins have no teeth, ants and termites enter the stomach uncrushed, where they must be mechanically ground by thick muscular stomach walls and small pebbles the animals ingest along with the insects.

Pangolins also have been observed performing a highly unusual feeding ritual known as an ant bath. The pangolin settles itself in an ant nest, and then raises its scales, allowing the ants to crawl underneath. It crushes the ants by depressing its scales. Then, it goes into water and raises its scales, allowing the dead ants to float to the surface to be retrieved and eaten.

Adult pangolins are generally solitary but sometimes associate in pairs. The female carries its offspring for three to five months before giving birth. Rarely is more than one baby born at a time. Only about 45 centimeters (17.7 inches) long at birth, the baby has soft scales that harden within two days. The young ride on the back or tail of the mother by clinging on tightly. When danger threatens, the mother conceals her offspring within her rolled-up body.

Scientists have not successfully documented the lifespan of these creatures in the wild. One specimen in captivity lived more than 13 years, but such longevity would be unlikely in a natural setting.

....

THREATS

The pangolin's low reproductive rate and large home range make it particularly vulnerable to over-exploitation. Both Asian and African species are in decline, although the animal's solitary nature and nocturnal lifestyle have made it difficult to determine the status of different populations.

Hunting has definitely taken a toll on pangolins in Asia, where they are sought for their meat, skins, and scales. Markets supply international trade, as well as domestic consumption. In China, pangolin scales are highly prized for their medicinal value. Demand for pangolin meat in that nation's restaurants also has contributed significantly to the decline of populations. In January 2002, for example, the Bangkok Post reported the seizure of 400 illegally acquired pangolins destined for medicine or food outlets. In New York's Chinatown, scales and meat labeled as pangolin products have been offered for sale on the street.

The unsustainable levels of pangolin hunting occurring throughout Asia are reflected in official export figures recorded in countries like Malaysia and Indonesia. From 1958 to 1964, for example, more than 60 tons of scales, estimated to represent more than 50,000 animals, were exported legally from the Malaysian state of Sarawak. Such commerce continued through the 1980s. From 1980 to 1985, the scales of an estimated 3,000 to 5,000 pangolins were exported annually to Taiwan and South Korea. The trade in skins has been even more extensive, with approximately 185,000 exported legally from 1980 to 1985. These hides, 90 percent of which went to the United States, were used to manufacture leather goods, principally boots and shoes.

Loss of pangolins to hunting is a concern not only in China and Southeast Asia, but in other parts of the animal's range on the continent as well. In India and Nepal, traditional hunters use trained dogs to track down these animals. Pangolin scales are extracted after the animal has been killed and skinned. Scales from one adult weigh an average of one kilogram. Oil is extracted from the fat and used for medicinal purposes. Practitioners of folk medicine also use the brain of the animal, and tribal people consider the flesh a delicacy.

African pangolin species are also reported to be decreasing in much of their range. Demand for scales by local doctors and herbalists encourage hunting. Other threats include loss of habitat to agriculture and the animal's susceptibility to insecticides.

....

Conservation Strategies and Research

As early as 1975, the member nations of CITES placed all pangolin species on Appendix II, a listing that required exporting countries to issue permits to authorize trade. Twenty-five years later in 2000, the CITES community also set a zero annual export quota for the three Asian species of wild pangolin. Nevertheless, this measure does not apply to domestic consumption, and large-scale smuggling also continues. Both factors further aggravate the pangolin's chance of survival. One African species, the Cape pangolin, also is listed as endangered under the U.S. Endangered Species Act.

Countries with pangolin populations also have taken steps to stem the unsustainable hunting and trade of these animals. Nationally legislated protections exist in Bangladesh, Thailand (where the animals are classified as protected), India (where two of the three Asian species are protected), Pakistan (where one of the three species is protected), and Indonesia (where *Manis javanica* has been protected since 1931). In China, the Chinese pangolin is listed as a Class II protected species in the Wild Animal Protection Law (1981). Catching or hunting wildlife under Class II protection requires a special license.

CITES data suggest that the country of origin for pangolins in international trade shifts as populations become depleted and protective measures are imposed. Until the mid-1980s, for example, most imports were declared as originating in Thailand, Indonesia, or Malaysia. Most documented trade now originates in Laos, which exported more than

70,000 skins between 1991 and 1996. The Pangolin Specialist Group reported the frequent confiscation of sacks of pangolins mixed with freshwater turtles, despite measures in Laos to protect the species. Lack of coordination between different departments was cited as a cause.

Despite national and international efforts, available information suggests that Asian populations are increasingly under threat due to market demand for live pangolins, skins, scales, and meat. Live pangolins fetch about US$100 per animal in wildlife markets across the region. In restaurants in China, diners pay as much for one kilogram (2.2 pounds) of pangolin meat. Rising prices indicate a high level of demand for this species and suggest that populations are declining despite official efforts to conserve them.

For example, a 1996 survey by TRAFFIC East Asia that analyzed the use of wildlife as medicine and food by Hong Kong Chinese showed that the Chinese pangolin was the third most frequently consumed animal after snake and civet cat. Consumers regarded pangolin meat as a health tonic that warms the body.

Pangolin scales were among the most frequently observed medicines during surveys conducted in 1996 by the Chinese Academy of Science in six medicine markets in China. That same year, the State Administration of Traditional Chinese Medicine noted that supplies from neighboring countries had alleviated the shortage of pangolin scales in China. A report issued two years later also noted that imports from Vietnam, Laos, and Myanmar were helping to meet the demand for scales in China.

Should the current demand trends continue alongside the current unsustainable management of wildlife resources, experts predict the three Asian pangolin species may become extinct in the near future.

SOURCES

Born Free Foundation website as of March 2006 available at: http://www.bornfree.org.uk/pangolins/pangolins.shtml

IUCN Pangolin specialist group Conservation and Management. As of March 2006 available at: http://protect.tfri.gov.tw/animal/pangolin/iucn_003_01.asp

TRAFFIC (2000) Dispatches, June 2000

Website as of March 2006, available at: http://animaldiversity.ummz.umich.edu/site/accounts/information/Pholidota.html

Website as of March 2006 available at: http://www.awf.org/wildlives/178

Website as of March 2006 available at: http://ladywildlife.com/animal/pangolin.html

Website as of March 2006 available at: http://www.bbc.co.uk/nature/wildfacts/factfiles/622.shtml

Website as of March 2006 available at: http://www.pangolin.com/PangolinPic.html

World Wildlife Fund (2004) "Armored but Endangered." Feature story, 9/16/2004. Available at: http://www.panda.org/about_wwf/what_we_do/species/news/stories/index.cfm?uNewsID=15278

Rhinoceroses

Michael Spencer
WildAid

Cornu Rhinoceri	Xī Jiǎo	Ceratotherium simum, Ceratotherium simum simum, Ceratotherium simum cottoni, Diceros bicornis, Rhinoceros unicornis, Dicerorthinus sumatrensis, Rhinoceros sondaicus

Rhinoceroses have existed for more than 50 million years. Ancient drawings of these animals, predating those in the caves of Lascaux, have been found in the Dordogne region of France. These sturdy, enduring animals have no predators other than humans. All rhinoceros species are severely threatened by poaching and habitat loss across their range in Africa and Asia. Concern about their decline has prompted increased support for rhino protection and stricter controls on the sale and trade of rhinoceros parts and products.

....

Distribution

Five species of rhinoceros survive today. Two live in Africa and three in Asia, with a total wild population of approximately 17,500 individuals.

The largest species, and also the most numerous, is the African white rhino (*Ceratotherium simum*). Afrikaans used the word "weit" to describe the animal's "wide" mouth, but English settlers later interpreted this word as "white," thus giving the animal its common name. This species consists of two distinct subspecies, the Southern white rhino (*Ceratotherium simum simum*) and the Northern white rhino (*Ceratotherium simum cottoni*). The former, located primarily in South Africa, is more numerous, while the latter is most severely endangered. Only approximately 30 individuals survive in Garamba National Park in the Democratic Republic of the Congo. The total overall population of the species is estimated to be 11,670.

The African black rhino (*Diceros bicornis*) is not black at all. Its name, derived from the dark local soil that colors its skin, serves perhaps to distinguish it from the white rhino. Unlike the squarish-lipped white rhino, which feeds by grazing, these animals are browsers. They have an upper prehensile lip adapted to feeding from shrubs and trees, and they inhabit dense thickets and dry scrublands. Although black rhinos once ranged across most of Africa, today they require protection in parks, reserves, and on private lands in order to survive. Between 1970 and 1992, the species suffered a 96 percent decrease in population; their numbers dropped from approximately 65,000 animals to 2,300. Thanks to active efforts to stem poaching, the population has grown to approximately 3,100 animals, which survive in isolated pockets dispersed across much of the species' former range. The largest remaining populations are found in South Africa, Namibia, Zimbabwe, and Kenya.

The three Asian species are the Indian rhino (*Rhinoceros unicornis*), Sumatran rhino (*Dicerorhinus sumatrensis*), and Javan rhino (*Rhinoceros sondaicus*). Of these, the Indian rhino is the most abundant, with just over 2,400 animals in India, Bhutan, and Nepal. Approximately 300 Sumatran rhinos are believed to survive in small, very isolated and fragmented groups, an estimate that represents a sobering 50 percent decline in the past 15 years.

Current estimates of the Javan rhino population suggest that this species is now the rarest of the rhinos. Fewer than 60 individuals are left in two locations—one in Vietnam and one in Indonesia. Habitat loss and poaching continue to put heavy pressure on this species.

....

BIOLOGY

After the elephant, the rhinoceros is the second largest land animal on earth. Under ideal conditions, rhinos may live 50 years and weigh as much as three tons. Although their eyesight is notoriously poor, they have excellent senses of smell and hearing, and they are fast and formidable foes when attacking an adversary. Their skin tones vary from red to gray, depending on the mud they wallow in each day to stay cool and protect themselves from biting insects.

Depending on the species, a rhino may have one or two horns on its forehead. The black, white, and Sumatran rhinos have two horns; the Indian and Javan rhinos have one. The horn is made of densely matted rough hair—a form of keratin, much like human hair and toenails. Rhinos use their horns for protection, to establish rank, and as a tool. The horn appears weeks after birth and continues to grow at six to eight centimeters per year. Some researchers suggest that the legendary explorer Marco Polo may actually have been describing Sumatran rhinos (which, unlike other essentially hairless species, have long, shaggy hair) when he wrote in 1298 of seeing "unicorns" with "hair like that of a buffalo, feet like those of an elephant, and a horn in the middle of the forehead, which is black and very thick."

Despite their fierce appearance, rhinos are herbivores. The African white rhino and the Indian rhino are grazers, consuming mostly grass. The African black rhino and Sumatran rhino are browsers that eat leaves and twigs of bushes and trees. While the Javan rhino seems to be a mixed feeder, it is likely the animal is primarily a browser.

Female rhinos can breed as early as age three; male rhinos reach maturity at age seven. Generally, female rhinos are attentive mothers, suckling a new calf for a full year and staying with it until ready to give birth again, usually after about four years.

Most rhinos are solitary, living in open grassland, savannah, scrub forest, or marsh. Indian rhinos live in seasonally flooded regions. Sumatran rhinos now are found only in deep forest. Black rhinos are unsociable and only come together to mate. They prefer dense thickets for browsing. White rhinos prefer open grassland for grazing, and they may live in small family groups of as many as 10 animals. All species need cover to keep cool, as well as water to drink regularly. All are territorial, marking their ranges with urine and dung.

....

THREATS

Rhinos have lost habitat to agricultural expansion, development, and deforestation and have been squeezed into smaller and smaller spaces to make room for growing human populations. Rhinos are also preyed upon for their horn, which is used in traditional Chinese medicine to reduce fever and hemorrhaging. It is also used ornamentally to make ceremonial daggers that are worn in some Middle Eastern countries.

Habitat loss and "harvest" for their horn have combined to decimate rhino populations. At the turn of the last century, evidence suggests that approximately 100,000 rhinos existed worldwide. One hundred years later, the population of all five species in the wild has shrunk to approximately 17,530 individuals, a loss of more than 80 percent.

Demand for rhino horn by users of traditional Chinese medicine continues to put pressure on rhino populations. Sixty percent of traditional medicine practitioners in East Asia stock rhino horn, with Asian horns preferred over their African counterparts. South Korea and China (including Taiwan and Hong Kong) are among the largest consumers of rhino products. While such demand keeps illegal poaching and trade alive, research suggests practitioners who purchase and prescribe rhino horn see it, not as a luxury, but as a life-saving necessity with significant medical value. Given the high price of horn (in 1994, a kilogram was worth about US $60,000 in the Far East), one might expect those who buy it to sell it quickly for profit. Studies by TRAFFIC (the trade monitoring network of the World Wildlife Fund and the IUCN), however, show just the opposite occurs. Practitioners typically recouped their investment only after seven years, suggesting that the medical value of the horn requires sparing and judicious use.

Conservation action has helped stem the other major use of rhino horn. In Yemen, rhino horn was used for hundreds of years to create the handles of traditional daggers, which were worn as symbols of wealth and status. But the scarcity of rhino horn and bans on its trade have changed this ancient practice. In the 1970s, economic conditions in Yemen made it possible to purchase traditional daggers with rhino horn handles, albeit at great expense. At that time, Yemen consumed as much as 40 percent of the horn being traded. Economic and political changes in the 1980s, coupled with protections for rhinos, resulted in the increased use of alternatives to rhino horn, including water buffalo horn. Since 1994, dagger handles made from jasper and locally quarried agate have proved to be a popular substitute, even though these materials cost more than water buffalo horn.

Despite the reduced demand for horn in some markets, rhino poaching in Africa continues to be a serious problem. In recent years, civil wars have increased the availability of high-powered weapons, making it easier for poachers to kill rhinos.

....

CONSERVATION EFFORTS AND RESEARCH

The member nations of CITES have placed all but one rhino species on the treaty's Appendix I, thus outlawing commercial trade in rhino products. South Africa's population of white rhinos is listed on Appendix II, with trade restricted to legally hunted trophies and live animals destined for appropriate and acceptable locations. These decisions were made early in the life of the convention, in 1975 and 1977, respectively.

In the early 1990s, however, the international community became increasingly concerned about the rate at which rhino populations were being decimated and realized that extinction was a real possibility for these magnificent animals unless something was done. Delegations traveled to key consuming countries to persuade them to increase their protection efforts. During this time, the United States imposed sanctions on Taiwan, one of the countries identified as a primary consumer of rhino horn. International pressure prompted the government of Taiwan to ban rhino trade, increase penalties, form a Wildlife Protection Unit, and expand public education efforts. Similar measures were implemented in Hong Kong and China.

Range countries also improved protections. Some nations closely guarded their remaining free ranging rhinos. South Africa formed a special police force called the Endangered Species Protection Unit (ESPU) to combat illegal smuggling of African horn through southern Africa for export to the Far East. In Nepal, 700 armed troops and rangers protected one population—a ratio of almost two guards per rhino.

The huge decrease in rhinoceros populations resulted in the evolution of new approaches to control poaching and protect the animals. Some programs introduced dehorning procedures and shoot-to-kill policies to deter poachers.

In 1991, the World Wide Fund for Nature (WWF) launched a conservation program for black and white rhinos in Zimbabwe, moving the animals from areas of high poaching activity to areas of relative safety, where they were dehorned. By August 1993, 122 black rhinos and 111 white rhinos had undergone the procedure. A similar dehorning program was started in Namibia in 1989.

The practice of dehorning rhinos had both advocates and detractors. Some argued that allowing trade in amputated horn could generate much needed revenue for conservation, while others maintained that such sales would only fuel demand. Questions also arose about how dehorning affected the species itself. Studies looked at such factors as horn growth and regrowth, reproductive behavior in rhinos with different horn sizes, and range size of males and females in relation to horn and body sizes. Even the efficacy of the procedure as a way to prevent poaching remains in doubt. Dehorned rhinos may be no safer than those retaining their horns, since poachers have been known to kill even for the sliver of horn that remains on dehorned animals.

As an alternative, some game preserves in the past adopted a controversial "shoot to kill" policy to protect rhinos. Wardens or other officers enforcing anti-poaching laws were trained to "shoot first, ask questions later." In 1984, for example, the government of Zimbabwe instituted such a policy as part of Operation Stronghold—an effort to prevent the poaching of elephants and rhinos. During its lifespan, 178 people suspected of being poachers were killed. Although the country's rhino population rose steadily from virtually zero to 260 in 1997, the recent political and economic crisis in Zimbabwe has undermined some of these gains.

Clinical trials to determine the pharmacological basis for efficacy of rhino horn in reducing fever and addressing other selected medical problems have proved problematic. According to an IUCN summary document, a study on rabbits demonstrated no fever-reducing properties, although a second study giving huge doses of horn to rats did reveal some cooling effect.

Although practitioners of traditional medicine continue to value rhino horn for its healing properties, workshops conducted in Asia in 1992 and 1995 by TRAFFIC also showed that the community regards conservation seriously and considers it within the rubric of its practice. Openness to further conservation-based action may ultimately provide the stimulus needed to ensure long-term survival of rhino species.

SOURCES

Emslie R and Brooks M (Compiled) (1999) African Rhino - Status Survey and Conservation Action Plan. IUCN/SSC African Rhino Specialist Group. 1999 International Union for Conservation of Nature and Natural Resources.

International Rhino Foundation website as of March 2006 available at: http://www.rhinos-irf.org/

Rhino Resource Center website at of March 2006 available at: http://www.rhinoresourcecenter.com

Save the Rhino website as of March 2006 available at: http://www.savetherhino.org/index.phtml

SOS Rhino website as of March 2006 available at: http://www.sosrhino.org/

Website as of March 2006 available at: http://www.achimerfriendsofrhino.de/Rhino/Rhino_Horn/IUCN_Notes/iucn_notes.html

Website as of March 2006 available at: http://www.bagheera.com/inthewild/van_anim_rhino.htm

SAIGA ANTELOPE

Grace Ge Gabriel
International Fund for Animal Welfare

Cornu Antelopis	Líng Yáng Jĭao	Saiga tatarica tatarica, Saiga tatarica mongolica

The saiga antelope (*Saiga tatarica*) is a small, nomadic species that inhabits the semi-arid rangelands of Central Asia. The animal's scientific name, *Saiga tatarica*, comes from the Russian word for antelope (*saiga*) and the area in eastern Russia that is its home—Tatary (*tatarica*). The common name for the saiga in Chinese is *Saijia Ling Yang*, in Japanese *Reiyokaku*, and in Korean *Yongyanggak*.

The bones of saiga antelope have been found buried in geologic deposits dating from the Pleistocene. These discoveries testify to the endurance of a species referred to by some as a "living fossil."

Throughout the past 400 years of human history, the rise and fall of saiga populations have been intricately linked to human occupation of the regions favored by these antelope. More recently, hunting of the saiga for its meat and horns has had a devastating impact. A mere 10 years ago, saiga populations appeared so healthy that some conservationists actively promoted using saiga horn as an alternative to rhino horn in Traditional Chinese Medicine (TCM). Today, biologists say the saiga population is in the midst of the most sudden and dramatic population crash of a mammal ever seen. They warn that the species is on a rapid trajectory toward extinction.

The case of the saiga antelope is a tragic example of how commercial trade in animal parts can rapidly affect a wild population. The future of this "living fossil" is now in doubt; its survival requires immediate action.

....

DISTRIBUTION

Saiga antelopes originated in central Asia between two and five million years ago. They ranged over a vast area, from the British Isles in the west to the Northwest Territories of Canada in the east, extending north to

Siberia and south to the Caucasus region. Their range dramatically diminished 10,000 years ago, when climatic changes melted the ice and flooded much of the grassland habitat on which the saiga relied.

Today, two subspecies of saiga remain: *S. t. tatarica*, found in Kazakhstan (three populations) and the Russian Federation (one population), and *S. t. mongolica*, found in Mongolia (two populations). Some herds from Kazakhstan migrate to Turkmenistan and Uzbekistan during the winter. Each of the species' populations is distinct, with limited intermixing. No saigas remain in their natural habitats in the Ukraine, but a large herd lives in an enclosure at the Askania Nova Biosphere Reserve.

....

BIOLOGY

Saigas inhabit the open dry steppe and semi-desert grasslands of Central Asia and the Pre-Caspian region. They prefer areas free of dense vegetation, where they can run quickly - up to 128 kilometers per hour (80 miles/hour) - to avoid predators such as wolves and humans. Saigas are herbivores, eating low-lying vegetation such as herbs, grasses, and shrubs.

Saiga antelope are usually found in herds of 30 to 40, but they will congregate in the thousands at calving grounds in spring and during spring and fall migrations. Migration is a way of life for the saiga. They spend the winter in desert areas, where the snow is not deep and vegetation is plentiful. In the spring, they move as much as 1,000 kilometers (620 miles) north to the steppes to take advantage of the rich grazing areas. In the autumn, they retrace their steps southward.

Saiga also migrate to avoid bad weather, food shortages, and predators. They have been known to travel 40 kilometers (25 miles) in a single day. This nomadic lifestyle is advantageous in a semi-desert environment, where food sources can be highly localized and far apart.

Saiga are small mammals. Females stand 106 to 124 centimeters (42 to 49 inches) tall and males are 109 to 140 centimeters (43 to 55 inches) tall. A short mane covers the back of the neck. Ears and tail are short, and the eyes appear to be supported on bony protrusions when viewed from directly in front of the animal. Although saigas' hearing is not acute, their eyesight is excellent, and they can see danger up to one kilometer (0.6 mile) away.

Only males have horns, which grow to 20 to 25 centimeters (8 to 10 inches) in length. The horns are ringed with prominent ridges near the base and have a semi-translucent, wax-colored appearance.

The most unusual feature of the saiga is its large nose, bulbous and thick, which at first glance appears swollen, as if battered in a fight. In reality, it contains a complex filtration system of convoluted bones, hairs, and glands that secrete mucus. This feature enables saiga to filter dust inhaled from their desert environment, extract valuable moisture from the dry air, and even warm up the air during the winter. The males' noses increase in size during the rut, and hair tufts below the eyes become thickened with gland secretions.

Saiga antelopes adapt to changes in climate by changing their coat. In warm summer months, the fur is sparse and light brown. In winter, their coat turns white and has a thick wooly under-layer covered by longer, coarser bristles that provide protection from the harsh climate. The saiga's winter coat may be twice as long and as much as 70 percent thicker than its summer coat.

Under the best conditions, saiga antelopes live between six and 10 years, with females reaching sexual maturity at eight months and males at 20 months. Mating occurs in December, and calves are born between late March and early May. Females breeding for the first time give birth to a single calf, while twins are common in successive years.

The saiga's early reproductive age and ability to give birth to twins mean that the species has potential for rapid population growth. Under optimum conditions, an entire population may be renewed every four years. This ability to recover quickly from heavy losses is an adaptation to the saiga's harsh and unpredictable environment, where drought and snowy winters may cause high mortality.

The ability to reproduce rapidly has helped the saiga recover from low population levels numerous times in recent history. In the early 20th century, the Russian subspecies *S. t. tatarica* was nearly hunted to extinction. Populations recovered in the aftermath of the Russian Revolution when reduced numbers of humans and livestock lived in the regions favored by saiga. In addition, the development of collective farms aggregated humans and livestock near the most desirable pasturelands, leaving the steppes available for saiga occupancy. The saiga received additional protection from a hunting ban imposed by the Bolsheviks, which lasted until 1951 in Kalmykia and 1954 in Kazakhstan.

In 1950, a first-ever aerial survey revealed a population of 100,000 animals. By 1958, the population had increased to an estimated 800,000 animals, despite the recurrence of hunting in the area. The fortunes of the saiga antelope rose and fell many times during the following decades. Sometimes populations edged up when hunting pressures diminished; they dropped when irrigation facilities came through the antelope's calving grounds. For a while, sheep competed with antelopes for habitat, but the former were removed in the mid-1980s in the first significant step to halt desertification of the saiga's northern range.

Census data from 1980-1994 showed the overall saiga population to be fairly constant at about one million individuals. Data for *S. t. mongolica* during this period is poor, but the population size was estimated to be 300 to 1,700 animals. Between 1995 and 1999, funding for surveys decreased along with knowledge of the saiga's status.

In 2000, scientists finally conducted thorough surveys of all four populations. The results were alarming: dramatic declines were observed in each population of *S. t. tatarica*, with the most dramatic loss occurring between 1999 and 2000. Surveys of saiga populations in Kazakhstan between 1999 and 2000 show a steep decline in regional saiga numbers. The number of saigas in Ural decreased from 84,000 to 17,500; the population in Ustiurt declined from 200,000 to 116,000; and in Betpakdala, the numbers dropped from 64,000 to 15,000. These new estimates represented a mere four percent, 15 to 20 percent, and 15 to 20 percent of the 1980-1990 estimated populations in each area.

Massive declines were again recorded in 2001, as saiga populations fell to 69 percent, 50 percent, and 54 percent, respectively, of the already dangerously low figures recorded for 2000. In 2002, the census once again showed a horrifying downward trend for all four *S. t. tatarica* populations. The total population estimate for all saigas in Russia, Kazakhstan, and Mongolia has fallen from around one million from 1980 to 1994 to fewer than 200,000 in 2000 and fewer than 50,000 in 2001. Current estimates now put the wild population at fewer than 30,000 animals.

....

THREATS

Saigas are listed as *critically endangered* by the Species Survival Commission of the IUCN. These animals face an extremely high risk of extinction in the wild.

The intensive, uncontrolled hunting of saigas for their horns and meat is the biggest threat to their continued survival. Since the collapse of the Soviet Union, a lucrative market for saiga horns has opened in China, where they are used in TCM. Organized gangs illegally export saiga horn by train from Moscow to Beijing, or across the border from Kazakhstan to China, where they fetch approximately US$100 a kilogram (2.2 pounds).

Trade in horn has prompted poachers to target males, since only they have horns. As a result, the population has become unbalanced in favor of more females, creating concern about sustainability of the species. Normally, a gender imbalance would not pose a problem, since saigas are polygamous (i.e., one male mates with numerous females each season). Traditionally, a male saiga keeps a harem of between 12 to 30 females, which he mates with and defends from other males. But with fewer males available, each now has to defend a larger harem of females. Some harems are as large as 700 females, making it impossible for all of them to be successfully impregnated.

As a result, the pregnancy and birth rates of saigas have dropped. For an animal with a short lifespan, missing one reproductive season may have major implications for a population that is already critically endangered. In addition, defending and mating with large numbers of females weakens male saigas, making them easy prey for predators and poachers and putting their survival at risk during harsh winters.

Both male and female saigas are also hunted for their meat, which is sold locally. Additional threats to the saiga include habitat degradation and loss due to agricultural development, desertification, irrigation, and road construction. Natural threats such as severe winters, drought, disease, and predation by wolves are also present, but their effect on the saiga population has been relatively minor compared with the impacts of human activities.

....

CONSERVATION STRATEGIES

Four hundred years ago, the nomadic people who came to the region that would later be named Kalmykia regulated their use of the then-abundant saiga antelope to maintain a healthy supply of wild game. According to scientist and researcher Anna Lushchekina, "Had it not been for the straightforward rules they designed for its protection, it is likely that the fate of the saiga in this corner of Europe would have been no different than the one that befell it throughout the rest of the continent's steppe belt."

The saiga has managed to survive the twists and turns of human occupation, and to also benefit from some national protection strategies. In Russia, a hunting ban has been instituted twice: once before 1950, which resulted in sufficient population recovery to allow resumption of regulated hunting, and again in 1991. A hunting ban was also instituted in 1998 in Betpak-dala (Kazakhstan) and throughout the rest of Kazakhstan in 1999. All three bans remain in effect. In Mongolia, the government is working with local shepherds to protect that nation's two saiga populations.

Increased regional cooperation among saiga range states will play an important role in ensuring the survival of the species. In 2002, for example, a workshop on the conservation of saigas convened in Elista, Kalmykia, Russian Federation, resulted in a draft Memorandum of Understanding among range states and an action plan for saiga antelope recovery.

On the international level, fear for saiga antelope survival prompted the member nations of CITES to list the species on the treaty's Appendix II, effective February 16, 1995. This listing requires the issuance of export permits to authorize international trade.

In 2001, however, continuing concern over the sustainability of trade prompted the CITES parties to recommend suspending imports of *S. t. tatarica* from the Russian Federation and Kazakhstan until a regional conservation strategy for the species was in place, and scientists could confirm that exports would not be detrimental to the survival of the species. Both range states have implemented this recommendation.

Although many of the laws needed to protect the saiga in its natural ranges are in place, increased enforcement is critical. Management authorities, in particular, require better training and equipment so they can conduct anti-poaching activities effectively. A longer-term initiative involves educating local people about saigas and finding ways to engage them in conservation. In addition, creating new reserves and strengthening existing ones can help increase and maintain the saiga's habitat, providing them with satisfactory places to live. Establishing protected corridors between reserves and parks where the animals migrate may also be integral to their conservation.

Since commercial trade is in part responsible for the saiga's current precarious status, a conservation strategy is needed that involves partnerships with those who sell and use products made from this species. Practitioners of Chinese medicine, and the patients who buy the remedies, are in the best position to reduce the demand for saiga horn, which is sold under the commercial name Cornu Antelopis. The Chinese name for saiga horn is "ling yang jiao." The thoughtful selection of replacements for saiga horn, ones that will themselves not become subject to overexploitation, will be critical in ensuring the saiga's future.

SOURCES

Anonymous (2002) Draft Action Plan Concerning conservation, restoration and sustainable use of the Saiga antelope (*Saiga tatarica tatarica*). Convention on the Conservation of Migratory Species (CMS) Secretariat. United Nations Premises in Bonn, Martin-Luther-King-Str. 8, D-53175 Bonn, Germany

Bekenov AB, Grachev IUA and Milner-Gulland EJ (1998) The ecology and management of the saiga antelope in Kazakhstan. *Mammal Review* 28:1: pp 1-52.

Bensky D and Gamble A (eds.). (1993) *Materia Medica: Chinese Herbal Medicine*. Revised Edition. Eastland Press, Seattle WA.

Chan S, Maksimuk AV and Zhirnov LV (eds.). (1995) From steppe to store: the trade in saiga antelope horn. TRAFFIC International, Cambridge: 47pp.

Coulson TN, Milner-Gulland EJ and Clutton-Brock T (2000) A comparison of the relative roles of density and climatic variation on fecundity rates in three contrasting ungulate species. Proceedings of the Royal Society of London, B, 267: 1771-1779.

Ginsberg JR and Milner-Gulland EJ (1994) Sex-biased harvesting and population dynamics: Implications for conservation and sustainable use, *Conservation Biology* 8: pp. 157-166.

GrachevYA (2001) Saiga in Kazakhstan, the Problem of Survival. Northeast and East Central Asia - National Biodiversity Strategies Action Plans Newsletter, Issue 3/4, 29 March 2001.

IUCN (1996) The IUCN Red List of threatened species. World Conservation Union, Gland, Switzerland.

IUCN (2000) The IUCN Red List of threatened species, World Conservation Union, Gland, Switzerland.

Lushchekina AA, Dulamtseren S, Amgalan L, and Neronov M (1999) The status and prospects for conservation of the Mongolian saiga *Saiga tatarica mongolica*. *Oryx* 33:1: pp.21-30.

Lushchekina A and Struchkov A (2001) The Saiga Antelope in Europe: Once Again on the Brink? *The Open Country* 3: pp. 11-24.

Mace GM and Balmford A (2000) Patterns and processes in contemporary mammalian extinction. In *Future Priorities for the Conservation of Mammalian Diversity.* A. Entwhistle and N. Dunstone (eds.), Cambridge University Press, Cambridge.

Mallon DP and Kingswood SC, in press. Antelopes: global survey and regional action plans—Part 4: North Africa, the Middle East and Asia. IUCN-SSC, Gland, Switzerland.

Milner-Gulland EJ, Bekenov AB, Grachev IA (1995) The real threat to the saiga antelope. *Nature* 377: pp. 488-489.

Milner-Gulland EJ, Kholodova MV, Bekenov A, Bukreeva OM, Grachev IA, Amgalan L., and Lushchekina AA (2001). Dramatic declines in saiga antelope populations. *Oryx* 35-4: 340-345.

Milner-Gulland EJ, Bukreeva OM, Coulson T, Lushchekina AA, Kholodova MV, Bekenov AB, Grachev IA (2003) Reproductive collapse in saiga antelope harems. *Nature* vol. 422, 13 March pp. 135.

Nowak RM (1999) *Walker's Mammals of the World.* Sixth edition. Johns Hopkins University Press, Baltimore MD.

Pearce F (2003) Rhino rescue plan decimates Asian antelopes. New Scientist print edition, February 12, 2003.

Pereladova OB and Lushchekina AA (2001) First urgent measures for supporting conservation of Kalmykian saiga population. *Steppe Bulletin* 9: pp. 56-58.

Robinson S (2000) Pastoralism and land degradation in Kazakhstan. PhD Thesis, University of Warwick, U.K.

Robinson S. and Milner-Gulland EJ (2003) Political Change and Factors Limiting Numbers of Wild and Domestic Ungulates in Kazakhstan. *Human Ecology* 31:1: pp. 87-142.

Sokolov VE and Zhirnov LV (eds.). (1998) *The Saiga antelope, phylogeny, systematics, ecology, conservation and use.* Russian Academy of Sciences, Moscow.

Teer JG, Neronov VM, Zhirnov LV and Blizniuk AI (1996) Status and exploitation of the saiga antelope in Kalmykia. In *The Exploitation of Mammal Populations,* V.J. Taylor & N. Dunstone (eds.). Chapman & Hall, London: pp. 75-87.

Seahorses

Sarah Foster
Project Seahorse

Seahorse	Hǎi Mǎ	Hippocampus spp. Including: Hippocampus kelloggii, Hippocampus histix, Hippocampus kuda, Hippocampus trimaculatus, Hippocampus japonicus, Hippocampus capensis, Hippocampus denise, Hippocampus abdominalis, Hippocampus ingens

Seahorses undeniably appeal to humans. They fascinated the ancient Greeks, who called them *Hippocampus*, meaning "sea monster," and they often depicted them as mythical half-horse, half-fish creatures. The biological reality is at least as curious—seahorses are the only known animals in which the male becomes "pregnant," carrying the eggs through to hatching in a specialized abdominal pouch.

Whatever their appeal, seahorses are traded for both practical and whimsical purposes. They are collected for aquariums, dried for souvenirs, and fished by the ton for use as traditional medicines throughout the world.

No one knows how many seahorses live in the world's coastal habitats. Their skillful camouflage helps them hide in plain sight, even from those who hope to study and protect them. As a result, IUCN listed 23 seahorse species as "data deficient" in the 2004 update of the Red List of Threatened Species.

Obtaining information on the life history and ecology of seahorses, and applying it to protect these undersea creatures and their habitats, is the work of an increasing number of organizations, as well as the communities that depend on them. Ultimately, hope for seahorses, and for all species used by humans, depends on humanity's growing awareness of the interconnections and interdependencies of all life on Earth.

....
DISTRIBUTION

Seahorses belong to a group known as syngnathids (from the Greek *syn*, meaning fused, and *gnathus*, meaning jaws). This group also includes pipefishes, pipehorses, and sea dragons.

If you are looking for seahorses, you need search no further than shallow, temperate, and tropical marine and estuarine waters off the Earth's continental shelves, between latitudes 50° north and south of the equator. Seahorse species can be found at depths between one meter and one hundred meters (3 to 330 feet), depending on the species and population.

Seahorse habitats include some of the Earth's most degraded coral reefs, mangroves, and seagrass beds. Seahorses can also be found on soft bottom habitats and man-made structures, such as jetties and nets.

Pipefishes have wider distribution. They range further north and south than seahorses and occupy freshwater and marine environments. Sea dragons have a more restricted range; they are found only off the continental shelf of southern Australia.

Population densities for seahorses are often low. Because seahorse populations are patchily distributed, density estimates may vary greatly within a small geographic area. For example, studies have reported average densities for the Knysna seahorse (*Hippocampus capensis*) of one seahorse per 100 square meters to one per five square meters (Bell *et al.*, 2003).

....
BIOLOGY

Morphology: While seahorses and other syngnathids appear to be very different from other fishes, they are fish nonetheless. Seahorses range in size from the tiny 16 millimeter (¾ inch) Denise's pygmy seahorse (*Hippocampus denise*) to the big-belly seahorse (*H. abdominalis*) and the Pacific seahorse (*H. ingens*), both of which can reach lengths of more than 300 millimeters (12 inches). With a horse-like head, monkey-like prehensile tail, and kangaroo-like pouch, seahorses are marine fishes with specialized form. In fact, even their eyes can be likened to those of a chameleon, in that they move independently of each other and in all directions.

As a group, syngnathids have bony skeletons arranged in a series of rings along the length of their bodies. Instead of scales, they have thin skin stretched over a series of bony plates that are visible as rings around the trunk. This skeleton is perfectly retained when dried. Some syngnathids also have spines or bony bumps protruding from these rings. Only seahorses, however, have a group of spines on the top of the head; referred to as the coronet, these spines look like a crown.

While seahorses have their heads angled 90 degrees to their body and lack a caudal (tail) fin, pipefishes are slender, straight fishes with most species retaining their caudal fin. Pipehorses seem to be positioned between the seahorses and pipefishes, with heads angled at about 30 degrees and slightly grasping tails. Sea dragons resemble pipehorses, but they have numerous leaf-like appendages.

Taxonomy: Seahorses and related syngnathids are included in the same order (*Gasterosteiformes*) as the trumpetfishes, snipefishes, cornetfishes, and pegasids (sea moths) (e.g., Vari, 1982; Orr, 1995). The taxonomy of seahorses still requires some clarification. CITES and the IUCN currently recognize 34 and 33 species respectively.

Descriptions of new species occasionally appear (the most recent in 2003), and the proliferation of names used in the early scientific literature (more than 150) often creates confusion. The names *H. histrix* and *H. kuda*, for example, have been used for virtually any smooth or spiny seahorse in the Indo-Pacific (Lourie *et al.*, 1999).

Movement: Seahorses swim using the propulsive force of the quickly oscillating dorsal fin; they employ the pectoral fins on either side of the body for steering and stability. More adapted for maneuverability than speed, seahorses apparently rely on camouflage rather than speed to escape predators,.

Most seahorses are of neutral color (ranging from beige to brown to black), but possible color changes include fluorescent orange and deep purple, depending on species. Encrusting organisms may also grow on their skin, improving their camouflage. Seahorses can blend into their underwater habitats through a number of mechanisms including immobility, cryptic color changes, and growth of skin filaments. Short-term color changes may also occur during courtship displays and daily greetings. For example, *H. whitei* of both sexes brighten from a dark brown or grey to a pale yellow or off-white during greetings (Vincent and Sadler, 1995).

Most seahorse species studied to date are "homebodies," exhibiting high "site fidelity" and small home range sizes, at least during the breeding season. The fact that most species tend to stay within one area may limit re-colonization of exploited areas. Seahorses moving into new areas are likely to be juveniles. Juveniles of at least some species appear to rise to the surface of the water column, where currents carry them away.

Survival: From laboratory observations, scientists estimate that lifespans for seahorses range from about one year for the very small species to three to five years for the larger species. Juveniles are most likely to fall victim to predators, such as fish and invertebrates. Adult seahorses presumably avoid this fate, thanks to their excellent camouflage and unappetizing bony plates and spines.

Crabs may be among the most threatening predators. Seahorses have also been found in the stomachs of large ocean fish such as tuna and dorado, and they are eaten by skates and rays (Herald, 1949; Alverson, 1963; Wilson and Beckett, 1970), penguins, and other water birds (Kuiter, 2000). Studies suggest that natural rates of adult mortality may be low.

Feeding: Seahorses are voracious feeders, typically relying entirely on live, moving food. They are primarily ambush predators. They anchor themselves by curling their tails around seagrass stems, corals, or other rooted objects and suck passing prey quickly out of the water with their long snouts. They ingest prey small enough to fit into their mouths, mostly small crustacea such as amphipods, but also fish fry and other invertebrates. Seahorses have neither teeth nor stomach; they pass food through an undifferentiated digestive system (Rauther, 1925; Stoskopf, 1993).

Reproduction: Male parental care is not uncommon among bony fishes (Blumer, 1982), but seahorses and other syngnathids have perhaps the most specialized practice; males brood the young. So if males get pregnant, why aren't they called females? The reason is that, like all other male and female animals, it is the male seahorse that provides the sperm and the female seahorse that provides the eggs.

The female seahorse deposits eggs into the male's brood pouch, where he fertilizes them. The pouch acts like the uterus of a mammal, complete with a placental fluid that bathes the eggs and provides nutrients and oxygen to the developing embryos while removing waste products (Linton and Soloff, 1964; Boisseau, 1967). During pregnancy, the pouch fluid changes from being similar to body fluids to being more like the surrounding seawater.

The timing of reproduction varies with location, but seasonal peaks may arise in response to environmental variables such as light and water temperature. Pregnancy typically lasts between two and four weeks, with colder temperatures increasing gestation time. At the end of gestation, the male goes into labor to release his brood.

The number of young released averages 100 to 200 for most species, but range from as few as five for the smaller species to as many as 2,000. Although these numbers are relatively small compared with the numbers of eggs or young produced by other commercial fish species (millions in some cases), and may limit the potential reproductive rate, the small brood size may be somewhat offset by the presumed greater survival of the well-developed young released from the pouch. The young resemble miniature adults. They are independent from birth and receive no further parental care. Newborns of most species measure 7 to 12 millimeters (¼ to ½ inch).

Most seahorse species studied to date are monogamous, forming pairs that endure for an entire breeding season. Pairing, which may be based on size, involves daily greetings to reinforce the bond; the seahorses come together each morning to hook tails and perform an elaborate dance. "Widowed" animals stop reproducing until they find a new partner. Low population densities, however, mean that lost partners are not replaced quickly.

....
THREATS

Globally, seahorses are threatened by direct exploitation, accidental capture in non-selective fishing gear (by-catch), and degradation of habitat. Biology and population dynamics may make them particularly susceptible to over-fishing (Foster and Vincent, 2004). As a result, the harvest and trade in seahorses may be unsustainable for many populations. The 2004 IUCN Red List recognized one seahorse species as endangered, nine as vulnerable, and all others as *data deficient* (denoting the need for more research) (IUCN, 2004).

Dried seahorses are sold as traditional medicines, tonic foods and curiosities, and live for ornamental display. As of 2001, at least 70 countries traded syngnathids (seahorses and their immediate relatives), with the trade in seahorses alone exceeding 24 million animals.

Medicinal Use: Traditional medicines, particularly traditional Chinese medicine (TCM) and its derivatives, account for the largest consumption of seahorses. Nearly 90 percent end up in this trade, where they are used to alleviate a variety of disorders. Medicinal use of syngnathids, which dates back thousands of years, also occurs in other traditional medicine systems such as *Jamu* (Indonesia), *Hanyak* (South Korea), *Kanpo* (Japan), and folk medicine in Vietnam, Malaysia, and Brazil.

Syngnathids are sold whole and dried; they may be fermented into a liquid or ground into a powder along with other ingredients. Although large, pale, smooth specimens are believed to have greater medicinal value, the growing use of prepackaged compounds has opened the door to increased collection of animals previously thought undesirable because they were dark, spiny, or too small. The prospect of large-scale consumption of juveniles is of particular concern.

Syngnathids are used primarily to treat respiratory complaints (such as asthma or bronchitis), sexual dysfunction, and as a general tonic. Seahorses and pipehorses are particularly valued in TCM.

Other Uses: Dried seahorses are also made into souvenirs, key chains, yo-yos, and even incorporated into toilet seats! Additionally, hundreds of thousands of live seahorses are traded internationally, with small specimens finding a ready market. For some populations (e.g., *H. reidi* in Brazil and *H. erectus* and *H. zosterae* in the western Atlantic), capture for the aquarium trade may be the main pressure.

Habitat Loss: Habitat degradation also threatens many seahorse populations, since they inhabit shallow coastal areas subject to intense pressure from human activities. Pollution from sources such as untreated waste runoff, destructive fishing practices such as trawling and dynamite fishing, and activities such as dredging all damage sea grasses, mangroves, and coral reefs. More research is needed to assess loss of seahorse habitat, especially sea grasses, and its impact on wild populations.

....

CONSERVATION STRATEGIES

The impacts of exploitation and trade on seahorse populations are considerable, especially when combined with the damage being inflicted on their vulnerable coastal habitats. It is impossible to determine exactly how many seahorses live in the wild, and it is difficult to assess how individual populations are being affected by commercial use, but customs records, quantitative research, and qualitative information collectively indicate that seahorse catches have declined markedly (A.C.J. Vincent and A. Perry, Project Seahorse, unpublished data).

In 2002, the international community responded to this challenge by adding all seahorses to Appendix II of CITES. This listing, which took effect in May 2004, requires all treaty member countries to ensure that exports do not compromise the long-term sustainability of seahorse populations. In addition, at least 13 nations and the European Union have introduced regulations that affect syngnathid populations or fisheries. Australia, home to almost half the world's syngnathid species, strictly controls the capture and export of these fish.

On a local level, merchants in consumer regions can help support syngnathid conservation. Project Seahorse has long collaborated with TRAFFIC and the TCM community in Hong Kong to find ways to adjust consumption of marine species. The Hong Kong Chinese Medicinal Merchants Association has called on its members and its collegiate organizations to take three voluntary measures to reduce pressure on wild seahorse populations: (1) avoid small animals; (2) avoid animals that are breeding; and (3) seek alternative medicines where possible. Such restraint may help ensure the continued availability of seahorses to treat diseases that most benefit from their use.

Trade regulation alone cannot secure seahorse conservation. Seahorse fisheries and habitats also need better management to ensure the long-term survival of seahorse populations and sustain adequate income levels for the communities that depend on them.

Successful recovery strategies will require implementation of a suite of well-established fishery management tools. "No take" marine protected areas, for example, can help safeguard seahorse populations that are caught as by-catch. Minimum size limits, where only animals over a certain size are allowed to enter trade, are also helpful (Martin-Smith *et al.*, 2004; Foster and Vincent 2005). These tools are already being implemented in certain parts of the world. Fishermen in Bohol province in the Philippines, for example, have set aside no-take marine protected areas and are pursuing alternative, environmentally sustainable livelihoods.

While the aquarium trade can place huge pressure on certain seahorse populations, it also provides key support for seahorse conservation. Reducing reliance on wild populations is an increasingly important goal for those working in marine aquaculture and the ornamental fish trade. Although many species remain difficult to maintain and breed in captivity, successes have been achieved with the big-bellied seahorse *(H. abdominalis)*, the dwarf seahorse (*H. zosterae*), the short-headed seahorse (*H. breviceps*), and Barbour's seahorse (*H. barbouri*).

An increasing number of public aquariums are also involved in conservation, educating their visitors about the problems facing seahorses and marine environments in general through exhibits as well as supporting research and community projects. With some 10 percent of the world's population visiting zoos and aquariums annually, these institutions are a tremendous resource for disseminating information (Hall and Warmolts, 2001).

Conserving seahorses and their relatives depends on a sophisticated understanding of the animals and their ecosystems, the establishment of marine protected areas, well-conceived and well-implemented regulations, stakeholder involvement, and improved environmental education. Seahorses serve as excellent flagship species for marine conservation. The experience in seahorse conservation has been cooperative and encouraging, providing a new opportunity for constructive action toward conservation of other marine species and systems. Saving seahorses means saving the seas.

SOURCES

Alverson FG (1963) The food of yellowfin and skipjack tunas in the eastern tropical Pacific Ocean. *Inter-American Tropical Tuna Commission Bulletin,* 7: pp. 293-396.

Anonymous (2003) Proposals for amendment of Appendices I and II Results. CITES Secretariat, Geneva. As of March 2006 available at: http://www.cites.org/eng/cop/12/prop/E12-P37.pdf

Bell EM, Lockyear JF, Schulz JM, Marsden ADM and Vincent ACJ (2003) First field studies of an endangered South African seahorse *Hippocampus capensis. Environmental Biology of Fishes,* 67(1): pp. 35-46.

Blumer LS (1982) A bibliography and categorization of bony fishes exhibiting parental care. *Zoological Journal of the Linnean Society,* 76: pp. 1-22.

Boisseau J (1967) Les régulations hormonales de l'incubation chez un Vertébré mâle: recherches sur la reproduction de l'Hippocampe. PhD thèses, L'Université de Bordeaux, France. 379 pp.

Foster SJ and Vincent ACJ (2004) The life history and ecology of seahorses, *Hippocampus* species: implications for conservation and management. *Journal of Fish Biology,* 65: pp. 1-61.

Foster SJ and Vincent ACJ (2005) Enhancing sustainability of the international trade in seahorses with a single minimum size limit. *Conservation Biology* 19: pp. 1044-1050.

Hall H and Warmolts D (2001). The Role of public aquaria in the conservation and sustainability of the marine ornamentals trade. Marine Ornamentals 2001: Collection, Culture & Conservation Program and Abstracts.

Herald ES (1949) Pipefishes and seahorses as food for tuna. *California Fish & Game,* 35: pp. 329.

IUCN (2003) IUCN Red List of Threatened Species. The World Conservation Union, Gland, Switzerland as of March 2006 available at: http://www.redlist.org.

Kuiter RH (2003) A new pygmy seahorse (Pisces: Syngnathidae: *Hippocampus*) from Lord Howe Island. *Records of the Australian Museum,* 55(2): pp. 113-116.

Linton JR and Soloff BL (1964) The physiology of the brood pouch of the male sea horse *Hippocampus erectus. Bulletin of Marine Science of the Gulf and Caribbean,* 14: pp. 45-61.

Lourie SA, Vincent ACJ and Hall HJ (1999) *Seahorses: An identification guide to the world's species and their conservation.* Project Seahorse, London, UK.

Lourie SA and Randall JE (2003) A new pygmy seahorse, *Hippocampus denise* (Teleostei: syngnathidae) from the Indo-Pacific. *Zoological Studies,* 42(2): pp. 284-291.

Martin-Smith KM, Samoilys MA, Meeuwig JJ and Vincent ACJ (2004) Collaborative development of management options for an artisanal fishery: seahorses in the central Philippines. *Ocean and Coastal Management,* 47: pp. 165-193.

Orr JW (1995) Phylogenetic relationships of Gasterosteiform fishes (Teleostei: Acanthomorpha). PhD Thesis. University of Washington, Seattle WA.

Rauther M (1925) Die Syngnathiden des Golfes von Neapel. Fauna e flora del Golfo di Napoli Monografia 36.

Stoskopf MK (1993) *Fish Medicine.* W.B. Saunders Company, Philadelphia, PA

Vari RP (1982) Fishes of the Western North Atlantic, Part 8. Order Gasterosteiformes, Suborder Syngnathoidea. Syngnathidae (Doryrhamphinae, Syngnathinae, Hippocampinae). Sears Foundation for Marine Research, Yale University, New Haven, CT.

Vincent ACJ (1996) The international trade in seahorses. TRAFFIC International, Cambridge, UK.

Vincent ACJ and Sadler LM (1995) Faithful pair bonds in wild seahorses, *Hippocampus whitei. Animal Behaviour,* 50: pp.1557-1569.

Wilson PC and Beckett JS (1970) Atlantic Ocean distribution of pelagic stingray *Dasyatis violacea*. Copeia 1970: pp. 696-707.

Tigers

Andrea Heydlauff
Wildlife Conservation Society

Os Tigris	Hŭ Gŭ	Panthera tigris

Tigers (*Panthera tigris*) are one of the world's most charismatic large mammals. They are ancient, both in their physical form and in their historical relationship with humans. Ancestors of the tiger, long bodied and flexible civet-like animals called miacids, evolved during the end of the dinosaur age, approximately 60 million years ago. Miacids evolved into hundreds of species that became cats, dogs, bears, and other land mammals.

Human relationships with most of these species have come down to us through stories and symbols, remembered for generations. These records document our complex feelings toward the big cats.

More than 5,000 years ago, the Indus people, who inhabited what is now Pakistan, imprinted images of tigers on seals they used to sign documents. Also, certain Buddhist temples depict monks riding tigers, demonstrating the tigers' supposed supernatural ability to overcome evil.

Shiva, a powerful god of the Hindus, sits on a tiger skin, signifying his role as destroyer and restorer. Also, China's Shang Dynasty (1700 to 1050 BC) regarded tigers as powerful, ghostly messengers that crossed back and forth between humans and the spirit world.

In some cultures, tigers represent both cunning and mischief, much like the coyote in traditional Native American stories told in the United Status of America. For example, the tiger appears in Korean myths as a mixture of supreme arrogance and foolishness, a lesson in traits that remain characteristically human.

Since tigers and humans have evolved together, they also have come to occupy some of the same landscapes. However, baseline numbers for both groups have shifted dramatically since their ancestors first appeared on Earth. Human populations now inhabit most of the land across which tigers once roamed freely, while tiger populations have plummeted dramatically, especially since the beginning of the 20th century. Experts estimate that more than 100,000 tigers ranged across Asia at that time.

In addition to loss of habitat, poaching of tigers and their prey continues to reduce populations across the species' range. As threats to these animals continue to increase, we must consider their importance to our lives, to the various environments they inhabit, and to the other wild creatures—both animals and plants—that benefit from their presence. Tigers are among the most studied of the world's megafauna. However, many questions about them remain unanswered and their relationship to human beings remains complex. Determining how to ensure their continued survival is a challenge that requires all of our support, commitment, and ingenuity.

....

DISTRIBUTION

At one time, the tiger's geographical range spanned from eastern Turkey to the Sea of Okhotsk near Kamchatka, and from as far north as Siberia to the southern Indonesian island of Bali (Norchi and Bolze 1995, Sunquist *et al.* 1999). According to Andrew Kitchener in his book, *The Natural History of Wild Cats*, "about two million years ago, tigers spread from their evolutionary center in eastern Asia in two directions…to the west and southwest…[and] to the east of the central Asian mountains."

About one million years later, tigers had adapted to an astonishing variety of habitats, from dry and moist deciduous landscapes to wet and semi-evergreen, riverine, swamp, and mangrove areas. Tigers also inhabited the coniferous-deciduous forests of Russia, tall grass environments south of the Himalayas, and the tropical forests of Sumatra and Malaysia (Sunquist *et al.*1999). They are now found in 13 countries, surviving in approximately 150 fragmented populations that cover less than five percent of their original domain (Karanth 2001).

Because they ranged far and wide, the definition of tiger subspecies is disputed. Yet, their disappearance from a wide part of their area is certain.

Fifty years ago, tigers disappeared from the Caspian region of Central Asia, where they filled a niche among the humid grasslands and forests of Afghanistan, Iran, Mongolia, and the central Asiatic areas of Russia.

Tigers also disappeared from two islands in Indonesia: 50 years ago from Bali, and, as recently as 25 years ago, from the Indonesian island of Java. In Indonesia, only the distinct Sumatran tiger, a well-recognized subspecies *(P. t. sumatrae)*, persists.

Recently, tigers are thought to have gone extinct in an isolated population in South China. Also, their numbers have been declining across Southeast Asia. Vietnam, Thailand, Cambodia, Laos, and Myanmar have all witnessed significant declines in the last few decades.

....

BIOLOGY

Where resources are abundant, and prey and space are available, tiger populations can grow quickly. Females breed early and come into estrous again rapidly, following the dispersal or loss of young (Sunquist *et al.*1999). Gestation lasts 103 days, a relatively short period.

The tiger's physiology is beautifully designed to ensure its survival. For example, the tiger's fur helps it maintain a constant body temperature. Where heat and cold reach extremes, tigers shed their coats twice a year, growing a longer coat in the winter and a shorter one in the summer.

Fur color varies across the animals' range; those from tropical forests have a deeper body color than those from colder climates or open areas (Karanth 2001). Tiger stripes provide remarkable camouflage by blurring the animal's outline and hiding it within the forest brush. Many stories have been told of hunters who, while stalking tigers, were themselves stalked by these well-muscled, powerful predators, capable of appearing and then disappearing into forest darkness with speed and ease. The white spots on the back of the animal's ears are thought to assist cubs in following their mother through dense forests and thick underbrush, as well as in following each other, another benefit of the animal's remarkable coloring.

With whiskers on their faces and pads on their feet, tigers use touch and smell to sense their surroundings. Smell helps them communicate with other tigers more than it does to identify prey. Tigers possess scent glands around their cheeks, toes, tails, and the ano-genital area. They scent-mark by rubbing these body parts on trees and by exuding scent through urine and fecal matter.

Tigers may be solitary animals, but they use well-developed methods to communicate with each other through scent and vocalizations. Some vocalizations can be heard from as far away as three miles. These sounds generally come from females in estrus or males searching for them. Males occupy large territories that include several females. They defend these territories mainly through scent marking, which warns other males of their presence while reducing chance contacts and fatal fights. However, if two animals refuse to yield, fights may ensue in defense of territories, females, cubs, or prey (Karanth 2001).

The tiger's biology—and its complex relationships with humans—evolved due to its most important feature: the canine tooth (Seidensticker *et al.* 1999; Karanth 2001). Tigers have shorter muzzles with fewer teeth than most carnivores, which give them the jaw power to deliver a lethal bite. Generally, tigers attack prey from behind, delivering a killing blow by severing blood vessels in the neck.

The Sunderbans, a 10,360 square kilometer (4,000 square mile) densely forested river delta region in India and Bangladesh, is home to approximately 250 tigers that hunt among its dense mangrove forests and swamps. This area once was sparsely populated with people. However, as human population grew, people moved into this tangle of roots and bushes to gather wood and catch fish. Unfortunately, human encroachment into dense, tiger-inhabited forest increased the frequency of attacks, most of them fatal.

One method that evolved to combat these tiger attacks was the creation of a mask depicting a human face, which was worn on the back of a person's head to deter a tiger's preferred attack from behind. Although this potentially mitigated some tiger-human conflicts in the beginning, tigers in the Sunderbans continue to kill dozens of people every year. Experts suggest that during prehistoric times, humans provided natural prey for tigers. Research indicates that tiger behavior in the Sunderbans—in a dense landscape where humans lack technology—is a remnant of the more "natural" relationship prevalent among these species in the past (Karanth 2001).

Tigers have acute eyesight that functions effectively even in broad daylight. They consume a large variety of prey, ranging from termites to elephant calves. However, meat from hoofed animals such as red deer, swamp deer, sambar, and wild pigs make up three-quarters of their diet (Karanth 2001; Sunquist *et al.* 1999).

As much as five to six kilograms (11 to 13 lbs) of meat each day is necessary to sustain a tigress. This translates to approximately 2,373 to 2,847 kg (5321 to 6276 lbs.) of meat per year—about 50 deer—taking into consideration that 30 percent of each carcass is inedible (Karanth

2001). Generally, only three out of ten attempts to bring down an animal succeeds. Tigers are not built to outrun prey. They depend on stealth, ambushing animals from the cover of trees or beneath tall grasses.

During the late afternoon, when temperatures start to fall, tigers begin their hunt for food. These forays can take them distances of more than 12 miles along game trails and human pathways. They are continuously alert to sound and movement. Using a camouflaged approach, a tiger will explode from cover to rush its prey. It knocks it off balance while being careful to avoid thrashing hooves, then delivers a quick and fatal bite to the neck. Depending on the size of the prey animal, a tiger can feed off one kill for several days, covering its food with leaves and other vegetation to hide it from marauders.

....

Threats

One of the greatest threats to wildlife in the 21st century is habitat loss. Forests are being felled, rivers dammed, and wild land developed, all in response to an ever-growing human population. As the human population increases, more space is needed for agriculture, shelter, and areas to generate income. Wherever people invade natural environments, they quickly come into contact with various types of wildlife, including those perceived to be dangerous. Chief among these are the predatory species. In Asia, the most skilled and successful predator is the tiger, which is also a source of conflict for those intruding on its habitat.

The tiger's endangerment has more than one cause, however. Over the decades, tigers have been hunted for sport, and to a lesser extent, killed to protect humans and their livestock. In addition, since ancient times, body parts of tigers—especially bones—have been traded for medical purposes (Nowell 2000).

One of the more critical factors influencing the presence of tigers in Asian forests is the elimination of their prey base. Many people who farm rural lands survive by hunting and eating wild ungulates. As a result, these populations continue to decline across the tigers' range, driving tiger populations to ever lower densities and diminishing the prey base that supports minimal tiger reproduction (Karanth and Stith 1999; Sunquist *et al.* 1999). In many areas where large cervids and bovids have been heavily poached, muntjac deer have become one of the only prey options for the endangered tiger (Karanth 2001).

ncake tortoises (***Malacochersus tornieri***)

Turtle (***Terrapene ornata***)

PHOTO COURTESY OF IF

ild Ass (***Equus hemionus***)

Asiatic Moon Bear (*Ursus thibetanus*)

Musk Deer (**Moschus spp.**) Sichuan Institute of Musk Deer Breeding

Pangolin (***Manis spp.***)

PHOTO COURTESY OF WILDLIFE AT RI

lack Rhinoceros (***Diceros bicornis***)

White Rhinoceros (***Ceratotherium simum***)

aiga antelope (*Saiga tatarica*)

Seahorse (*Hippocampus reidi*)

ger (***Panthera tigris***)

Agarwood flowers (*Aquilaria spp.*)

garwood seed (*Aquilaria spp.*)

Aloe (***Aloe ferox***)

Bletilla orchid (***Bletilla striata***)

inseng (***Panax quinquefolius***)

Euphorbia (***Euphorbia pekinensis***)

In equal measure, as the human population has increased in Asia, so has the need for farmland to supply food and support families. Forests that were once home to tigers have been leveled and replaced with rice, wheat, and sorghum, all of which lack the biodiversity of the original forest environment. The global commercial demand for coffee, tea, rubber, and palm oil, as well as the rise of the small-scale homesteader, is transforming even the few remaining landscapes that still contain suitable habitat for these animals. With the advancement of the agricultural frontier and the growth of monoculture farming, tigers and tiger habitats are hugely threatened (Karanth 2001).

This new world order has also brought with it an increase in livestock and the diseases they carry. Many of these diseases have proved capable of being transmitted to wildlife, including wild ungulates, which ultimately impacts the tigers' prey base.

The availability of livestock presents yet another challenge, particularly if the animals live or graze within tiger habitat. Tigers have no way to distinguish between wild and domestic ungulates, except that the latter may be easier to hunt. This proclivity of tigers for domestic livestock has led to human-wildlife conflicts and to a reduced tolerance of tigers by herders. Often, killing tigers that cause conflicts is considered an acceptable retaliatory measure.

Both legal and illegal logging for oaks and pines in temperate forests, and for timbers used in decorative laminates and perfumeries, as well as the exploitation of bamboo, has further reduced tiger forests and displaced or reduced tiger prey. Logging also necessitates roads, and roads bring more people into tiger habitat, as well as more advanced threats (Karanth 2001). The shift from traditional methods of hunting and trapping to the use of guns, advanced ammunition, flashlights, all-wheel-drive vehicles, lethal poison, bombs, and dynamite have made hunters more successful at catching and killing tigers and their prey (Karanth 2001). All these factors conspire to reduce tiger populations.

In the long run, agriculture and hunting may be the most significant threats to the tiger's survival (Seidensticker, *et al.* 1999). However, killing tigers to supply the demands of traditional Chinese medicine poses perhaps the most immediate threat to existing populations (Karanth 2001, Mills and Jackson 1994, Hemley and Mills 1999). Folk traditions are powerful in Asia. Thus, tiger lore is deeply intertwined with strong personal beliefs in the curative powers of the animal's body, including its bones, blood, tail, and eyes. People believe that applying medicines made from tiger parts to such ailments as arthritis, skin diseases, and cataracts can reverse them or, at the least, provide relief. Wildlife traders manage highly organized networks that seek out poachers in tiger habitats to secure a supply of the animal's parts (Karanth 2001).

....

Conservation Strategies and Research

Several national governments spearheaded international tiger conservation efforts in the 1970s. By 1987, international trade in tigers had been banned. However, trade statistics monitored by international agencies during the early 1990s revealed an increase in tiger consumption.

At that time, a possible solution seemed imminent, due to discussions concerning the replacement of tiger parts used for healing with substitutes from domesticated or otherwise abundant animals (Karanth 2001). Subsequently, the sale, possession, and use of tiger parts and products, even those that falsely claimed to contain tiger products, were banned in the United States, under the Rhinoceros and Tiger Conservation Act, as amended in 1998.

Formal tiger missions from CITES emphasized the need to implement the treaty's provisions to their fullest extent in all CITES signatory nations with tiger trade concerns. Since then, proposals have been suggested that would increase penalties for trade violations and fully enforce these penalties in order to provide effective deterrents to the tiger trade (Norchi and Bolze 1995). Nevertheless, the trade continues, jeopardizing the survival of tigers throughout their range.

Currently, long-term, in-depth ecological studies on tigers, as well as status surveys and the monitoring of populations are continuing. Establishing the presence and relative abundance of tigers and their prey is essential. Other strategies include the creation of new legal and policy initiatives to protect tigers in their natural habitats. Such strategies include legally empowering law enforcement officers to prohibit the hunting of prey species and to search for and seize any animals that may have been hunted.

To accomplish this, however, more officers are needed in the field. Anti-poaching patrols require better training to become more effective. Ultimately, more personnel need to be trained in enforcement techniques, though this can be achieved only when incentives such as better and more dependable salaries become available (Norchi and Bolze 1995).

Ensuring that tigers remain on the earth, not only for future genera-tions of humans, but also to fulfill their roles within their ecosystems, will require unwavering commitment and international support from all sections of society. Some dramatic measures have been taken in the past few years, indicating that many are prepared to make this long-term commitment. In India, with government support, conservation initia-tives have included assistance in relocating local people and their live-stock to help protect critical tiger habitat.

However, other issues, such as tiger poaching for trade and the deci-mation of tiger prey, remain significant. Conserving and monitoring timber and non-timber forest products extracted from protected areas is also critical if we intend to maintain some tiger habitat relatively free of human influence. Dam building, mining, and road building need to be limited, if not completely halted, within tiger habitat. These and similar activities are worthy conservation endeavors that could help preserve ti-gers for future generations.

The long-term survival of the tiger depends on many factors. Shifts in government as well as environmental agendas continually offer chal-lenges. Funds for conservation are always needed. In addition, a more permanent, though more time-consuming, investment in the future of the tiger is education. People can only be inspired to save tigers if they understand the role these animals play in the ecosystem, as well as their relevance to human culture and traditions.

Education, conducted within an appropriate cultural context, pro-motes awareness of the protected status of tigers and helps people re-member their own unique relationships with these animals. Engaging associations of Chinese medicine practitioners, academic institutions, and conservation organizations to help protect tigers could make a dif-ference in the tiger's ability to survive the challenges of the present tech-nological age.

SOURCES

Hemley G and Mills JA (1999) The beginning of the end of tigers in trade? In *Riding the Tiger: Tiger Conservation in Human-dominated Landscapes*. J. Seidensticker (ed.) Cambridge University Press, Cambridge UK: pp 217-229.

Karanth KU (2001) *The Way of the Tiger*. Voyageur Press, Osceola WI.

Karanth KU and Stith M (1999) Prey depletion as a critical determinant of tiger population viability. In *Riding the Tiger: Tiger Conservation in Human-dominated Landscapes*. Cambridge University Press, Cambridge UK: Pp. 334-337.

Mills JA, and Jackson P (1994) *Killed for a Cure: A Review of the World-Wide Trade in Tiger Bone*. TRAFFIC International, Cambridge UK.

Nowell K (2000) Far From a Cure: The Tiger Trade Revisited. TRAFFIC International.

Norchi D and Bolze D, (1995) Saving the Tiger: A conservation strategy. WCS Policy Report Number 3. New York: Wildlife Conservation Society. 24 pp.

Seidensticker J, Christie S, and Jackson P (1999). Epilogue – vision and process in securing a future for wild tigers. In *Riding the Tiger: Tiger Conservation in Human-dominated Landscapes*. J. Seidensticker (ed.) Cambridge University Press, Cambridge UK: pp 334-337.

Sunquist M, Karanth KU and Sunquist F (1999) Ecology, behavior and resilience of the tiger and its conservation needs. In *Riding the Tiger: Tiger Conservation in Human-dominated Landscapes*. J. Seidensticker (ed.) Cambridge University Press, Cambridge UK: pp 5-18.

Chapter 5
PLANT SPECIES PROFILES: "THE WARP"

Elizabeth Call

....
INTRODUCTION

Conservation issues associated with plants tend to echo those associated with animals. However, the public's interest in and understanding of the importance of plant conservation is still in its infancy. There is also less media interest in plant conservation than in animal conservation. Therefore, little awareness has been generated about these all-important elements of the Chinese medicine practitioner's art. While substitutions for endangered plants are always an option, at present, identifying replacements for plants is a gray area, depending on the perspective of the practitioner and needs of the patient. Indeed, the aim of Chapters 7 and 8 is to provide a context for understanding and using replacements more actively within the practitioner community. First, it is important to recognize some of the conservation concerns for plants as a whole. We can then get better acquainted with the plants used in Chinese medicine that are listed on CITES Appendix II.

As stated earlier, while China cultivates about 15 percent of the medicinal plant species, wild harvesting of plants continues to occur, including wild harvesting of plants listed on CITES Appendix II. Wild plants often have a knobbier, rougher, less consistent appearance than their cultivated relatives, whose size, appearance, uniformity and hardiness are calculated to appeal to domestic and international markets. However, wild forest, desert, or mountain plants can be mixed with their cultivated cousins as they travel the supply chain that brings us the raw materials we convert into medicine.

Conservationists have long known that plant shipments from Asia, exported to Europe mix both wild and cultivated plants (Hamilton,

2003). American ginseng, a perennial favorite, appears as wild and cultivated roots, especially now that wild cultivated ginseng is available.

China has similar problems with wild plants. One botanist and researcher reported tubers of wild *Tian Ma* (*Gastrodia elata*) for sale in local villages (Leon, 2004), where it claims a higher price than cultivated
gastrodia. This is not unlike our own experience with American ginseng.
Since wild ginseng has been finding its way to Asia along clearly defined
trade routes from the time of the European exploration of North America, it is highly probable that wild gastrodia has also made its way into the
exported supply chain of supposedly cultivated plants reaching America.

Ginseng, gastrodia, and many other species comprise the ever-expanding *illegal* global trade in endangered species parts and derivatives,
valued at approximately $10 billion annually (Sharma, 2003-4). Given
these amounts, it becomes increasingly clear that preserving medicinal
plants requires coordinated international efforts, good scientific data on
their status in the wild, and increased consumer education. To begin this
process it is essential that practitioners gain a better understanding of
cultivation, harvesting, collection, and marketing protocols—essentially,
the supply chain.

....

CULTIVATED VERSUS WILD

For many reasons, the exact status of CITES listed plants is generally
not known. Research dollars are limited and are not able to cover the
diversity of wild plant varieties for which information may be needed.
Though certain plants are listed in CITES and their trade is regulated
(the plants included in this book, for example), researchers in academia,
as well as in the conservation community lack sufficient information to
determine consistently effective cultivation practices. Data is also lacking regarding the population status of wild plants and the impact of
cultivation on biodiversity. Another complex debate in the wild-versus-
cultivated distinction among plants concerns the clinical efficacy of wild
plants as opposed to cultivated ones.

Researchers at the Jiangsu Institute of Botany in China have been
studying *Atractylodes lancea* (*Cang Zhu)*, an herb collected from the wild
whose population has decreased seriously as a result of over-collection.
They suggest a link between the genetic diversity found in wild plants
and key chemicals that might imply clinical efficacy (He and Ning,

2001). Such research gives credence to the importance placed on collecting herbs from the wild in almost all traditional medicine practices around the world. Historically, wild herbs have been considered to be more desirable than cultivated ones, a condition that has changed substantially as global interest in medicinal herbs has grown. As an ever-increasing human population has expanded into undeveloped areas, pressure has intensified on the ecosystems supporting wild medicinal plants. This has accelerated efforts to uncover techniques for cultivating larger numbers of the heavily traded ones. Because researchers still are in the early stages of understanding some of these plants, cultivation has not always kept up with demand.

Another element of the cultivated versus wild issue may very well be our own concepts of what wild collecting looks like. We may imagine wild-collected plants growing in a pristine wilderness. Although that may be the case for some, many "wild" herbs grow in polluted environments. They are sometimes collected from roadsides, farms, and industrial zones that might expose them to chemicals and heavy metals from vehicular exhaust, agricultural inputs, and industrial pollution (Sturdivant, 1999). Research indicates that plants grown in contact with lead-contaminated soil tend to accumulate lead and other heavy metals in the skin of the root. In addition, plant leaves accumulate substantial amounts of lead and other heavy metal particles, as well as other toxins, from the air (Garden Organic, 2006). These factors make the case all the more compelling for quality cultivation with organic farming methods.

While we recognize the need to cultivate medicinal plants, we also need to appreciate the fact that their cultivation has never before been undertaken on such a large scale. Most herb manufacturers desire high quality cultivated herbs to meet customer demand. However, for certain herbs, demand still may exceed supply, depending on factors that range from weather conditions to cultivation and transportation costs. To ensure a steady supply of the raw materials of herb products, we may also need to consider which herbs are vulnerable to market demands and fluctuations, and then develop mechanisms that alert practitioners to changing conditions. Under such circumstances, the temptation to exploit wild resources might lessen.

Unfortunately, herbs continue to be collected from the wild on a global scale, without easily replicated procedures to help researchers determine the status of wild populations and any changes that such collection may cause. Though sophisticated research data used for trend analysis may project possible outcomes, confirming those projections on the ground would require coordinated efforts of the public and botanists alike. Regrettably, plant conservation efforts have not enlisted knowledgeable local volunteers to collect visual data on the status of local plants. A good model is the way the Audubon Society enlists the public to help count birds during seasonal migrations. If this could be done for plants, it would provide a more tangible framework for estimating plant populations than currently exists.

We are familiar with the results of over-collection through the historical data available to us on Asian ginseng. This popular plant was over-collected in China as early as the 17th century, forcing Chinese doctors to search for other sources. Fortunately for China, the new world opened up. In 1704, a Canadian priest found an American plant similar to Asian ginseng. This discovery of American ginseng (*Panax quinquefolius*), along with its medicinal effectiveness with certain ailments, has made it a popular export to China since the earliest years of the United States (Foster, 1992).

Nevertheless, the cultivation of American ginseng since the 1800s has not substantially diminished demand for wild ginseng roots. This is validated by the fact that the price for wild roots continues to exceed that of cultivated ones, even though wild roots are increasingly difficult to find. As of this writing, a certification process for wild cultivated ginseng is being developed in New York State, with the expectation that it will reduce pressure on wild ginseng populations by making wild cultivation a selling point.

Herbalists and growers in China are also researching ways to conserve the integrity of wild plant resources. Researchers in Jiangsu point out that, for most plant species collected from the wild, "the natural reserves are exhausted within 10 to 20 years of collection." They also note that "the loss of genetic variation within a given species is usually much more serious and occurs much earlier than the total extinction of the species itself." (He and Ning, 2001). This makes the use of replacements all the more critical for preserving endangered plants in the wild. Replacing a particular plant can act as an additional safeguard until "wild quality" cultivation can be maintained at levels that meet demand. Once this is attained, wild-simulated plants may provide a viable category for buyers to consider.

Although more and more plants may require cultivation to preserve the diversity of our medical choices, wild species and the ecosystems in which they grow will still require protection as cultivation techniques are developed. Why? Because wild species are the repository of a plant's genes, which contribute to the long-term health of that plant species, as well as to the overall diversity and health of ecosystems. In the seed of the plant is the genetic code for its continuance. Without a diversity of wild plant genetics, a diverse ecosystem is less assured.

The process associated with selecting genetic traits for their medicinal value is a recent imperative and an area with many unknowns. If the Jiangsu researchers are correct in their theory that genetic diversity is linked with higher numbers of certain key chemicals in a given plant, then selecting certain plant traits to produce specific health-related outcomes is still filled with uncertainty. In addition, when plants are cultivated, factors such as soil quality, spacing, plant genetics, and the influence of other plants and wildlife nearby come into play, adding an as-yet-unknown dimension to the mix.

Despite the unfamiliar territory we may explore, either when using medicinal plants that have been cultivated or perhaps cultivating them ourselves, we might remember that humans have a long relationship with plants. As some have observed, humans developed alongside plants, eating them, smelling them, touching them, admiring their beauty, and using their curative powers (Buhner, 2002). We have always had a relationship with the plants and trees of the Earth; in fact, we may be under their spell more than we think. They have compelled us to tend, breed, and spread them in ways we cannot quite explain (Pollan, 2001). Perhaps as we continue to learn about and care for our medicinal plants, we will come to better understand their needs and medicinal uses in a more connected and profound way.

SOURCES

Anonymous. Lead and the Gardener, fact sheet GG3. As of March, 2006 available at: www.organicgardening.org.uk/factsheets/gg3.php

Buhner SH (2002) *The Lost Language of Plants*. Chelsea Green Publishing Company, White River Junction VT.

Foster S (1992) *Herbal Emissaries: Bringing Chinese Herbs to the West.* Healing Arts Press, Rochester VT.

Hamilton A (1992), International trade in medicinal plants: conservation issues and potential roles for botanic gardens. WWF International, Surrey, UK. As of March 2006 available at: http://www.bgci.org/congress/congress_rio_1992/hamilton.html

Leon C (2003) Royal Botanical Gardens, Kew. Personal Communication.

Pollan M (2001) *The Botany of Desire: A Plants Eye View of the World.* Random House, New York NY.

He S and Ning S (1997) Utilization and Conservation of Medicinal Plants in China, With Special Reference to Atractylodes lancea. In *Medicinal Plants for Forest Conservation and Health Care.* G Bodeker, KKS Bhat, J Burley and P Vantomme (eds.) Food and Agriculture Organization of the United Nations, Rome (Non-wood Forest Products 11). As of August 2006, available at: http://www.fao.org/docrep/W7261E/W7261E13.htm

Sharma C (2003-2004) Enforcement Mechanisms for Endangered Species Protection in Hong Kong: A Legal Perspective. *Vermont Journal of Environmental Law*, vol. 5.

Sturdivant L and Blakley T (1999) *Medicinal Herbs in the Garden, Field and Marketplace.* San Juan Naturals, Friday Harbor WA.

Agarwood

Michael Spencer
WildAid

Robert Blanchette
University of Minnesota

Aquilariae Lignum resinatum	chén xiāng	Aquilaria sinensis (Lour.) GILG

Agarwood, aloeswood, eaglewood and gaharu—all are common names for the same aromatic, resinous heartwood collected for generations from trees of the Aquilaria genus. Though less familiar to the people of the West, these trees are very old and have long been significant to the aromatic, medicinal, and spiritual histories of the world. Their extensive contributions in diverse cultures and regions around the world are reflected in numerous myths, stories, and documented research. Among these is an account that myrrh and agarwood, mixed together, helped prepare Christ's body for burial.

Agar, the Hindi term for the wood, also is used in the trade when referring to trees in this genus. In Japan, the common name is jinko, and in Indonesia and Malaysia it is called gaharu. In Chinese, agarwood is called chén xiāng, which literally means "sinking fragrance," as it sinks when it is put in water. Its old Latin name is lignum aloe, from which its English equivalent, aloeswood, is taken. The span of cultures with differing words for this species indicates the range of influence these trees have had through time. This is particularly true in the Middle East and Asia, where agarwood is considered one of the four original incenses, with the others being sandalwood, frankincense, and myrrh.

For thousands of years, agarwood has provided fragrant perfume, reliable medicine, and quality cosmetics, as well as precious ornamental wood. Mixed with a carrier oil, such as sandalwood, agarwood becomes a fragrant perfume. Muslims use "Attar oil," a water-based perfume containing agarwood, to scent prayer cloths.

As a medicinal ingredient, agarwood appears in Ayurvedic, Tibetan, and traditional Chinese medicine for ailments as diverse as paralysis, pleurisy, cancer, asthma, dysentery, rheumatism, and jaundice. Chinese medicine also uses it to improve circulation. The *Sahih Muslim*, which dates back to the eighth century, and the *Susruta Samhita*, an ancient Ayurvedic medical text, reference agarwood. As incense, it is used by Buddhists, Hindus, and Muslims and even appears as an ingredient in some Taiwanese wines.

Hand-carved beads and small boxes of agarwood may be used ceremonially, while the wood also has been presented as a diplomatic gift, exchanged between kings. The revival in Japan of the 800-year-old "koh doh" incense ceremony rekindled interest in agarwood in recent years.

The popularity of aromatherapy also developed a new market for this ancient incense. Shops in Europe and America sell agarwood products, and internet outlets also contribute to their sale. Pure agarwood oil distilled from the wood is known as Oud. Rare and expensive, it is often mixed with other scented oils and perfumes.

····························

DISTRIBUTION

The genus Aquilaria comprises 15 species, all of which may be potential sources of the fragrant agarwood resin. The trees are large evergreens growing from India, Bhutan, Myanmar, and Bangladesh to Malaysia, Indonesia, and the Philippines. Their historical range extended from Iran and the Indian subcontinent through all of Southeast Asia to Papua New Guinea, including Hainan Island and Southern China, the furthest extreme of their range.

Aquilaria sinensis, as well as *A. agallocha*, *A. malaccensis*, *A. secundaria*, and *A. ovata* are imported from parts of Asia. The Missouri Botanical Garden's Tropicos database lists *A. sinensis* and other Aquilaria species, which are accessible by going to http://mobot.mobot.org/W3T/Search/vast.html, and typing in "Aquilaria." Many of these species appear to be facing extinction due to over-collection. These trees may be found on hillsides and ridges of primary and secondary forests up to 1000 meters in altitude.

Trees in Papua New Guinea and parts of Indochina that contain the fragrant resin appear also to include the genus *Gyrinops*, which has seven species. New molecular studies indicate that these species may not be appropriately placed taxonomically in *Gyrinops* and appear better designated as species of Aquilaria, a discovery presented at the 2003 Agarwood Conference in Asia.

Gyrinops ledermannii grows in lowland forests on mountains, hills, and slopes below 1000 meters, where water is easily available but the ground is not saturated. Soils have been identified as yellow or red clays with a thin humus layer and thick root mass.

Like other resinous trees, these fragrant specimens appear to clump in localized areas and are not equally distributed throughout the forest. One of the last bastions of wild harvesting, Papua New Guinea has been experiencing gold-rush style collection since the late 1990s, when the commercial value of these trees was recognized.

With the exception of a few attempts at cultivation, almost all remaining populations of Aquilaria species exist in the national parks and protected areas of Southeast Asia. Collecting in these protected areas is illegal in all of the countries where the trees are found.

....

BIOLOGY

Left undisturbed, Aquilaria trees grow 20 to 40 meters high and up to 2.5 meters in girth. They bear sweetly scented white, green, or yellow flowers. Seedlings grow fast in the presence of sufficient shade and water and produce seeds in approximately four years. The wood of the Aquilaria species is normally light and white-colored, much like balsa. In the presence of resin deposits, the wood becomes dark and hard in patches or nodules. Only a small proportion of the tree mass is affected.

Scientists are still trying to understand the conditions under which agarwood resin forms. However, they believe the process may begin when the trees are infected with a decay-causing fungus. The formation of the aromatic oleoresin that impregnates the tree's trunk wood and roots may be a response to the infection. In wild trees, ten percent or less develop these oleoresin deposits. Theories suggest that the resin is the immunological defense of the tree to a fungal infection, a wound, or a combination of the two. Generally, the older the tree, the more well developed the resin deposits. Trees between 25 and 75 years of age contain the greatest stocks, though the presence of the resin is determined only once the trees are cut. This contributes to serious declines, since only approximately ten percent contain these deposits.

Five genera within the Thymelaceae family have been analyzed to determine their potential for producing agarwood resin: Aquilaria (8 or more species out of the 15 are known producers); Aetoxylon (1 species reported); Gyrinops (out of the 6 species, *G. ledermanii* and *G. versteegii* are reported as producers); Phaleria (the 2 species have not been assessed); and Gonystylus (27 species, with only 1 reported as an agarwood producer).

Agarwood consuming cultures have many myths and legends as to the provenance and formation of the resin. In China, it was believed that agarwood developed over thousands of years in trees that were already dead. Some cultures also believe that the resin-rich wood develops in trees that already have been cut, though until commercial demand intensified, local people tended to harvest only those trees where the presence of the resin was clearly visible.

....

THREATS

Populations of eight Aquilaria species have declined to the point that they are categorized as threatened according to the IUCN Red List Categories. Nevertheless, even though most Aquilaria are threatened in the wild, only one species, *A. malaccensis*, was listed on Appendix II of CITES. This changed during the 13th meeting of the Congress of the Parties (COP) to CITES, held in Thailand in October 2004. At that time, all agarwood trees (*Aquilaria* spp. *Gonystylus* spp., and *Gyrinops* spp.) were listed on Appendix II.

Typically, traditional methods of collecting agarwood involve chipping or cutting away the infected part of the tree. The older, high quality wood is the first to be collected. However, as this wood becomes more scarce, harvesters turn their attention to lightly infected trees that are felled entirely and reduced to chips for resin extraction.

Since external signs of the resin may be difficult to determine, trees are felled indiscriminately, merely in hope of finding resin. Also, carefully chipping out infected wood to conserve the tree is more time consuming than cutting and splitting it. Local communities trained to cut out only small portions of the resin and leave the tree standing are reported to still cut the tree because of easier access to the resin.

The growing scarcity of agarwood and its tendency to cluster in small tree groups rather than spread evenly throughout a forest also has led to helicopter exploration in the most remote regions of the species' range. The net effect on Aquilaria populations is severe. Regeneration is reported to be scarce in areas of heavy exploitation, as entire trees are felled whether they contain resinous wood or not.

The most significant impact of rampant Aquilaria harvesting is its unsustainability. Such harvesting has led to the disappearance of the species over much of its range. India is a good case in point. Once a leading exporter of agarwood, India is now a net importer, and its existing populations are considered critically endangered.

Collecting agarwood in the wild has an impact on other species also, as harvesters typically snare and poach wild animals to supplement their food while in the forest. As supplies of agarwood dwindle and prices rise, the potential increases for violent conflict between harvesters illegally cutting the trees and park protection staff. A Thai park ranger died in a confrontation with agarwood poachers in 2000.

From the perspective of a local harvester, trends may be difficult to determine. However, the effects of all actions are cumulative, and agarwood collection throughout its range involves not only wood but also wood chips, powder, oil, and finished products such as perfumes, incense and medicines. Based on recorded export data, Indonesia, Papua New Guinea, Malaysia, and Cambodia appear to be the main sources of agarwood in international trade. And most of this is illegally collected in protected areas.

Once major suppliers of agarwood to international markets, India and Thailand now act primarily as processing centers. These countries' reserves have been largely depleted by overexploitation. Myanmar, Vietnam, and Laos all formerly had large stocks of agarwood. According to reports from traders, these are largely depleted.

Bangkok, Singapore, Hong Kong, and Vietnam are all major re-export locations. In locations like Thailand, which are close to the source countries, agarwood costs between US $600 – US $1,500 a kilo, depending on the grade. Agarwood oil costs anywhere from US $5,000 – US $30,000 on the world market—the purer the oil, the higher the price.

Traders now are using the internet to source customers and to market agarwood. Customers include not only their traditional clients, but also new customers from the growing aromatherapy market in North America and Europe

....

CONSERVATION STRATEGIES AND RESEARCH

The burgeoning international demand for agarwood has put the reserves in the wild under severe pressure. Low intensity collecting of high-grade wood may be sustainable, as long as only small sections are carved out over infrequent intervals. However, harvesting of low-grade white wood for oil distillation is less sustainable, because it involves felling the entire tree.

Attempts have been made in various Aquilaria range countries to cultivate the trees commercially. Plantations have been reported in Thailand, India, Malaysia, Indonesia, and Vietnam. Plantations in India, developed in the early 1990s, reportedly are struggling to produce viable products in a timely manner.

A long-term project of The Rainforest Project Foundation and the University of Minnesota involves wounding Aquilaria trees, and then treating them in ways that encourage the trees' own natural defenses. This can produce sustainable yields of resin while trees are reasonably young. These methods have produced large quantities of resin in trees that are four to six years old. Primarily, these studies have been conducted in Vietnam. Concern for the future of Aquilaria trees in the wild is fueling this and other research, in addition to the exchange of information at such events as the First International Agarwood Conference in Vietnam in 2003.

SOURCES

Al-Absi A (1998) Incense: To Scent or to Exorcize? *Yemen Times*. As of March 2006 available at: http://www.yementime.com/98/iss16/culture.htm

CITES News (2000) *Plants, A Newsletter for the European region of the CITES Plants Committee.* Issue 7, July 2000.

Forest Research Institute Malaysia. The Investigation of the Formation of Gaharu in Aquilaria malaccensis Through Inoculation and Wounding. As of March 2006 available at: http://www.frim.gov.my/tu/gaharu.htm.

Harris T. Agarwood - Gem of Truth. As of March 2006 available at: http://www.enfleurage.com/articles.html.

Hongthong P (2002) Stolen Scent. *The Nation Newspaper, Thailand.* 8/3/2002. As of March 2006 available at: http://www.nationmultimedia.com

LaFrankie JV (1994) Population Dynamics of Some Tropical Trees that Yield Non-Timber Forest Products. *Economic Botany*, Vol. 48, 1994.

McMahon C (2001) "#29 Agarwood," 8/25/2001. As of March 2006 available at: http://www.whitelotusaromatics.com

Paoli GD, Peart DR, Leighton M and Samsoedin I (2001) An Ecological and Economic Assessment of the Non-timber Forest Product Gaharu Wood in Gunung Palung National Park, West Kalimantan, Indonesia. *Conservation Biology*, vol. 15, no. 6 pp. 1721-1732.

Peters CM (1994) Sustainable Harvest of Non-timber Plant Resources in Tropical Moist Forest: An Ecological Primer. Institute of Economic Botany, New York Botanical Garden.

Pope L. Aromatic Illumination. As of March 2006 available at: http://www.alshindagah.com/august/aroma.htm.

Barden A, Noorainie AA, Mulliken T and Song M (2000) Heart of the Matter: Agarwood: Use and Trade and CITES Implementation for Aquilaria malaccensis.

Traffic. As of March 2006 available at: http://www.traffic.org/news/agarwood/pdf.

Moresby P (2001) The Last Frontier of Agarwood: Under Threat in Papua New Guinea. Traffic Oceania and WWF South Pacific. As of March 2006 available at: http://www.traffic.org/news/agar2.html.

UNEP-WCMC (2005) Tree Conservation Information Service. United Nations Environment Programme/World Conservation Monitoring Centre. As of March 2006 available at: http://www.unep-wcmc.org/tree/trade/aqu_mal.htm.

Watson L and Dallwitz MJ. The Families of Flowering Plants. As of March 2006 available at: http://en.wikipeda.org/wiki/Flowering_plant.

Wildlife Conservation Society/WildAid (1999) The Aloewood Crisis in Khao Yai: How to Reduce the Poaching of Aloewood and Wildlife in Khao Yai National Park. The Khao Yai Conservation Project.

World Wildlife Fund. (2001) Wood Used in Perfume and Incense Threatened. Available at: http://www.ecoworld.org/Trees/ecoworld_tree_articles.cfm.

Zich F and Compton J (2001) The Final Frontier: Towards Sustainable Management of Papua New Guinea's Agarwood Resource. Traffic Oceania Report/WWF South Pacific Programme. 10/2001.

Zain S (2005) Losing Its Fragrance. Traffic International. As of March 2006 available at: http://www.traffic.org/news/agarwood/html.

Aloes

Jean Giblette
High Falls Gardens

Herba Aloes	lú huì	Aloe vera L. var. chinensis (Haworth) A. Berger A. vera (L.) Burm. f. (syn. A. barbadensis Mill.) A. ferox Mill.

Aloe vera is a plant familiar to most indoor gardeners. Its glossy, succulent, spiked rosettes of leaves grow in pots on windowsills, where they may be broken off and squeezed for fresh gel to treat a burn or similar emergency. Asian grocery stores sell fresh mature leaves in bulk for cooking.

Though aloes resemble a type of cactus, they were classified until recently as members of the lily family (Liliaceae), keeping company with onions, garlic, and others in this expansive taxonomic grouping. Now the plant belongs to its own family, Aloaceae, with four other genera and 350 to 400 species in the genus Aloe (Chen and Gilbert 2000).

Used extensively since ancient times, aloe has been stripped, ground, scraped, cooked, compressed into molds, crystallized, and otherwise manipulated for all manner of purposes. The mild, colorless gel exuded from the leaves is distinct from the bitter yellow sap, known as lú huì or drug aloe, which is extracted from beneath the rind of the leaf and is a strong cathartic (Foster 1998). Beverages, skin products, and the like are made from the gel, while lú huì and other laxatives are made from the sap.

Water-soluble lú huì powder is usually made into pills or capsules and administered with other herbs, but it is not decocted (Bensky et al 2004). Traditional Chinese medicine distinguishes among the crystal products, including "lucid" aloe (toù míng lú huì), a dark reddish brown or black mass with glassy-smooth broken edges, and "liver colored" aloe (gān sè), which is a black, translucent mass with waxy broken edges (Yen 1992).

This versatile medicinal plant is widely cultivated, and its quality is strictly controlled. Unlike other aloes protected under either CITES Appendix I or II, aloe vera (except for the Chinese cultivar, *Aloe vera* var. *chinensis*) was delisted from this international trade treaty in 1994. Distinguishing one aloe from another may be difficult, complicating efforts to protect these plants. As a result, CITES lists many species in Appendix II that are "look alikes"—they resemble species at risk but are not themselves endangered.

Differences among species challenge even the experts. Such is the case with *Aloe vera* var. *chinensis*, which is closely related to *Aloe indica* from northern India, Nepal, and Thailand. Given the long history of cultivation and trade in aloe vera, and lacking verifiable wild populations, botanists have concluded that these two species were introduced to Asia long ago (Chen and Gilbert 2000). The first mention of aloe as an imported medicine appears in the *Bencao Shiyi*, written by Chen Cangqi in 739 A.D. References to viable plant populations occur as early as 969 A.D. (Xie et al 2000). Despite extensive cultivation, the Chinese variety remains protected by CITES as a safeguard for a family with a high percentage of endangered members.

....

DISTRIBUTION

Most of the aloes are distributed throughout tropical and southern Africa, including Madagascar and tropical Arabia. *Aloe ferox* grows widely on rocky hillsides in South Africa, often in large groupings. Ferox means "fierce," apparently referring to the plant's spiny edged leaves. In Afrikaans, it is referred to as "bitteraalwyn" and in Zulu, "iNhlaba" (Aubrey 2001). The plant is commonly called a "cape" aloe due to its location near the South African coast, where it grows from the southern to the eastern Cape, including Kwazulu-Natal and Lesotho. It occupies a wide niche, choosing open as well as shrubby areas, and may respond with slight shifts in appearance to different growing conditions. For example, southeastern Free State winters differ from those on the eastern Cape. A form of *Aloe ferox* found in Kwazulu-Natal (formerly identified as *Aloe candelabrum)* appeared distinctly different, due to the slight downward curve of leaf tips and spines on both the upper and lower surfaces (Aubrey 2001).

Aloe vera (=barbadensis) and its cultivars are not known in the wild. In the United States, aloe vera is cultivated in the Rio Grande Valley of South Texas, in Florida, and in Southern California. The Chinese cultivar of aloe vera is grown throughout southern China, in Guangdong, Guangxi, Fujian, Sichuan, and it is possibly naturalized in southern Yunnan (Chen and Gilbert 2000).

BIOLOGY

Aloe ferox is a tall, single-stemmed aloe, usually two meters high, although older plants may grow up to five meters. Attractive to sunbirds and weavers, as well as bees and other insects, its broad greenish-gray leaves, 40 to 60 centimeters in length, appear slightly blue with a tinge of red in sunlight. Its flower forms as a lush, branched, orange-red candelabra of five to 12 upright spikes that bloom from May to August, except in colder regions where bloom time may advance to September through November. The flowers graduate in color from yellows and oranges to reds.

Aloe ferox grows in well-drained soil in full sun and becomes diseased when stressed by poor drainage, too little sun, or cycles of excess water or drought. As the plant ages and gains height, bottom leaves desiccate and hang below the younger upper leaves like a skirt, before eventually decomposing and dropping off. In the wild, aloe nectar is popular with baboons and monkeys (Aubrey 2001).

Aloe vera is a succulent herb with short stems that sucker freely to form dense clumps, rarely more than one meter in width. The smooth, hairless, pale green leaves, which are usually 15 to 35 centimeters long, have toothed margins and pointed tips. Greenish-white spots may dot the leaves of young plants. The flower stalk is erect, measures 60 to 90 centimeters in height, and supports a raceme of numerous pale yellow flowers. The Chinese cultivar is slightly smaller overall (Chen and Gilbert 2000).

Both aloes grow readily from seed and may cross-pollinate with others that are flowering at the same time. Aloe vera also may be propagated from its pups (root suckers).

THREATS

According to the IUCN Red List, 206 of the 700 species in the five genera of the family Aloaceae are threatened. This number accounts for 29 percent of the species in the family, an alarmingly high proportion. Of the threatened species, the majority belong to the genus Aloe (Walter and Gillett 1998.)

All aloes, other than *A. vera*, receive some level of protection under CITES, chiefly because of habitat loss. Native to hot, dry regions with some winter precipitation and infrequent fires that build genetic endurance, they grow in areas where overgrazing or human occupation have altered the landscape. Depending on the aloe variety, plants popular with hobbyists may have been over collected. Dry desert areas with small human populations are common sites for dams, so certain areas may have been altered by these artificial water bodies, which are disruptive to native habitat.

Even cultivation is not clear-cut assurance of species conservation. Commercial demand for aloe is met primarily from cultivated sources. However, conservation concern still exists for isolated pockets of wild aloes that may be collected locally, which can then end up passing through brokers for eventual commercial use.

CONSERVATION STRATEGIES AND RESEARCH

The aloes used for lú huì, other than *A. vera*, are listed as CITES Appendix II species, making permits necessary for all live plants, parts, products, or derivatives if import or export activities are being conducted. This provides one strategy for protection, by using the negotiated authority of an international treaty to encourage conservation while sustaining trade.

Since habitat loss is a significant factor for certain aloes, the creation of nature reserves, development of cultivation techniques, and encouragement of educational efforts to assist local communities are useful tools to help sustain species. For medicinal plants in Africa, the wildlife trade monitoring group TRAFFIC has suggested that collaboration with traditional healers' associations can be beneficial to plant conservation programs (TRAFFIC 1998).

In Africa, *Aloe ferox* is collected and processed in the wild. A description, including photographs of traditional harvest, is published on the website of the Aloe Ferox Trust (www.aloeferoxafrica.com), a commercial group based in Albertinia, South Africa. According to this model, a basin or bowl is dug in the ground; it is then covered with plastic to hold leaves removed from the wild plants. Responsible collectors ("tappers") harvest only the lower leaves of mature plants, cutting close to the stem. The leaves are stacked—two or three hundred leaves in a circle, filling the basin—with the cut ends overlapping downward so that their sap drains into the depression. Eventually the sap is collected from each of the sites. It is then boiled in a metal drum over an open fire to produce the raw material for the crystalline form. The leaves are then crushed to produce the aloe gel.

The encouragement of sustainable harvest practices is a top priority in the case of *Aloe ferox* and other plants collected from the wild. Certification of traditional harvesters, analogous to the licensing of wild ginseng collectors in the United States, could be effective in conservation.

Certification of cultivated sources is already in place. Aloe vera is commercially important enough to have its own nonprofit trade association, the Texas-based International Aloe Science Council (www.iasc.org). This industry group estimates the worldwide market for aloe vera raw materials at US $85-100 million. Since the 1980s, the council has certified the aloe content of products and raw materials to protect consumers from false advertising. The council certification label ensures, among other things, that the aloe used in the product comes from a certified source, and thus has no impact on wild plant populations. The council has contributed to the sustainability of this plant by working within the parameters of cultivation to create an equivalent of the Good Housekeeping Seal of Approval for aloe.

A nonprofit organization called the Institute for Aloe Studies, based in Oakland California, is involved in propagating and distributing aloes to plant lovers in the United States (www.aloestudies.org). As is true of each of our CITES listed medicinal plants, demand generated by plant enthusiasts has led to sometimes devastating over-collection from the wild. Our contemporary challenge is to channel this fervor into educated consciousness and a positive force for conservation. For example, funds raised from the many plant societies could be used for research, monitoring of wild stocks, and to develop sustainable harvest methods, including support for responsible farmers and wild-crafters.

SOURCES

Aubrey A (2001) Monograph on Aloe Ferox. National Botanical Institute of South Africa, Capetown SA. As of March 2006 available at: www.plantzafrica.com/plantab/aloeferox.htm.

Bensky D, Clavey S and Ströger E (eds.) (2004) *Chinese Herbal Medicine Materia Medica, 3rd Edition*. Eastland Press, Seattle WA.

Chen X and Gilbert M (2000) Liliaceae Chapter 29 ALOE. In *Flora of China Vol. 24: Flagellariaceae through Marantaceae*. Z. Wu and P. Raven (eds.), Science Press, Beijing PRC/Missouri Botanical Garden Press, St. Louis MO.

Foster S (1998) *101 Medicinal Herbs: An Illustrated Guide*. Interweave Press, Loveland CO.

TRAFFIC (1998) Searching for a Cure: Conservation of Medicinal Wildlife Resources in East and Southern Africa. As of March 2006 available at: www.traffic.org/africa/executivesummary.html

Walter K and Gillett H eds (1998) *1997 IUCN Red List of Threatened Plants*. International Union for Conservation of Nature and Natural Resources, Gland, Switzerland and Cambridge UK.

Xie Y, Li Z, Gregg W and Li D (2000) Invasive species in China: an overview. In *Biodiversity and Conservation* 10(8): pp. 1317-1341. As of March 2006 available at: http://www.chinabiodiversity.com/shwdyx/ruq/ruq-index-en.htm.

Yen K (1992) *The Illustrated Chinese Materia Medica: Crude and Prepared*. SMC Publishing Inc, Taipei Taiwan.

American Ginseng

Jean Giblette
High Falls Gardens

Radix Panacis Quinquefolii	xī yáng shēn	Panax quinquefolius L.

Since the time of the great Swedish botanist Linnaeus, scientists have been aware that the flora of eastern Asia and eastern North America bear close similarities. In 1751, another Swedish botanist, Pehr Kalm, published an account of his travels in North America. He noted *Panax quinquefolius* and its recognized medicinal value, and he reported that the French were importing the root from Canada and exporting it to China (Boufford and Spongberg 1983).

The medicinal plants of the two continents' eastern woodlands—black cohosh, coptis, mayapple, and Solomon's seal, among others—are closely related. The ginsengs, members of the family Araliaceae, provide perhaps the best-known example: *Panax ginseng* (rén shēn) is the primary Asian species, and *P. quinquefolius* is American.

The Chinese named the American plant "western seas root," probably in reference to the early shipments through Europe, and deemed that its nature and properties provide a desirable complement to their own native species. China still imports economically significant quantities of American ginseng, even though *P. quinquefolius* is commercially cultivated in that country.

....

Distribution

Panax quinquefolius is endemic to the mountainous areas of eastern North America, from southern Canada (Quebec and Ontario) south through Georgia and the Carolinas, and has been found in some regions to the west. Records of Native American usage are scant, although several nations (including the Oklahoma Seminoles) knew of its medicinal applications (Foster 1999). The plant is now field cultivated in several locales, including Wisconsin, British Columbia, and Jiangxi, China.

In the wild, the species depends on a stable, undisturbed ecosystem. It also requires shade and does not emerge in spring until the trees have leafed out. Therefore, the practices of the European settlers in logging and clearing the forests for farming and grazing were the primary disruptors of ginseng habitat. The decline of agriculture in the eastern United States since the 19th century has restored ginseng habitat to some extent. Replanting projects are underway, and wild cultivation is now seen as an attractive component activity for agroforestry (Jacobson and Burkhart 2004).

....

Biology

American ginseng is a long-lived herbaceous perennial, which dies back to the ground each autumn and sends up new shoots in the spring. Plants in the wild have been observed with an estimated age of 50 years or more. If moisture and temperature are not conducive to growth in the spring, the le.aves will die back early, and the plant will appear to be dormant for the season. This characteristic has fueled ginseng lore, with observers noting magical reappearances of plants long thought dead.

In the wild, healthy ginseng plants live in family groups of varying ages, dispersed among companion plants or "indicator" plants such as maidenhair fern, baneberry, elderberry, and others, depending on the site (Beyfuss 2000). They have perfect flowers, with both male and female parts, with a high rate of self-fertilization. Small bees and flies assist in pollination, although cross-fertilization over long distances does not occur.

Seed production increases with the age and size of the plant, and it seems to depend on the plant's energy reserves for reproduction in any given year. This, in turn, depends on resources available in the immediate environment. The number of fruiting plants within a population varies from year to year. If conditions are optimal, a single four-year-old plant may produce as many as 40 fruits—bright red berries with two seeds each. In the wild, the fruits are eaten by animals or they drop off, typically remaining within two meters of the parent. Germination rates in the wild are low, although the seeds that germinate are likely to survive (USFWS 2003).

Ginseng leaves are whorled and palmately compound, with three to five leaflets. Each leaf with its petiole is called a "prong." The approximate age of the plant can be estimated by the number of prongs, with one prong usually indicating a two-year-old plant, two prongs 3 to 6 years old, three prongs 7 to 9 years, and four prongs 10 to 11 years (USFWS 2003). Plants with five or more prongs are now rare. Flowering and seeding begins at the two-prong stage. The sequence of stages is not foolproof, as less-than-favorable conditions will retard growth, although the plant can survive for many years.

The plant forms a thick taproot that sometimes divides to form "legs," prompting its common name "man root." Thin roots may also branch to the sides. A special rhizome formed on top of the taproot sends up the stems each season. Annual stem scars on this rhizome or "neck" can be counted to estimate the age of the root. Although wild collectors have often replanted the rhizome for successful propagation, the legal requirement to retain the neck for purposes of determining age interferes with this practice (Jacobson and Burkhart 2004).

The root is cylindrical or spindle-shaped, 2 to 6 centimeters long and 0.5 to 1 centimeter in diameter. The exterior surface has varying shades of pale to medium brown, with transverse rings or wrinkles that are denser toward the neck or head of the root. The interior is off-white to pale yellow in color (Yen 1992). Fresh and dried ginseng root breaks smoothly, like a carrot.

The size, shape, and age of the root, as well as its "wild" qualities, determine value, since ginseng dealers can tell the difference between roots grown under artificial and natural conditions (Jacobson and Burkhart 2004). A harvest of wild roots would be considerably varied in shape and size, even though the plants might be of similar age, compared to those cultivated with extra water and fertilizer, which would be larger and more uniform in shape.

....

Threats

Two species of ginseng appear on the 1997 IUCN Red List: *Panax vietnamensis* Ha & Grushv., and *P. zingiberensis* C.Y. Wu & K.M. Feng (Walter and Gillett 1998). In the China Plant Red Data Book, *P. ginseng* is listed as vulnerable. Extensively cultivated, it has almost disappeared from the wild.

In North America, research shows that the harvest of ginseng from the wild removes the oldest and largest plants from the population, thus eliminating the individuals that produce the most seeds. Such a practice is problematic for a slow-growing species with low seed production and minimal natural dispersal of seed (Gagnon 1999). Research indicates that small stands of wild ginseng may be vulnerable to an Allee effect, referring to a critical threshold of population size below which the individuals cannot maintain fertility and reproduction (Levin 2001). The minimum viable population size has not yet been determined.

Poaching has been a serious problem, particularly on public lands such as Great Smoky Mountains National Park (Gagnon 1999). Even licensed wild collecting can be a threat, as responsible collectors may have no way to know how many collectors have preceded them in removing individuals from a given population.

Populations seem to be highly adapted to local conditions, and there is considerable genetic variation from one population to the next. Seed from cultivated ginseng may have been introduced into certain wild populations, thereby making the group less distinct (USFWS 2003). Conscientious land stewards are aware that artificial seeding can erode the genetic distinctiveness of their wild stands.

Given ginseng's dependence on species-specific forest ecology, especially its preference for trees that concentrate calcium in their leaves (such as maple and tulip poplar), any threats to those tree species represent a potential loss of habitat. Acid rain has adversely affected ginseng populations, particularly in Quebec (Beyfuss 2000). Ginseng is also dependent on a symbiotic relationship with a vesicular-arbuscular mycorrhizal (VAM) fungus (Whitbread *et al* 1996). These complex interdependencies within the ginseng ecosystem suggest that climate change could precipitate a chain reaction of events that would adversely affect habitat and the species.

....

CONSERVATION STRATEGIES AND RESEARCH

American ginseng root has been listed on CITES Appendix II since 1975, and its root products and derivatives (powders, pills, tonics, etc.) since 1985. The US Fish and Wildlife Service and individual states license and monitor harvesting and trade in ginseng.

In 1999, the US Fish and Wildlife Service determined that wild ginseng roots must be at least five years of age to receive a permit for export. In 2005, they increased this requirement to ten years (USFWS

2005), prompting protest from ginseng growers that demand for their cultivated product may be affected.

Given the three centuries of international trade in American ginseng and its increasing scarcity in the wild, cultivation would seem to be a desirable means of conservation. However, the history of ginseng cultivation tells a cautionary tale. Beginning in Virginia after the Civil War, cultivation was encouraged by a USDA Bulletin published in 1895 (Foster 1999). By the 1990s, production had concentrated in Wisconsin, where industrial agriculture techniques were used to grow plants under shade cloth in monocultures. Monocultural cropping systems (the practice of concentrating plants of only one kind in a particular cultivation area) lead almost inevitably to attack by disease organisms. Facing loss of the crop, especially one that has taken many years to produce, growers feel compelled to use fungicides and pesticides to save their investment.

Current attention to non-timber forest products has resulted in advances in ginseng cultivation. The land-grant colleges and USDA Cooperative Extension in several eastern states have provided training for growers in recent years. Two methods of production, known as woods-cultivated and wild-simulated, each with economic trade-offs, have become prevalent (Jacobson and Burkhart 2004). Landowners are in a good position to monitor their own stands and to create conditions that lead to a truly sustainable harvest. The recent controversy over the 2005 ginseng finding suggests that the perceived quality gap between wild and cultivated product may have narrowed.

Continued training programs, lower taxes on forest reserves, measures to control animal overpopulations (notably deer), stewardship payments, and a dependable market are measures that would encourage the land-owning forest farmers.

Research on sustainable harvest strategies should continue. Research and control measures related to climate change are required. Subjects to study include acid rain, exotic pests that attack native plants and trees, and invasive plants that displace natives and interfere with ecosystem processes. Other promising lines of research deal with population dynamics, effects of soil chemistry on ginseng growth, effects of soil preparation, mulching and plant density in different types of deciduous forests, studies of the colonization of roots by soil fungi, and development of *in vitro* germination of ginseng plantlets.

SOURCES

Acres USA (1995) Bulletin on the Wisconsin Ginseng Crop Improvement Project. *Acres USA: The Voice of Eco-Agriculture*, Austin TX.

Beyfuss R (2000) Soil nutrient characteristics of wild ginseng populations in NY, NJ, ME and TN. In *American Ginseng Production in the 21st Century: Sept. 2000 Conference Proceedings*, Cornell Cooperative Extension of Greene County, Cairo NY: pp. 105-114.

Boufford D and Spongberg S (1983) Eastern Asian - Eastern North American phytogeographical relationships - a history from the time of Linnaeus to the twentieth century. *Annals of the Missouri Botanical Garden* 70: pp. 423-439.

Foster S (1999) *Botanical Series No. 308: American Ginseng*. American Botanical Council, Austin TX.

Gagnon D (1999) An analysis of the sustainability of American ginseng harvesting from the wild: the problem and possible solutions. US Fish and Wildlife Service. As of March 2006 available at: http://www.nps.gov/plants/medicinal/pubs/ginseng.htm.

Jacobson M and Burkhart E (2004) *Opportunities from Ginseng Husbandry in Pennsylvania*. Penn State College of Agricultural Sciences, University Park PA.

Levin S ed-in-chief (2001) *Encyclopedia of Biodiversity, Vol. 1*. Academic Press, San Diego CA.

USFWS Division of Scientific Authority (2003) Convention permit applications for wild ginseng (*Panax quinquefolius*) harvested in 2003 and 2004. As of March 2006 available at: http://international.fws.gov/ginseng/2003-2004ginsengfinding.htm.

USFWS Division of Scientific Authority (2005) Convention permit applications for wild American ginseng harvested in 2005. As of March 2006 available at: http://www.fws.gov/international/pdf/2005ginsengfinding.pdf.

Walter K and Gillett H eds (1998) *1997 IUCN Red List of Threatened Plants*, International Union for Conservation of Nature and Natural Resources, Gland Switzerland and Cambridge UK.

Whitbread F, McGonigle T and Peterson R (1996) Vesicular-arbuscular mycorrhizal associations of American ginseng (*Panax quinquefolius*) in commercial production. *Canadian Journal of Botany* 74: pp. 1104-1112.

Yen K (1992) *The Illustrated Chinese Materia Medica: Crude and Prepared.* SMC Publishing Inc, Taipei Taiwan.

Chain Fern Rhizome

Jean Giblette
High Falls Gardens

Rhizoma Cibotii Barometz	gŏu jĭ	Cibotium barometz (L.) J. Smith

Like most of our medicinal plants protected under CITES, *Cibotium barometz* belongs to a class of organisms that have long been the subject of popular fascination. The members of the hairy tree fern family Dicksoniaceae resemble palm trees, but their trunks actually are frond stalks growing together in tight spirals that can reach more than 15 meters in height. Botanical gardens commonly exhibit mature tree ferns growing in large tubs.

Like orchids, ferns are beloved to the point of mania. The story of the fern craze in 19th century Britain illustrates our modern compulsion to domesticate wild and exotic plants. In 1795, the infamous Captain William Bligh had recovered sufficiently from the *HMS Bounty* mutiny to bring 37 species of ferns back to England from the West Indies. In almost the same time, John Lindsay, an English physician living in Jamaica, discovered how to propagate ferns. Although he did not understand the details of the process, he reported the procedure to a London botanical society. Decades later, another physician and amateur botanist named Nathaniel Ward made a serendipitous discovery that his ferns survived better in a glass bottle, and thereby set off a fad. Miniature greenhouses, known as Wardian cases, became an essential decor element in Victorian homes. At its height, fern mania caused the areas around London to be stripped of wild ferns, and conservationists called for restraint (Allen 1969).

Cibotium barometz is a uniquely notorious plant. Known as "Scythian lamb," the "vegetable lamb of Tartary," or simply the "Barometz," this particular tree fern is the subject of a legend traced to 5th century Talmudical writings. They describe a curious part-animal, part-plant creature that is attached to the soil with a kind of umbilical cord and feeds on the products of dying organic matter in its vicinity. (How interesting that the myth conveys the principle of the saprophytic organism! Although, in reality, tree ferns produce chlorophyll.) This creature was said to inhabit Scythia or Tartary, a region north of the Black Sea.

The Barometz legend reached European academic circles in the 16th century. In the late 19th century, a London scientist reviewed the legend and concluded that its subject was the cotton plant (Lee 1887). In 1955, however, the fern expert Alice Tryon published a journal article that juxtaposed a drawing from a 1725 Latin treatise with a modern photo of Chinese artifacts made for tourists. The treatise author, Prussian scientist Dr. Breyn of Danzig, had argued that the Barometz was made from the stem of a fern. His drawing was remarkably similar to the photo of small dog- or lamb-shaped toys made from woolly pieces of *Cibotium barometz* rhizome, stem stubs attached, and garnished with glued-on bits for eyes and ears (Tryon 1955).

Gǒu jǐ, "dog spine," has been known by the Chinese for a very long time. *The Divine Farmer's Materia Medica* lists it as a middle-grade herb, saying "it benefits old people very much." The rhizome's enduring popularity probably is related to its Yang-tonifying properties. Sometimes called "golden-haired dog" in southern China, *Cibotium barometz* has been kept as a houseplant for use in minor emergencies—a few hairs pulled from the rhizome will help stop bleeding from a skin cut.

....

DISTRIBUTION

In the wild, tree ferns inhabit the misty cooler regions of the tropics and subtropics. *Cibotium barometz* is native to South China, Assam, and Malaysia (Graf 1985). In China, varying concentrations of *C. barometz* occur in the southern and southwestern provinces. Populations are usually found in valleys and forest margins at elevations ranging from 200 to 600 meters (Jia and Zhang 2001).

....

BIOLOGY

Cryptogams are non-flowering plants without stamens or pistils. Of these, the Pteridophytes do not produce true seeds. The Filices (ferns) are among this group. The families Dicksoniaceae and Cyatheaceae constitute the tree ferns. The former are distinguished by their hairs and the latter by scales. Reproduction depends on the presence of external water (Graf 1985).

Cibotium barometz has fragrant, light green, one- to two-meter fronds of leathery texture. The wiry frond stalks or stipes, are covered with light brown hairs. Unlike other tree ferns, the plant forms no trunk. The rhizomes, actually prostrate stems, are covered with golden brown hairs, and the stipes grow directly out of the stems. Hardy to USDA climate zone 9, this plant prefers light shade and temperatures of 10 to14 degrees Celsius (Perl 1977).

Like other ferns, its life cycle alternates between two distinct generations. The leafy phase is the sexless or sporophyte generation, producing seed-like spores in cases (sporangia), usually in clusters known as sori on the underside or margin of the leaf. The dust-like spores are ejected when mature. When alighting on a moist surface, the spore forms a small, shield-like structure called a prothallus, rarely more than one centimeter in diameter. The prothallus contains separate male and female sexual organs, each with its haploid gametes. Moisture causes the cell wall to rupture. The sperm swim to unite with the eggs, and their union forms the diploid sporophyte. Cibotiums can be propagated by spores or by division (Graf 1985).

....

Threats

Cibotiums are popular in the ornamental trade and with botanical gardens. The 1997 IUCN Red List states that four of the 41 species of the family Dicksoniaceae are threatened (Walter and Gillett 1998). While this percentage is significant, the list of threatened species does not include *Cibotium barometz*. Thus, once again, collection pressure and loss of habitat for the family as a whole justify CITES Appendix II protection.

....

Conservation Strategies and Research

A recent study found wild stocks of *C. barometz* to be seriously depleted in certain parts of its range. A detailed assessment was undertaken with the support of Fauna and Flora International and the CITES Management Authority of China. Each county in the southern provinces was assessed and ranked in one of four categories, according to the size of its *C. barometz* population. Sample plots in each category were dug up and the rhizomes weighed in order to estimate the national inventory and evaluate sustainability (Jia and Zhang 2001).

Based on responsible local practices of harvesting only rhizomes of two kilograms or more, the study estimated national reserves at 39,140 tons, of which 3,131 could be harvested each year without impairing natural regeneration of the stands. The investigators estimated that internal trade currently involves 3,000 tons per year, while exports number 90 tons. Overall, therefore, harvests seem to be close to sustainable capacity at present. Scientists, however, recommend government restriction of exports, export of only finished products and not raw materials, encouragement of sustainable harvests through education and forestry management practices, establishment of nature reserves where no collection is allowed, and research into cultivation methods (Jia and Zhang, 2001).

Considering the interest in tree ferns perpetuated by botanical gardens and enthusiasts, perhaps sustainably propagated *C. barometz* featured in more collections could be a valuable adjunct to cultivation research. The means are available. "Pteridomania" still lurks in the hearts of many plant lovers, and the American Fern Society maintains a spore exchange service.

SOURCES

Allen D (1969) *The Victorian Fern Craze: A History of Pteridomania.* Hutchinson, London.

Graf A (1985) *Exotica Series 4 International: Pictorial Cyclopedia of Exotic Plants.* Roehrs Company Publishers, East Rutherford NJ.

Jia J and Zhang X (2001) Assessment of resources and sustainable harvest of wild *Cibotium barometz* in China. In *Medicinal Plant Conservation*, newsletter of the Medicinal Plant Specialist Group, IUCN Species Survival Commission, *Bundesamt für Naturschutz, Bonn*, Vol. 7: *pp. 25–27.*

Lee H (1887) *The Vegetable Lamb of Tartary, A Curious Fable of the Cotton Plant.* Sampson Low Marston Searle and Rivington, London.

Perl P (1977) *The Time-Life Encyclopedia of Gardening: Ferns.* Time-Life Books, Alexandria VA.

Tryon A (1955) The vegetable lamb of Tartary. *Missouri Botanical Garden Bulletin* XLIII No. 2, February 1955, pp. 25-28.

Walter K and Gillett H eds (1998) *1997 IUCN Red List of Threatened Plants.* International Union for Conservation of Nature and Natural Resources, Gland Switzerland and Cambridge UK.

EUPHORBIAS

Jean Giblette
High Falls Gardens

Herba Euphorbiae Helioscopiae	zé qī	E. helioscopia L.
Radix Euphorbiae Kansui	gān suì	E. kansui Liou ex S.B. Ho
Radix Euphorbiae Pekinensis	jīng dà jǐ	E. pekinensis Rupr.

The genus Euphorbia of the Spurge family, Euphorbiaceae, encompasses 2,000 species and is one of the six largest genera of flowering plants. Most Euphorbias are tropical and subtropical; they are found in nearly every kind of habitat from desert to jungle.

Spurges include many useful genera besides Euphorbia. Several are poisonous, such as the source of tung oil, *Aleurites fordii*, yóu tóng zǐ; the purgative bā dòu, *Croton tiglium;* and castor oil, *Ricinus communis*, bì má zǐ (Duke and Ayensu 1985).

Many spurges resemble cactuses; some are shrubs or the size of trees. They can boast exotic or even weird forms and large and/or sharp spikes and thorns. Other spurges have soft, lovely foliage, and their yellow-green colors offer a pleasing contrast in the perennial bed. A large number of ornamentals are in worldwide trade, especially the genus Codiaeum (Crotons), which has hundreds of cultivars (Graf 1985). *Euphorbia pucherrima*, poinsettia, threatens to overwhelm the north during the winter holidays with its showy colored bracts.

The genus Euphorbia is a favorite, attracting its own societies of plant enthusiasts and their associated websites, especially in Europe. A sizeable percentage of Euphorbias are succulents, fleshy and juicy, similar to the leaves of aloe. Like the aloe family, succulent Euphorbias merit blanket protection from CITES due to collectors' appetite for cactuses and cactus-like plants, especially those considered most exotic and rare. A few of the many Euphorbia species recognized as medicinal in the Chinese traditions are listed on CITES Appendix II (see table). However, the three most familiar to American students (zé qī, gān suì and jīng dà jǐ) are not succulents and thus are not CITES-protected.

Sun spurge, *E. helioscopia*, is one of the world's most ubiquitous weeds of temperate origin (Turner 1995). Listed as an inferior grade herb in *The Divine Farmer's Materia Medica*, zé qī ("marsh lacquer") is toxic but transforms phlegm, dissipates nodules, reduces edema, and otherwise regulates fluid metabolism (Yang 1998, Bensky et al 2004).

Gān suì and jīng dà jǐ are considered strong expellants and are toxic in traditional Chinese medicine; consequently, they seem less useful in modern times. Gān suì is also noted in *The Divine Farmer's Materia Medica* as an inferior grade herb (Yang 1998). Hóng dà jǐ, *Knoxia valerianoides*, a less-toxic cousin in the Euphorbia family, now is used more often than jīng dà jǐ (Bensky et al 2004). Throughout history, however, many other Euphorbia species have been recognized as having medicinal properties, as the following table attests.

Names of the Genus EUPHORBIA in Traditional Chinese Medicine

Latin Binomial	Plant Name (Pinyin)	Medicine/Literature Name*	Latin Binomial	Plant Name (Pinyin)	Medicine/Literature Name*
E. antiquorum**	jin gang zuan	huo yang	E. luticola	huang tu da ji	tu da ji*
E. adenochlora	ling ru	ling ru	E. maculata	ban di jin	di jin cao
E. atoto**	hai bin da ji	bin da ji*	E. makinoi	xiao ye hong ru cao	
E. chrysocoma:	huang bao da ji	shui huang hua	E. marginata	yin bian cui	yin bian cui
E. cyanophylla	lan ye da ji	da lang du (local name Yunnan)	E. milii (= E. splendens)**	tie hai tang	tie hai tang
E. ebracteolata (= E. sieboldiana auct. non Morr. et Decne.)	yue xian da ji	lang du	E. nematocypha	da lang du	da lang du
E. erythraea	san duo yun	tie kuai zi	E. nematocypha var. induta	mao da lang du	bei gai da lang du*
E. esula	ru jiang da ji	ru jiang cao	E. neriifolia**	jia zhu tao ye da ji	ba wang bian*
E. esula var. cyparisioides (= E. kaleniczenkii)	song ye ru jiang da ji	ru jiang cao	E. pekinensis	da ji	jing da ji

Species		
E. fischeriana (= E. pallasii)	lang du da ji	lang du
E. fischeriana var. komaroviana	duan zhu lang du da ji	lang du
E. fischeriana var. pilosa	mao lang du da ji	lang du
E. formosana	da jia cao	ba gua cao (local name Taiwan)
E. helioscopia	ze xi	ze xi
E. henryi	chang yuan ye da ji	gua jin ban (local name Hubei)
E. heterophylla	xing xing cao	yi pin hong
E. hippocrepica:	ma ti ye da ji	niu nai jiang cao
E. hirta (= E. hirta var. typica)	fei yang cao	fei yang cao
E. humifusa	di jin	di jin cao
E. hylonoma	jiu niu zao	jiu niu zao
E. hypericifolia (= E. indica)	tong nai cao	da di jin

Species		
E. peplus	xian cao	shui jing (local name, Fu Jian)
E. pilulifera	taiwan di jin cao	mao guo da ji*
E. pinus	tu gua lang du	tu gua lang du
E. prolifera	xiao lang du	xiao lang du
E. prostrata	pu di cao	hong ru cao
E. pulcherrima	yi pin hong	xing xing mu (local name Jiangsu, Taiwan, Guangxi, Yunnan)
E. rapulum	kuai jing da ji	xiao luo bo da ji*
E. resinifera**	da ji ru zhi shu	xian ren zhang da ji*
E. rothiana	chang jiao da ji	qian da ji*
E. royleana**	ba wang bian	ba wang bian
E. sessiliflora**	bai bu hui yang	can dou qi (local name Yunnan)
E. sieboldiana	gou xian da ji	cao ling ru

Species		
E. jolkiki	nan da ji	shan da ji
E. kansui	gan sui	gan sui
E. kozlowii	qing hai da ji	ta ri qing (local name Qing Hai)
E. lamprocarpa (= E. soongarica ssp. lamprocarpa)	guang guo da ji	da ji (local name, Xin jiang)
E. lathyris	xu sui zi	qian jin zi
E. lunulata	mao yan cao	mao yan cao
E. lucorum	lin da ji	lin da ji
E. soongarica	zhun ge er da ji	xin jiang da ji
E. stracheyi (= E. megistopoda)	zang xi da ji	tu gua lang du*
E. supina	xue jin cao	di jin cao
E. thymifolia	qian gen cao	xiao fei yang cao
E. tirucalli**	lu yu shu	lu yu shu
E. vachellii	xi ju ye di jin	xi ju ye di jin

* Literature names (wén xiàn míng), as distinct from current accepted medicine names, are given to the plant species in context of a historical discussion, usually in older texts.

** Species listed in CITES Appendix II

Distribution

The spurges are found worldwide, but especially in Africa, tropical Latin America, and central and southwest Asia. About 75 species, 10 endemic, occur in China (Ma and Gilbert draft).

Euphorbia kansui inhabits steppes, slopes, valleys, fields, scrub, and forest margins. Its range is in north-central China, from Hebei, Nei Mongol, and Gansu to northwest Sichuan. *E. pekinensis*, Peking (Beijing) spurge root, is considered common all over China except in Xinjiang, Xizang, Yunnan, and Taiwan (Ma and Gilbert draft). The plant is also found in the Russian Far East, Inner Mongolia, Japan, and Korea (Turner 1995).

Sun spurge, *E. helioscopia*, inhabits fields, roadsides, scrub, or mixed forest margins throughout every province of China except Nei Mongol, Jilin, and Heilongjiang. The plant has spread to other parts of Asia, as well as to North Africa, Europe, and North America (Ma and Gilbert draft). In the continental United States, however, only cypress spurge (*E. cyparissias*) and leafy spurge (*E. esula*) appear on the list of "alien plant invaders" compiled by the Plant Conservation Alliance.

Biology

Euphorbias can be annual, biennial, or perennial. Sun spurge is an annual, while the other two medicinal species under consideration are perennials. The distinguishing characteristics of Euphorbias include: 1) small, simple flowers with specialized leaves called bracts, whose color attracts insects, and 2) stems that contain a milky, usually poisonous, juice called latex (Turner 1995).

E. kansui is a bright green perennial herb approximately 25-40 centimeters in height, with smooth-edged oblong leaves (Yao and Zhang 1995). The fleshy root is pale brown outside and white inside, round in cross-section, and about 3-9 centimeters long (Yen 1992). The plant flowers and sets fruit from April through June. The inflorescence, unique to the Euphorbias, is called a cyathium, a cup-shaped organ containing tiny flowers, one female surrounded by several males. The rounded cyathia of *E. kansui* have four lobes, with the male flowers protruding out of the cup. The fruit is a smooth capsule about 6 millimeters in diameter (Ma and Gilbert draft), which splits open to release its seeds when ripe.

Peking spurge, *E. pekinensis*, is a delightful, reliable foliage plant, clump-forming but non-invasive. The foliage turns fiery red on a pink stem in autumn. The herbaceous stems are 20 to 80 centimeters tall with simple leaves. The bracts are lime-yellow. The cyathia are 3 to 4 millimeters in diameter, with four lobes (Ma and Gilbert draft). The fruit capsule bears smooth seeds that pop out when ripe. The seeds germinate readily, and the plant will self-sow under the right conditions. The plant can be propagated by seed or division (Turner, 1995).

Sun spurge reaches 10 to 50 centimeters, with fibrous, branching roots and one or more smooth stems growing from its base. Spoon-shaped leaves alternate along the stem. The flowering and fruiting period extends from April through October. Smooth, five-lobed, 2 millimeter cyathia appear singly at the ends of branches, with male flowers extended out of the cup. The smooth capsule has three conspicuous furrows and bears dark brown, ovoid seeds (Ma and Gilbert draft).

....

THREATS

The 1997 IUCN Red List records 933 of the 7,500 species in the spurge family (12 percent) as threatened. Of these, about 300 are in the genus Euphorbia. Habitat loss and pressure from plant collectors are the greatest threats (Walter and Gillett 1998). While populations of the three medicinal spurges under consideration continue to thrive in the wild, CITES protections reflect efforts to safeguard a threatened family of plants by listing all species under at least Appendix II.

Threats to this group resemble those that threaten aloes. The attractiveness of cactus-like plants to collectors, slow growth and reproduction rates, and the sensitive qualities of preferred habitats, such as regions of Africa and Madagascar, all combine to justify blanket protection for the entire category of succulent Euphorbias.

....

CONSERVATION STRATEGIES AND RESEARCH

Why should we discuss conservation strategies for a plant such as sun spurge, which is widespread on several continents? Such a case provides an opportunity to re-think the human sense of entitlement to harvest wild plants wherever they appear abundant, if their sustainability is not considered. While acknowledging very old hunter-gatherer instincts, we may come to appreciate "weeds" and wild plants in a new way, simply by taking time to get to know their growth patterns and biological needs before collecting them.

A responsible wildcrafter encountering a plentiful stand of wild plants in any area will harvest them only after verifying positive answers to three questions:

- Is this "weed" abundant elsewhere, or only here? (Even if abundant in your state or region, ensure that it is not one of the few places the plant is found. Otherwise, harvest may pose a threat.)
- Can this stand of wild plants recover easily after the loss of what I take?
- Can the species in its entire distribution recover after the loss of what others are taking, including those less responsible than I am?

We may wish to debate variations on this monologue. However, only such a level of global awareness allows us to prevent cumulative impacts on the viability of plant species. The spirit of CITES protection is to raise our collective level of consciousness so that we develop habits of stewardship beyond the letter of the law—habits that extend to long-term plant sustainability as the goal.

SOURCES

Bensky D, Clavey S and Ströger E (eds.) (2004) *Chinese Herbal Medicine Materia Medica, 3rd Edition*. Eastland Press, Seattle WA.

Duke J and Ayensu E (1985) *Medicinal Plants of China, Vols. I&II*. Reference Publications Inc, Algonac MI.

Graf A (1985) *Exotica Series 4 International: Pictorial Cyclopedia of Exotic Plants*. Roehrs Company Publishers, East Rutherford NJ.

Ma J and Gilbert M (draft) Euphorbiaceae. In *Flora of China Vol. 11: Oxalidaceae through Aceraceae*. Z. Wu and P. Raven (eds.), Science Press, Beijing and Missouri Botanical Garden Press, St. Louis MO. As of March 2006 available at: http://flora.huh.harvard.edu.

Turner R (1995) *Euphorbias: A Gardener's Guide*. BT Batsford, London.

Walter K and Gillett H eds (1998) *1997 IUCN Red List of Threatened Plants*. International Union for Conservation of Nature and Natural Resources, Gland Switzerland and Cambridge UK.

Yang S translation (1998) *The Divine Farmer's Materia Medica*. Blue Poppy Press Inc, Boulder CO.

Yao D and Zhang J (eds.) (1995) *A Coloured Atlas of the Chinese Materia Medica Specified in Pharmacopoeia of the PRC*, Joint Publishing Company Ltd, Hong Kong.

Yen K (1992) *The Illustrated Chinese Materia Medica: Crude and Prepared*. SMC Publishing Inc, Taipei Taiwan.

ORCHIDS

Jean Giblette
High Falls Gardens

Rhizoma Bletillae	bái jí	*Bletilla striata* (Thunb.) Reichb. *Bletilla ochracea* Schltr.
Pseudobulbus Cremastrae seu Pleiones	shān cí gū	*Cremastra variabilis* (Bl.) Nakai (=*C. appendiculata* (D. Don) Makino *Pleione bulbocodioides* (Franch.) Rolfe *Pleione yunnanensis* Rolfe
Herba Dendrobii	shí hú	*Dendrobium candidum* Wall. ex Lindl. *Dendrobium chrysanthum* Wall. *Dendrobium fimbriatum* Hook. var. *oculatum* Hook. *Dendrobium loddigesii* Rolfe. *Dendrobium nobile* Lindl.
Rhizoma Gastrodiae	tīan má	*Gastrodia elata* Blume

.....and many other orchid species (see Table A below)

The orchid family, Orchidaceae, comprises approximately 700 to 800 genera, at least 20,000 (some sources estimate 35,000) species worldwide, and more than 30,000 hybrids (Graf 1985). Even with so many hybrids, and more being introduced continuously, the orchids that are important in the ornamental trade belong to only a small number of genera in the family. Most orchids are not cultivated (Romero-Gonzalez et al 2002).

Few other families of plants have cast such a powerful spell over humankind, who from ancient times has sought their varied, exotic forms, exquisite colors, and delightful fragrances. One of the first flowers mentioned in a recorded text that survives to this day, and one of the oldest cultivated orchids, is the orchid genus Cymbidium. Confucius (551-479 BCE) called it "the king of fragrant flowers" (Isaac-Williams 1988).

A few orchids have been used as food. Salep, a type of flour used in northern Africa, the Middle East, and Asia, is ground from the dried roots of some Dactylorhiza, Eulophia, and Orchis species. The ubiquitous spice vanilla consists of the dried fruits of several species in the genus of that name (Romero-Gonzalez et al 2002).

The orchid family is a very old source of medicinals. The Chinese have recognized medicinal properties in at least 245 species, as the list in Table A confirms (Han and Newman 1996). Three of the four orchid medicinals identified at the beginning of this profile, which are most familiar to students of traditional Chinese medicine in North America, were noted in *The Divine Farmer's Materia Medica.* Shí hú is of the superior class of herbs, with tīan má a middle grade and bái jí an inferior grade herb (Yang 1998).

....

TABLE A

NUMBER OF ORCHID SPECIES RECOGNIZED AS MEDICINES IN CHINA
(Listed by Genera)

Acampe	1	Epipactis	3	Oreorchis	3
Aerides	1	Eria	3	Paphiopedilum	4
Amitostigma	1	Galeola	2	Pecteilis	1
Anoectochilus	2	Gastrochilus	1	Perisylus	3
Apostasia	1	Gastrodia	6	Perularia	1
Arundina	1	Geodorum	2	Phaius	2
Bletilla	3	Goodyera	8	Phalaenopsis	2
Brachycorythis	1	Gymnadenia	5	Pholidota	4
Bulbophyllum	9	Habenaria	13	Platanthera	6
Calanthe	15	Hemipilia	3	Pleione	5
Cephalanthera	2	Herminium	3	Pogonia	1
Changnienia	1	Holcoglossum	1	Renanthera	1
Cheirostylis	1	Ischnogyne	1	Robiquetia	1
Cirrhopetalum	2	Liparis	12	Sarcanthus	2
Cleisostoma	4	Listera	1	Sarcochilus	1
Coeloglossum	1	Ludisia	1	Satyrium	2
Coelogyne	7	Luisia	2	Sedirea	1
Collabium	1	Malaxis	2	Spathoglottis	1
Cremastra	1	Neofinetia	1	Spiranthes	1
Cymbidium	10	Neottia	1	Thunia	1
Cypripedium	13	Neottianthe	1	Tulotis	2
Dendrobium	30	Nervilia	3	Vanda	2
Diploprora	1	Oberonia	3	Vanilla	2
Ephemerantha	. 3	Odontochilus	1	**Total number**	
Epigeneium	2	Orchis	3	**of species**	**245**

terrestrial: a ground-dwelling plant that grows in any of a variety of habitats.

epiphyte: a plant that grows on a host, which can be a tree or a rock, not as a parasite, but by absorbing moisture and nutrients from the air or surface of the host. Mainly tropical and subtropical, many can tolerate long dry periods.

saprophyte: generally terrestrial plants with no leaves that do not produce chlorophyll but instead absorb nutrients from decaying organic matter.

monopoidal: one stem, flowers from the leaf axils.

sympoidal: many stems, often have pseudobulbs at stem base to store food and water (like Dendrobium).

....
DISTRIBUTION

While orchids are distributed worldwide, even in the Arctic, 85 percent are endemic to the tropics and sub-tropical regions. Tropical Asia is probably the richest location for orchids, including Cymbidium, Dendrobium, and other genera popular as ornamentals, such as Bulbophyllum, Calanthe, Coelogyne, Paphiopedilum, Phaius, Palaenopsis, and Vanda (Graf 1985).

Approximately 173 genera and 1,247 species are native to China (Chen et al draft). By this estimate, about 5 percent of the known species are recognized as having medicinal properties. The descriptions that follow of the ranges of the species most familiar to students of traditional Chinese medicine show the adaptability of these plants to a variety of habitats.

Bletilla

Bletilla striata (=hyacinthina) is found from northern Myanmar through China to Japan. In China in the wild, Bletilla inhabits evergreen broad-leaved and coniferous forests at altitudes of 100 to 320 meters. Also found along roadsides, among grasses, and in crevices, it ranges from southeast China north and west to Shaanxi and southern Gansu.

Bletilla is cultivated in Beijing and Tianjin (Chen et al draft). Winter hardy with protection, Bletilla is available commercially from U.S. nurseries. A stand of Bletilla grows in the Asian Woodland of the National Arboretum in Washington, D.C., which is located in USDA climate zone 7. According to unconfirmed reports, it also has escaped from cultivation and grows along roadsides in Florida (Romero-Gonzalez et al 2002).

Cremastra and Pleione

One of four species of Cremastra found in China, *C. appendiculata* dwells in damp places in forests in southeast China and in wet ditches at altitudes of 500 to 2,900 meters. The plant's northern range is Henan, Anhui, and Jiangsu, west to the southern part of Yunnan and east to Taiwan. Two of the Chinese Cremastra species also occur in Bhutan, northern India, Japan, Nepal, Sikkim, Thailand, and Vietnam (Chen et al draft).

Pleione bulbocodioides inhabits evergreen broad-leaved forests in the humus-rich soil of scrub margins at 900 to 3,600 meters. It is found in Anhui, Hubei, Hunan, Guizhou, Sichuan, southern parts of Shaanxi and

Gansu, northern parts of Guangdong and Guangxi, northwest Yunnan, and southeast Tibet (Chen et al draft). The Yunnan *Pleione* occurs in Yunnan, Sichuan, and Guizhou, inhabiting the forested slopes of mountains or gully rocks at altitudes of 2,000 to 2,800 meters (He 1998).

Dendrobium

Of the approximately 1,000 *Dendrobium* species distributed throughout tropical and subtropical regions of Asia, 74 are endemic to China, where they are found mostly in southern Yunnan. The group that includes the medicinal species also occurs in southwest Guizhou and the northwest and south of Guangxi, as well as in Bhutan, India, Laos, Myanmar, Nepal, Sikkim, Thailand, and Vietnam. *G. loddigesii* is found also in Guangdong province. In the wild, *D. nobile* and the four other medicinal species listed above cling to tree trunks in dense forests or to rocks in mountain valleys at altitudes ranging from a few hundred to 2,500 meters (Chen et al draft).

Gastrodia

Gastrodia elata is one of 13 *Gastrodia* species in China, with 7 others occurring in other parts of Asia to Oceania. This orchid grows wild in the understories of open forests, in canopy gaps, forest margins, and scrub margins at altitudes of 400 to 3,200 meters. Its range is scattered but wide, from Jilin, Nei Mongol, and Gansu in the north to Sichuan, Yunnan, and Tibet in the west, and Taiwan in the east. Outside China, *G. elata* is found in Siberia, Korea, Japan, Nepal, Bhutan, and India.

There are four recognized, medicinally important forms of *G. elata*, each with a specific wild range, summarized in Table B below (Chen et al draft).

....

TABLE B

FORMS OF *GASTRODIA ELATA* AND THEIR RANGES

Gastrodia elata f. *elata*	Provinces along the Yellow and Yangtze rivers
Gastrodia elata f. *viridis* (Makino) Makino	Provinces from northeast to southwest China
Gastrodia elata f. *glauca* S. Chow	Western Guizhou and northern Yunnan
Gastrodia elata f. *alba* S. Chow	Northwest Yunnan in pine and oak forests

....
BIOLOGY

Orchids are perennial herbs (rarely, vines) that grow on the ground or on the surface of trees or on rock. They are monocotyledons like palms, lilies, and grasses—seed plants having an embryo with a single first leaf and usually parallel-veined leaves.

Orchids that grow on the ground are called terrestrial, while their cousins, the epiphytes, cling to trees or rocks. Another type is the saprophyte, which has no green parts (no chlorophyll) but instead obtains nourishment by absorbing the byproducts of organic decay in its vicinity.

The most prominent characteristic of the orchids is that the stamen (the organ that produces the male gamete) and pistil (the organ that produces the ovule) are united to form a column. The flowers can be borne on a spike, raceme, or panicle. Typically, the showy and/or fragrant flowers have three sepals and three petals, of which one is noticeably different in the form of a larger or smaller lip or pouch (Graf 1985). The variety of flower shapes, colors, and fragrances seems endless, especially to orchid breeders and fanciers, who are now so numerous they need a clearinghouse to keep track of their websites (http://www.orchidmall.com/society.htm).

Orchids are unique among the monocots, in that their pollen aggregates into discrete masses; various features help attach the unit to a pollinator. The pollen is usually not available as a nutrient source, and orchids have a complex relationship with their pollinators. Several genera have evolved a strategy known as pseudocopulation, in which the flower mimics the smell, appearance, and movements of a female wasp to attract a male wasp, which will succeed only in carrying off the pollen package to another orchid (Romero-Gonzalez et al 2002). Orchid seeds are very small with no endosperm, but the quantities are large. For some species, seeds number in the millions.

Other features of the orchid family vary greatly. Species range in size from a few millimeters long to over 13 meters in height. Some flowers are barely visible to the naked eye, while others measure up to 76 centimeters in diameter. Fragrances run the gamut from enchanting to unbearably repulsive. Habitats range from the driest and warmest places on earth to the wettest and coolest (Romero-Gonzalez et al 2002). Within this wide spectrum of diversity, the medicinal orchids have their own specialized adaptations.

Bletilla

A terrestrial orchid 30 to 60 centimeters high, Bletilla sprouts leafy stems from tuberous rhizomes bearing three to five thin plaited leaves. An erect, leafless stalk rises from the center of new shoots, bearing a terminal cluster of 3 to10 light purple flowers, 3 to 5 centimeters in diameter, in June or July. The blooms usually do not open fully (Graf 1985).

The tuberous rhizome, the medicinal portion, is fat and brown with one or two branches and an overall length of 1 to 5 centimeters. Rhizomes from previous years persist, bearing a scar left by the old stalk, and are connected in a series, with several thin roots extending downward (Yen 1992).

Bletilla ochracea Schltr., listed as a substitute species used in northern China, has yellowish-white flowers (Chen et al draft).

Cremastra and Pleione

Both these genera are terrestrial orchids with pseudobulbs just below ground. *Cremastra appendiculata* forms a series of closely connected, small pseudobulbs, 1 to 3 centimeters in diameter, buried near the surface with their stem node pointed upward and many dense roots at their base. Each pseudobulb sprouts one narrow leaf with a 7 to 17 centimeter stem and a blade ranging from 18 to 34 centimeters. The 27 to 70 centimeter flower stalk emerges from the top of the pseudobulb and produces a raceme of fragrant, medium-sized (2 to 3 centimeters) purplish-brown flowers. The pollen masses are waxy and adhere to a sticky structure, the viscidium, which pastes itself to the pollinator (Chen et al draft).

Pleione, "mother of the Pleiades," is a small group of about 15 species of beautiful deciduous orchids (Isaac-Williams 1988). Smaller than Cremastra, the pseudobulbs are closely arranged and flask-shaped, like little figs with their necks pointing up out of the ground. *P. bulbocodioides* is actually semi-epiphytic and may grow in relatively soil-less conditions on rocky mountain slopes. While the single leaf is still immature, the 7 to 20 centimeter long flower scape grows from the prominent neck of the pseudobulb and sprouts usually only one large, showy purple-pink flower with petals 3 to 7 centimeters wide (Chen et al draft). Yunnan Pleione, *P. yunnanensis*, grows 13 to 30 centimeters tall and also has one leaf and a solitary, terminal pale violet flower (He 1998).

Dendrobium

The species within the large genus Dendrobium that include the medicinal orchids are no less lovely and exquisite for being useful. Dendrobiums are tropical or subtropical epiphytic orchids that cling to tree trunks in dense forests. Their sympoidal stems, in clusters, are often stout and fleshy with conspicuous nodes that may be more prominent when the plant is dry. The numerous flowers sprout in a raceme, or more rarely an umbel, from nodes above the middle of the stem, sometimes pendulous (Chen et al draft). Relatively large, the flowers have sepals and petals more than one centimeter in width, and flower form is fairly consistent throughout the genus (Isaac-Williams 1988).

Some texts list 15 or more Dendrobium species as used for shí hú ("bushel of stone"). One visible commonality is the golden yellow color of the stems (the medicinal portion) when dried (Yen 1992). Of the medicinal species listed above, *D. nobile* has erect, thick stems over one centimeter in diameter and 10 to 60 centimeters in length. *D. loddigesii* and the others have soft, pendulous shorter stems that are only 3 millimeters in diameter (Chen et al draft).

In *D. nobile*, the flower raceme arises in April or May before or after the leaves have fallen. The flower is white to pale purplish-red. In *D. candidum*, *D. chrysanthum*, and *D. fimbriatum* the flowers are varying shades of yellow (Yao 1995).

The flowers of *D. loddigesii*, the "Anemone Dendrobe," are truly exquisite. Appearing singly from the stem nodes, the 4 to 5 centimeter wide lavender-mauve flowers have a large lip that is ringed with short hairs, pale mauve around the edge with a white band inside, and a deep orange-yellow blotch in the center. The short-lived flowers bloom in April or May (Isaac-Williams 1988). The species also has a white variety (Chen et al draft).

Gastrodia

Tiān má, "heavenly hemp," comes from a saprophytic species of the orchids. *Gastrodia elata*, "tall Gastrodia," is 0.3 to 1.5 meters in height (He 1998). Depending on the form (see Table B), the leafless stem is orange, yellow, grayish-brown, or blue-green. The flowers in a terminal raceme are colored orange, pale yellow, bluish green, or yellowish white, but are not as decorative as those of the other medicinal orchids described above. The rhizomes may be dumbbell-shaped, elliptical, oval, or spindle-shaped (Chen et al draft).

With no chlorophyll, *G. elata* depends entirely upon the symbiotic fungus *Armillariella mellea* (Vah. ex Fr.) Karst for the absorption of nutrients. Fleshy, tuberous underground rhizomes are of a shape and size similar to fingerling potatoes. Fresh rhizomes, which are 70 to 90 percent water, can weigh as much as one kilogram each (Chen et al draft). The orchid's development from germination to maturity takes three years. First a primary tuber forms, then secondary tubers appear. From the sprouting of flower scapes to dispersal of seed takes 62 to 65 days. The plant flowers from May to July, and the fruits ripen in July and August (Fu 1992). Pollen masses are granular and lack special structures to attach to pollinators (Chen et al draft).

....

THREATS

The 1997 Red List published by the Species Survival Commission of the IUCN records 1,779 of the world's orchid species as threatened. This number represents 5 to 8 percent of the species, depending on whether the total is 20,000 or 35,000. The list includes about 70 Dendrobiums, 2 Pleiones (including *P. formosana*), and 8 Gastrodia, not including *G. elata* (Walter and Gillett 1998).

The *China Plant Red Data Book* states that, though *Gastrodia elata* is widely cultivated in its range, the wild population is shrinking and even extinct in some places due to constant wild-harvesting and deforestation (Fu 1992).

In general, over-collection and habitat loss are the most common threats to orchid survival in the wild. The fervent popularity of orchids in the ornamental trade, enduring since 1850 and underscored by the existence of at least 30,000 hybrids, fuels an unrelenting appetite for new or rare species. For example, plants of *Vanda caerulea* sent back to England in the late nineteenth century by Veitch Nursery plant hunter Thomas Lobb were sold for 300 pounds (Musgrave et al 1998). CITES has responded to this pressure by listing a large number of orchids (7,816 records in the database) in an attempt to deter uncontrolled trade.

While attitudes toward the plunder of species from the wild have changed in the last 150 years, the example of Victorian Britain illustrates the role of inexpensive energy and technology in supporting popular demand for orchids and other exotic tropical plants. Repeal of the Glass Tax in 1845 caused an 80 percent drop in prices by 1865. In mid-century, cast iron came into use for glazing of windows, curved structures, boilers, and pipes for heating in conservatories or "hothouses." The Great Exhibition of 1851, with its centerpiece Crystal Palace, provided a vivid demonstration of England's consolidation of power (Musgrave et al 1998). From then until the outset of World War I, both middle and upper classes created an intense demand for exotic plants that could be displayed in both indoor and outdoor settings.

Our ubiquitous tropical houseplants of today seem humble by comparison, though hobbyists may invest plenty of money in an orchid collection, complete with a greenhouse. Yet, conservationists can benefit from understanding the history, psychology, and opportunism that underlie the cravings represented by "orchidmania."

······································

CONSERVATION STRATEGIES AND RESEARCH

In addition to international monitoring of trade and protection in nature reserves, strategies for orchid conservation focus on cultivation. Orchid fanciers have developed indoor cultivation, propagation, and breeding into an art form, and a vast amount of information is available to hobbyists and horticulturalists. A hardy orchid such as *Bletilla striata* makes an easy, entertaining houseplant, even for the brown-thumbed. It sprouts and blooms in May and June, the leaves wither in autumn, and the dormant rhizomes can be set in a cool room to over-winter without much water.

Whether the cultivation techniques devised for ornamental horticulture are adequate for medicinal plants remains a subject for additional research. The example of *Gastrodia elata*, which is cultivated extensively in northeast China, can help illustrate the scope of the problem (Fu 1992). Although hardy to −15° C, Gastrodia's symbiotic relationship with its fungus, and their joint dependence on damp, humus-rich soil in a sheltered woodland, makes cultivation outside its range very difficult (Bown 1995).

Gastrodia plants are grown using a pile of oak logs on well-drained, sandy slopes. Each layer of logs is inoculated with fungus cultured from hyphae taken from Gastrodia rhizomes. Then the spaces are stuffed with humic soil. A wood box may be used in place of the stacked oak logs (Fu 1992).

Note that in this type of operation, the use of artificial fertilizers, pesticides, or fungicides would kill the Armillariella fungus and, thus, the orchids. Gastrodia's symbiotic relationship with its fungus is quite evident but hardly unique. In recent decades, research has demonstrated that most plants have symbiotic relationships with myriad soil-dwelling organisms, some specific to the plant species. Therefore, soil biodiversity and perhaps even a special constellation of microorganisms are important to plant health and may affect even the tree-dwelling Dendrobiums.

These ecosystem relationships must be discovered and understood before orchids can be cultivated extensively for medicinal purposes. Those who assume that the challenges of cultivation may be surmounted by mass propagation (for example, cloning techniques or tissue culturing, or the use of artificial media such as hydroponics) ignore the role of natural ecosystem biodiversity in contributing to a plant's medicinal properties. True conservationists look to nature as a guide in finding ways to protect plant populations, whether wild or cultivated.

SOURCES

Baker M (1996) *Orchid species culture: Dendrobium*. Timber Press, Portland OR.

Bown D (1995) *Encyclopaedia of Herbs and Their Uses*. Dorling Kindersley, London.

Chen X et al (draft) Orchidaceae. In *Flora of China Vol. 25: Burmanniaceae through Orchidaceae*. Z. Wu and P. Raven (eds.), Science Press, Beijing and Missouri Botanical Garden Press, St. Louis. As of March 2006 available at: http://flora.huh.harvard.edu.

Fu L ed-in-chief (1992) *China Plant Red Data Book: Rare and Endangered Plants*. Science Press, Beijing/New York.

Graf A (1985) *Exotica Series 4 International: Pictorial Cyclopedia of Exotic Plants*. Roehrs Company Publishers, East Rutherford NJ.

Han W and Newman R translation (2004) Data excerpted from *Quan Guo Zhong Cao Yao Ming Jian* (A Compilation of Names of All of China's Herbal Medicines), 1996, People's Health Publishers, Beijing.

He S ed-in-chief (1998) *Rare and Precious Plants of China*. Scientific and Technical Publishers, Shanghai.

Isaac-Williams M (1988) *An Introduction to the Orchids of Asia*. Angus and Robertson, North Ryde NSW Australia.

Musgrave T, Gardner C and Musgrave W (1998) *The Plant Hunters: Two Hundred Years of Adventure and Discovery Around the World*. Ward Lock, London.

Romero-Gonzalez G et al (2002) Orchidaceae. In *Flora of North America* Vol. 26:230. Harvard University Herbarium, Cambridge MA. As of March 2006 available at: http://www.efloras.org/florataxon. aspx?flora_id=1&taxon_id=10638.

Walter K and Gillett H eds (1998) *1997 IUCN Red List of Threatened Plants*. International Union for Conservation of Nature and Natural Resources, Gland Switzerland and Cambridge UK.

Yang S translation (1998) *The Divine Farmer's Materia Medica*. Blue Poppy Press Inc, Boulder CO.

Yao D and Zhang J eds (1995) *A Coloured Atlas of the Chinese Materia Medica Specified in Pharmacopoeia of the PRC*. Joint Publishing Company Ltd, Hong Kong.

Yen K (1992) *The Illustrated Chinese Materia Medica: Crude and Prepared*. SMC Publishing Inc, Taipei Taiwan.

PART III

That which interacts with the world is called the heart-mind.
When the heart-mind reflects, this is called consciousness.
When consciousness persists this is called will.
When will is resilient and adaptable, this is called thought.

Chapter 6

U.S. Conservation Laws and Treaties: Support for the Web

Sandra Cleva
US Fish and Wildlife Service

The world's animals and plants—including a number of species used in traditional Chinese medicine—face threats from sources that range from habitat loss to global trade.

Human interaction with wildlife and plant populations increasingly provides a measure of the long-term viability of a species.

Countries around the world recognize the importance of preserving the diversity of animal and plant life on Earth. Many nations—including the United States—have laws that protect their native species. Most—more than 160—have signed CITES, a global treaty designed to ensure the trade of wild animals and plants does not threaten their survival.

In the United States wildlife conservation has been a concern for more than a century. The nation's first federal wildlife protection law—the Lacey Act—was passed in its original version in 1900. Its purpose was to stem interstate commerce in game birds and other wildlife that were killed in violation of state law.

Designed to support states in controlling commercial exploitation of native wildlife, the Lacey Act embodied a recognition that even a nation with abundant resources and wilderness areas could not indefinitely allow "harvest" and use of wildlife without limits or restrictions. This law committed the federal government to helping states protect wild birds and other animals, which were perceived as resources of the people that warranted government safeguarding on their behalf.

The wildlife protection laws that followed over the next 10 decades drew on and expanded this concept of public stewardship. Animals and plants know neither state boundaries nor international borders. During the course of the last century, the United States came to perceive the preservation of animal and plant species as a national mandate—a mandate that covered the protection of natural resources not only in this country, but around the world.

Today, in addition to the CITES treaty, the United States is party to a plethora of conventions, treaties, and agreements addressing conservation concerns that range from protecting wetlands to safeguarding arctic resources. Some of these agreements are implemented through laws that regulate the activities of individuals and businesses. For example, the Migratory Bird Treaty Act upholds four treaties with other countries (Canada, Mexico, Japan, and Russia) that protect migratory birds as an international resource. This U.S. law limits human interaction with more than 800 avian species whose migration routes span countries, continents—and, in some cases, oceans.

Other U.S. wildlife laws focus more exclusively on protecting species native to this country. Examples include the Bald and Golden Eagle Protection Act and the Marine Mammal Protection Act. The Endangered Species Act promotes the recovery of animal and plant populations that are in danger of extinction; species "listed" for protection are primarily native to the United States, although a number of foreign animals and plants are also protected.

Special U.S. wildlife laws also regulate trade in African elephants, wild exotic birds, and rhinos and tigers. Although these species are not native to the United States, laws providing additional protections for them in this country recognize that the United States has played a major role as a "consumer" in putting pressures on populations in the wild.

This chapter provides an overview of the CITES treaty and U.S. wildlife laws that protect species used in traditional Chinese medicine. Practitioners, patients, and suppliers of medicinal products need to understand these laws and how they affect the legal availability of some traditional medicines in the United States.

....

CITES: A Global Commitment To Conservation

CITES provides a framework for nations to work together to prevent the decline in wild populations of commercially traded species worldwide. When CITES member nations decide that a species warrants protection under the treaty, they "list" the animal or plant on one of three appendices. The type of listing reflects the severity and scope of the threat to the species, as well as the CITES community's collective judgment about the types of controls on trade needed to ensure the continued viability of the species in the wild. CITES countries meet approximately every three years in a "Conference of the Parties" to review CITES implementation and assess the status of species in trade.

Each CITES appendix sets specific requirements that must be met before a listed species can move in trade. Appendix I—the highest level of protection—is reserved for species that are so close to extinction that commercial use is no longer viable, and even non-commercial trade must be evaluated and approved in advance. For example, this would include the transfer of animals between scientific institutions in different countries or the placement of a specimen in a foreign zoo to support captive-breeding research.

A CITES Appendix I species can only be moved from one nation to another if both the exporting and importing countries approve the transaction and issue permits to authorize it. Such permits are not issued for commercial import or export. An application for a CITES Appendix I permit must be reviewed by government scientists and CITES implementation officials in each country (entities officially designated in the treaty as "Scientific Authorities" and "Management Authorities"). For example, if a zoo in the United States wants to import a giant panda from China (an Appendix I species), the institution must obtain a CITES export permit from that country before the bear is shipped. The zoo must also obtain an Appendix I import permit from the U.S. Fish and Wildlife Service, which issues CITES permits in this country.

Officials in both countries must answer two questions before they issue such a permit. First, they must conclude that the transaction in question will not negatively affect the continued survival of the species in the wild (a "scientific finding of non-detriment"). Then they need to look at how the specimen itself was obtained to make sure that no laws were violated (a finding of "legal acquisition"). If the proposed trade passes both of these "tests," CITES Appendix I import and export permits can be issued to authorize the transaction. CITES permits from both the exporting and importing countries must be obtained before the shipment leaves the exporting country and before it enters the importing nation. Permits cannot be obtained "retroactively" to cover animals and plants that have already entered trade.

Species listed on Appendix I of the CITES treaty include some that have been used in the past in traditional medicine. Examples include

- Tiger
- Rhinoceros
- Asiatic black bear
- Leopard
- Some orchids

Because these animals and plants are listed on Appendix I, they and the products made from them cannot be imported into or exported from any CITES country for commercial use. Even individuals cannot buy a product made from an Appendix I species in one country and bring it to another for personal use without the required permits.

The CITES treaty provides two other levels of protection for animals and plants moving in international trade. If a species is listed on the treaty's Appendix II, the world community has decided that trade in that species warrants a certain level of scrutiny and control to ensure that it does not contribute to the decline of wild populations. Appendix II species can be commercially traded, but shipments must be accompanied by a CITES export document from the country of origin or the country that is re-exporting the species.

When CITES officials in a country issue an export permit for an Appendix II species, they are certifying that the proposed trade will not have a negative impact on the species in the wild. They are also confirming that the species has been legally acquired. As with permits for Appendix I species, the Appendix II export permit must be obtained before the species leaves the exporting country. The permit must be presented, validated, and collected on entry when the shipment arrives in the importing country.

Species used in traditional medicine that are listed on CITES Appendix II include:

- American black bear
- Saiga antelope
- Cobra
- Crocodilians
- Pangolin
- Seahorses
- American ginseng
- Goldenseal
- Himalayan nard

An individual or business that wants to commercially import these animals or plants or their products into the United States must first obtain a CITES Appendix II export permit from the country of origin or a CITES Appendix II re-export certificate from the country of re-export. The United States allows individuals to import products, parts, and derivatives of legally acquired CITES Appendix II species as personal effects (items carried with them in their personal baggage) or as household goods (belongings being moved back to the United States) without a CITES permit. Not all CITES nations, however, recognize such an exemption. If the exporting country requires individuals to obtain permits for personal items, such permits must be presented when the item is brought into the United States.

A third level of protection under the CITES treaty helps countries protect their native wildlife and plants, even if the species is thriving elsewhere in the world. A CITES member nation can unilaterally list its population of a species on Appendix III. An export of specimens from the protected population requires a permit from the listing country certifying that the wildlife or plant was legally obtained under that country's resource protection laws. The United States waives this permit requirement for personal and household effects, provided the exporting country has a similar exemption.

All CITES member nations (which number over 160) essentially require the same permits for species listed on any one of the treaty's three appendices. CITES requirements will thus apply to wildlife imports and exports virtually anywhere you live and anywhere you travel.

Penalties for violating the CITES treaty, however, vary from country to country. The United States, for example, upholds the treaty under the Endangered Species Act. If companies or individuals import CITES species without the required permits, they have violated the Endangered Species Act and are subject to the penalties of that law. Those penalties are described in the next section of this chapter.

U.S. WILDLIFE LAWS

A number of U.S. laws regulate the import, export, and interstate sale of wildlife and plants harvested from the wild. Prohibitions also exist in this country outlawing the possession of some species. In two cases of concern for those working with traditional medicine, there are laws against the import, export, and sale of products *labeled* as containing particular species, whether or not they actually do so.

This section presents brief summaries of U.S. laws that regulate species used in traditional medicine. It explains the prohibitions in each law and the penalties for violating them.

Endangered Species Act: The Endangered Species Act is perhaps the most widely known U.S. wildlife law. Passed by Congress in 1973, this law regulates a variety of activities involving animals and plants that have been designated by government scientists as either endangered or threatened. It provides measures to stem the loss of species, support the recovery of wild populations of imperiled animals and plants, and protect the habitat necessary for their survival.

The Endangered Species Act also implements the CITES treaty in the United States. It prohibits the importation and exportation of CITES species without the required permits and makes it unlawful to possess any CITES-listed animal, plant, or product that was not legally exported and imported under the treaty.

The list of animals and plants protected under the Endangered Species Act includes more than 1,250 native species and more than 550 foreign species. An "endangered species" is one that is in danger of extinction. A "threatened species" is one that is likely to become endangered in the foreseeable future. The status and level of listing of a species can change over time, depending on how well or poorly the animal or plant is faring in the wild.

Listed species include representatives from every branch of the animal kingdom, as well as more than 740 different kinds of plants. The status of a particular species or groups of species can be checked on the internet at http://www.fws.gov/endangered/. A complete list of animals and plants listed as endangered or threatened under this U.S. law appears in Title 50, Chapter 17 of the Code of Federal Regulations and is updated each year.

Species listed for protection under the Endangered Species Act that have been used in traditional medicine include:

- Asiatic black bear
- Tiger
- Musk deer

- Rhinoceros
- Leopard
- Smooth coneflower
- Tennessee purple coneflower

The Endangered Species Act protects imperiled plants and animals by preventing people from removing them from the wild. The law prohibits "take" and "attempt to take," meaning that you cannot hunt, shoot, wound, or kill a listed species (or try to do so) in the United States or in international waters. It is also illegal to harass, harm, pursue, trap, capture, or collect protected animals. Nor can you remove and take possession of a listed plant from federal lands or in violation of state law.

Prohibitions under this law also limit human use of protected species and products made from them. The Endangered Species Act prohibits import and export of listed animals and plants (whether commercial or not). It is also illegal to sell listed species and products, or offer and advertise these items for sale, in interstate or foreign commerce. And while the act does not ban the sale of listed animals and plants within a state, many states have laws that prohibit such commerce.

Permits are sometimes issued to allow an activity that would otherwise be prohibited, such as the importation of an endangered species for scientific research. Permits, however, are not issued to authorize international trade or interstate sale of protected animals and plants.

Individuals and businesses that violate the Endangered Species Act face penalties that range from simple fines assessed by the federal equivalent of a "ticket" (called a Notice of Violation) to imprisonment and fines imposed by a federal judge as part of a criminal prosecution. Anyone who violates the law can be fined up to $500 (this civil penalty can be assessed whether or not the person knew he or she was breaking the law). Higher civil penalties exist for offences that are knowingly committed (up to $25,000 when the violation involves an endangered species, and up to $12,000 when the animal or plant is threatened). The government can also seek forfeiture of the wildlife or plants involved.

Criminal prosecution can be sought when violations are knowingly committed. For example, an individual found guilty of selling products made from an endangered species in interstate commerce could be sent to prison for up to one year and fined $100,000 (the fine can jump to $200,000 for a business or other organization). Someone who imports products made from threatened species could end up going to prison for six months and paying a $25,000 fine. Property subject to forfeiture in connection with criminal violations includes not only the wildlife or plants involved, but also guns, nets, traps, other equipment, vessels, vehicles, and aircraft used to commit the crime.

Rhinoceros and Tiger Conservation Act: The Rhinoceros and Tiger Conservation Act was passed in 1994 to help protect rhinoceros and tigers. The act supports and funds conservation programs of nations whose activities affect populations of these species in the wild. The act was amended in 1998 to address problems with products intended for human use that are made from or labeled or advertised as containing parts from rhinoceros and tiger. Examples include such products as tiger bone plasters and rhinoceros horn pills and tea balls. Under the amended law, it is illegal in the United States to sell, import, or export—or attempt to sell, import, or export—any product, item, or substance intended for human consumption or application containing, or labeled or advertised as containing, any substance derived from any species of rhinoceros or tiger.

While some products that claim to be made from rhinoceros or tiger do not actually contain any material from these animals, such claims promote the continued use of real tiger and rhinoceros parts—and thus the continued killing of these animals in the wild. For this reason, the Rhinoceros and Tiger Conservation Act bans selling, importing, and exporting products that claim to contain rhinoceros or tiger on their labels, as well as products actually made from these animals.

A person doing business as an importer, exporter, or distributor who knowingly violates this ban may be fined up to $5,000 and imprisoned for up to six months. A person who knowingly violates the law, and anyone engaged in business as an importer, exporter, or distributor who violates the law, may be assessed a civil penalty of up to $12,000. In addition, the U.S. government may seize and seek forfeiture of any product, item, or substance that someone sells, imports, or exports (or attempts to sell, import, or export) in violation of this law.

Migratory Bird Treaty Act: Passed in 1918, the Migratory Bird Treaty Act is one of the oldest U.S. wildlife protection laws. Originally crafted to implement a treaty acknowledging migratory birds as a valuable international resource shared by the United States and Canada, this law now upholds similar agreements with three other countries: Mexico, Japan, and Russia.

Today, the Migratory Bird Treaty Act protects more than 800 species of birds—species that range from songbirds and waterfowl to raptors and sea birds. Under this law, it is illegal to kill, capture, possess, buy, sell, barter, import, or export any migratory bird. These prohibitions apply to all birds, alive or dead, and their feathers, parts, nests, and eggs.

The federal government sets hunting seasons for some traditional game species (including waterfowl and doves) if population levels warrant. The government can also issue permits to authorize certain activities that would otherwise be prohibited. Wildlife rehabilitators, for example, can obtain permits allowing them to possess migratory birds. Permits, however, would not be available to authorize commercial use of protected species or their parts, eggs, and nests, or to accommodate the import or export of birds or bird parts.

Violations of the Migratory Bird Treaty Act include both misdemeanor and felony offenses. Anyone who commits a prohibited act can be charged with a misdemeanor violation; the maximum penalty for such offenses is six months in prison and a $15,000 fine.

Individuals or businesses that knowingly buy or sell migratory birds or their parts, eggs, and nests can be charged under the law's felony provisions. Penalties include prison terms of up to two years, fines up to $250,000 for individuals and $500,000 for organizations, and forfeiture of the wildlife and any weapons, equipment, and vehicles used to commit the crime.

Marine Mammal Protection Act: Passed in 1972, the Marine Mammal Protection Act imposed a moratorium on the take and importation of marine mammals and their parts and products, and it gave the federal government specific responsibility for conserving this group of animals. Species protected include seals, polar bears, and whales, all of which have been used in traditional medicine. The law also applies to walruses, sea otters, porpoises, sea lions, dugongs, and manatees.

In general, this act makes it illegal to take, import, transport, buy, sell, or offer to buy or sell any marine mammal or marine mammal parts or products. Possession of illegally taken marine mammals (or parts and products made from such animals) is also prohibited.

The Marine Mammal Protection Act provides for both civil and criminal penalties for those who engage in prohibited activities. Anyone who violates this law may be subject to a civil penalty of up to $10,000. Those who knowingly violate this law may face criminal charges with maximum penalties of up to one year in prison and a $100,000 fine (or $200,000 for a business or other organization).

Lacey Act: The United States enforces international, tribal, and state wildlife laws under the Lacey Act. While this law originally was intended to help states protect their wildlife resources, its reach was expanded over the years to support global conservation as well.

Today, the Lacey Act prohibits the import, export, transport, sale, receipt, acquisition, or purchase of any wildlife in interstate or foreign commerce that was taken, possessed, transported, or sold in violation of state, tribal, foreign, or U.S. law. The act makes trafficking in virtually any illegally acquired animal a federal crime. It also prohibits the import, export, transport, or sale in interstate and foreign commerce of any plant taken in violation of state law.

The violation of a state, tribal, foreign, or other federal wildlife law is a prerequisite for Lacey Act charges. The Lacey Act also makes it illegal to mislabel wildlife shipments, bring injurious species into the country, and import live wildlife under inhumane conditions.

Those who knowingly violate the Lacey Act face maximum penalties of up to five years in prison and fines as high as $250,000 for individuals and $500,000 for organizations.

Civil penalties may run as high as $10,000. Those convicted of felony offenses under the Lacey Act may be required to forfeit vehicles, aircraft, vessels, or other equipment used to commit the crime, in addition to any fish, wildlife, or plants involved.

Other Federal Laws: Individuals and businesses that violate the laws described above may also face prosecution under other U.S. statutes. For example, someone who unlawfully imports a shipment of Asiatic black bear bile for sale in the United States could be charged not only with violating the Endangered Species Act (a misdemeanor violation) but also with smuggling (a felony offense). If this individual worked with other people to smuggle the bile, he or she could also be charged with conspiracy (also a felony offense). Charges of smuggling and conspiracy to smuggle each carry a possible penalty of up five years in prison and a $250,000 fine ($500,000 for a business or organization).

·····························

Regulation of Wildlife Trade in the United States

Although a number of federal agencies are involved in regulating the import, export, and sale of wildlife and wild plants in the United States (see "Supporting Resource Conservation" below), the U.S. Fish and Wildlife Service—an agency within the U.S. Department of the Interior—has primary responsibility for enforcing the CITES treaty in this country and upholding U.S. laws that regulate the take and trade of protected species.

To facilitate enforcement of CITES and the import/export provisions of the Endangered Species Act, Congress authorized the Fish and Wildlife Service to monitor and regulate all U.S. wildlife trade. Congress also assigned responsibility to federal agricultural authorities for inspecting imports of CITES and Endangered Species Act-listed plants for compliance with permit requirements.

Importing/Exporting Wildlife: Under federal regulations, most wildlife imports and exports (including wildlife products and parts as well as live specimens) must enter or leave the United

States through a port designated by the Fish and Wildlife Service to handle such trade. Wildlife imports and exports are processed at the following designated ports:

- Anchorage, Alaska
- Atlanta, Georgia
- Baltimore, Maryland
- Boston, Massachusetts
- Chicago, Illinois
- Dallas/Fort Worth, Texas
- Honolulu, Hawaii
- Houston, Texas
- Los Angeles, California
- Louisville, Kentucky
- Memphis, Tennessee
- Miami, Florida
- New Orleans, Louisiana

- New York, New York
- Newark, New Jersey
- Portland, Oregon
- San Francisco, California
- Seattle, Washington

Some wildlife shipments may be imported or exported at authorized border ports or special ports. Border ports may only be used if the wildlife itself originally comes from the United States, Canada, or Mexico and the shipment is being sent from or going to one of these countries. Shipments cannot be processed at border ports if the wildlife originates outside of North America or the species requires a permit under CITES or U.S. wildlife laws.

Special ports are located in Alaska, Puerto Rico, and Guam. These ports may be used to import wildlife if these places are the shipment's final destination. Wildlife that originates in these locations may be exported from a special port in that specific state or territory. Special ports, however, cannot be used if the wildlife requires a permit.

Commercial importers and exporters must declare shipments to the Service using a special form (hardcopy and on-line filing options are available). They must make their shipments available for physical inspection and receive clearance for shipments from a Service wildlife inspector before release by U.S. Customs and Border Protection. Wildlife inspectors are uniformed import/export control officers with the authority to clear, hold, or seize wildlife shipments imported or exported in violation of U.S. laws, treaties, and regulations.

Anyone engaging in business as an importer or exporter of wildlife must obtain a license from the Fish and Wildlife Service. Commercial importers and exporters must also pay user fees for each shipment.

Anyone who imports wildlife products for personal use in accompanying baggage must declare the item or items as wildlife on the passenger declaration form distributed by Customs and Border Protection to travelers visiting or returning to the United States. Individuals entering the United States at a land border must also declare any wildlife items to Customs and Border Protection officers. Items mailed to the United States or shipped as cargo must be declared to, and cleared by, the Fish and Wildlife Service

Importing/Exporting Plants: The U.S. Department of Agriculture (USDA) regulates the import and export of plants, including species listed under the CITES treaty as well as those protected under the Endangered Species Act. Anyone engaged in commercial plant trade must possess a valid USDA general permit. Importers dealing in live plants and seeds must also obtain other USDA permits.

CITES import permits from the Fish and Wildlife Service (which serves as the CITES scientific and management authorities in the United States) are required for wild collected Appendix I species. Appendix II plants and plant products must be accompanied by valid CITES export permits from the country of origin.

CITES protected plants and plant products must enter the United States through a port designated for this trade by the Agriculture Department. Such shipments are inspected by agricultural specialists working with Customs and Border Protection.

All CITES plants and plant products can be processed at the following locations:

- Nogales, Arizona
- Los Angeles, California
- San Diego, California
- San Francisco, California
- Miami, Florida
- Orlando, Florida
- Honolulu, Hawaii
- New Orleans, Louisiana
- Hoboken, New Jersey
- New York, New York
- San Juan, Puerto Rico
- Brownsville, Texas
- El Paso, Texas
- Houston, Texas
- Seattle, Washington

USDA also routes some specific types of CITES plant imports through special locations. Shipments of ginseng, for example, can be handled in Atlanta, Chicago, Baltimore, St. Louis, and Milwaukee. Other ports process orchids, plants from Canada, and logs and lumber.

....

SUPPORTING RESOURCE CONSERVATION

Those who work with, use, or deal with importers or suppliers of traditional medicines and herbal products can support resource conservation in a number of ways.

Knowing about the status of species in the wild and the laws and regulations that protect them is the first place to start. Learn about and consider the use of alternatives that do not rely on the harvest and use of imperiled animals and plants. Some of those alternatives are discussed in this book.

If you are traveling overseas and buy wildlife or plant products, check local laws, CITES requirements, and U.S. import/export rules before you return to the United States. Even personal items are subject to seizure. Be aware that an importation of more than eight similar items is considered "commercial" and subject to Fish and Wildlife Service license, declaration, inspection, and user fee requirements.

If you are offered products made from endangered species (species that cannot legally be imported into the United States or sold here in interstate commerce), do not buy them. Ask the retailer or importer if he or she is aware that such products are unlawful. Point out the existence of alternative products and your interest in purchasing them if they were available.

If you encounter illegal activity involving medicinal products but do not wish to confront those involved, consider contacting the U.S. Fish and Wildlife Service Office of Law Enforcement. The Fish and Wildlife Service can also answer any questions you might have about laws and regulations governing the import, export, sale, and use of wildlife and protected plants in the United States.

A number of other federal agencies also regulate the import and export of wildlife and plants. If you plan to engage in such trade, you may want to consult the U.S. Fish and Wildlife Service and the other organizations listed below for additional information. You should also be aware that many states have laws and regulations dealing with the sale and use of wildlife and wild plant products.

U.S. Fish and Wildlife Service
Office of Law Enforcement
4401 N. Fairfax Drive, MS-3000-LE
Arlington, Virginia 22203
http://www.fws.gov/le/

Customs and Border Protection
Office of Public Affairs
U.S. Department of Homeland Security
1300 Pennsylvania Avenue, N.W.
Washington, D.C. 20229
http://www.customs.ustreas.gov/xp/cgov/toolbox/contacts/

U.S. Department of Agriculture
Animal and Plant Health Inspection Service
Plant Protection and Quarantine, Unit 136
4700 River Road
Riverdale, Maryland 20737
http://www.aphis.usda.gov/ppq

U.S. Department of Agriculture
Animal and Plant Health Inspection Service
Veterinary Services
National Center for Import and Export
4700 River Road, Unit 39
Riverdale, Maryland 20737
http://www.aphis.usda.gov/NCIE

National Marine Fisheries Service
1315 East West Highway
Silver Spring, Maryland 20910
http://www.nmfs.noaa.gov/

U.S. Public Health Service
Centers for Disease Control and Prevention
1600 Clifton Road, NE, Mailstop E-03
Atlanta, Georgia 30333
http://www.cdc.gov

U.S. Food and Drug Administration
Office of Regulatory Affairs
Division of Import Operations and Policy
HFC-170, 5600 Fishers Lane
Rockville, Maryland 20857
http://www.fda.gov

PART IV

When thought is far-reaching this is called foresight.
When foresight is exercised in managing the affairs of the world this is
  called wisdom.

Chapter 7

RATIONALE FOR REPLACEMENTS: "WEAVING VARIATIONS"

Elizabeth Call

Chinese medicine has a long, distinguished history dating back thousands of years. Within the context of this medical tradition, the substitution of ingredients in prescriptions is not a new phenomenon. Based on careful, thorough observation, Chinese medicine has evolved as a flexible healing modality, relying on ingredients easily available near villages or small communities where practitioners first treated illness. If weather or other natural cycles limited the availability of necessary ingredients, practitioners could determine replacements through observation of their effects, or substitute with an appropriate herb in the same category.

If the use of replacements is not new, the intense global pressure on natural resources is a recent and alarming development. As stated earlier, the viability and vitality of species traditionally used by local people for food and medicine around the world are being compromised. Some of the factors are habitat loss, increased human population, global climate change, over-collection, and a range of related problems that, taken together, may seriously compromise our ability as practitioners to provide herbs needed by an ever-expanding clientele.

How should we respond? How can a long and effective tradition of health care such as ours address threats that ultimately will affect both our livelihood and the health of the environment that sustains our practice?

Like the use of replacements, the idea of polling Chinese medicine practitioners on the subject of replacements for endangered species is not new. Conservation organizations have explored this avenue since the mid-1990s. As a result, lists of replacements for certain wildlife species have been circulated to the public, as well as to some professionals. Nevertheless, the source for the replacements or the criteria used to determine their efficacy is unknown. Also, the replacements selected have not been reviewed by the Chinese medicine community, making validation of their clinical use unclear and, in some instances, irresponsible.

What is new, however, is the willingness of the Chinese medicine community to seek its own answers to concerns about the use of endangered species in their medicine. The survey analyzed in the following chapter was created out of the need to determine baseline information on clinically effective substitutions whose efficacy does not require the use of species protected under CITES.

Since earlier lists of replacements offered no justification for suggested substitutions, we were determined to survey practitioners to identify the range of alternatives they might use. In addition, we felt that by drawing on the practitioner knowledge base, the Chinese medicine community would be able to reach consensus on selected effective replacements for endangered species, thus providing more options for patients and practitioners alike. Sharing results of the survey among practitioners also unifies the community's awareness of the rationale for selecting the replacements listed here. It also provides a model for the decision-making process when, and if, other replacements may need to be selected in the future.

Building consensus in the community regarding replacements is critical, because Chinese medicine has a large number of herbs in common use. Practitioner-recommended replacements help build a base of common clinical knowledge, ensuring that practitioners use herbs in efficacious ways for specific ailments. Chinese medicine practitioners are fortunate that contraindications, dosage, and actions of herbs are known as the result of centuries of clinical use. Rather than seeking replacements on a one-to-one basis for a particular species, we chose to explore an approach that takes into account nuances in the multiple actions of the substance itself. This increases the options and the subtlety with which one can find substitutes, and it avoids the cycle of unsustainable overuse, high price, and unavailability.

Thus, we wanted to identify replacements from a broader perspective, which includes discussion of the medicine in conjunction with awareness of species needs. In short, the concept was to take all stakeholders into account, bringing practitioners closer to the foundation of the medicine itself, as well as its origins in the herbs we use. Since Chinese medicine practitioners do not rely on lab tests and mechanical diagnostics to evaluate their patients, they readily understand that now, more than ever, we need life to heal life. We need to be able to count on a supply of raw materials that are themselves in a condition of vitality, if we want to promote vitality in our patients. Indeed, the effectiveness of our medicine depends on the quality of our herbs, as well as the soil and ecosystems that nurture them. To preserve the biological diversity of our *materia medica*, and by extension its effectiveness, we must retain our sense of the living nature of the herbs and become more sensitive, in our roles as healers, working within the life span of all living things. In this way, we come to recognize that plants and animals have their own life cycles in which they begin, multiply, and end, and that working out of sync with those rhythms creates insufficiencies, such as the ones we currently face. Thus, we acknowledge and preserve the sacred connection between the herbs and the people they heal. We hope that this survey is one step that will lay the foundation for further discussion in this direction.

We would take great satisfaction if cultivation and conservation efforts would achieve sustainability in the near future for the species covered here, and this information would be rendered irrelevant. Indeed, some of the species discussed are being cultivated successfully and may even be rebounding in the wild. However, reality suggests that the achievement of species sustainability in the wild remains a long way off.

Just because a species is cultivated does not mean it is safe in the wild. As long as we are unsure of the source and quality of many herbs and herb products, we cannot always make an informed choice. However, the more we know about the species themselves, the more we can extend that knowledge to making choices, because we will know the right questions to ask regarding the source of a particular species. And, until we can be assured of the source of a particular species, we can err on the side of caution and use a substitute.

Our intent here is to help all who practice and respect Chinese medicine to embrace the fact that each and every plant and animal has its own story, its own place in an ecosystem, and its own unique place in the universe. As practitioners, we can take action to help protect these species in the wild, support cultivation for those we can, and ensure that the biodiversity of our time is passed on in its multiplicity to future generations.

By making the effort in the short term to seriously consider replacements in a manner based on community consensus, our profession will have gained practice as a group in identifying substitutes. This is an activity that should prepare us for further discussions and decision-making if and when additional species become threatened or endangered. As practitioners, we need a sense of the connection between our actions and the various outcomes.

For example, we need to understand the implications of heavy reliance on particular herbs—even identified replacements. Importers and practitioners in the United States have very little knowledge of the supply chain and often fail to ask important questions. Where do bulk raw herbs or prepared medicines originate? How are they grown or collected? Who handles them? What toxins and chemicals have they been exposed to, either in growing or processing? How are herbs processed? How much time elapses from collection to use? Gaining this information from China is difficult—internet searches may not be reliable and cannot be easily verified, and Chinese government sources are not always forthcoming.

We can only hope that there will be more communication concerning the supply chain for Chinese herbs in the future, resulting in less speculation about which species are being used, which are endangered and more information about what plants are cultivated. That being said, when practitioners learn more about the individual plants and animals they use, they can already begin to understand the basis of the supply chain. This puts them in the position to make conscious choices about the herbs and herbal products they use.

Chapter 8
SURVEY OF REPLACEMENTS: MENDING THE WEB

Elizabeth Call

In early 2002, a survey was mailed to 2,611 practitioners who were certified in Chinese herbology through the National Commission for the Certification of Acupuncture and Oriental Medicine (NCCAOM). Exactly 301 practitioners (11.5%) responded. Contact information was optional, with 12 (4%) submitting survey responses anonymously. We also requested information on training and years in practice. Information ranging from suggested replacements to opinions about the following fourteen endangered species was solicited.

Plants
Lú huì (Herba Aloes)
Gǒu jǐ (Rhizoma Cibotii Barometz)
Tiān má (Rhizoma Gastrodia Elatae)
Xī yáng shēn (Radix Panacis Quinquefolii)
Shí hú (Herba Dendrobii)
Bái jí (Rhizoma Bletillae Striatae)

Animals and Animal Derived Substances
Xióng Dǎn (Vesica Fellea Ursi)
Xī Jiǎo (Cornu Rhinoceri)
Hǔ Gǔ (Os Tigris)
Shè Xiāng (Secretio Moschus)
Chuān Shān Jiǎ (Squama Manitis Pentadactylae)
Líng Yáng Jiǎo (Cornu Antelopis)
Hǎi Mǎ (Hippocampus)
Guī Bǎn (Plastrum Testudinus)

Information Entry and Analysis

Information from the 301 returned surveys was entered into Microsoft Excel spreadsheet software for analysis. Few respondents answered every question for every substance. However, since the purpose of the survey was to elicit a wide range of information on usage, importance, and suggested replacements, all responses were included. For example, the fact that a respondent did not use a substance (answered "no" to the usage question), or left the question blank, did not negate that person's responses to other questions regarding that particular substance. Therefore, the number of respondents to each question is given along with the percent of the total survey population (301) for comparison in the results section.

·······························

Gathering Information

Practitioners were asked to respond to the same four questions for each substance as follows:

Establishing Usage (A)

Respondents identified their usage for each substance by using a box to provide a "yes" or "no" answer to the question, "Have you ever used (substance)?" This feedback is given under section A.

This question was purposely broad to capture past and present experience, so there was no exclusion regarding how long ago a practitioner might have used a particular substance. For example, some practitioners had experience using one or both Appendix I species previously and a few indicated they did not use them any more.

Perceived Importance (B)

Respondents were asked to reply to the question "How important do you think (substance) is to the practice of Chinese Medicine?" Four response categories were provided: "Crucial," "Important," "Helpful," "Minimal." This information is given under section B.

Opinions on perceived importance were requested to establish how strongly practitioners felt about the importance of the substance in question to clinical practice, to provide some indication about how well substitutions might be accepted.

Perceived Frequency of Use (C)

Respondents were asked, "How often do you use (substance) in your practice?" with a blank line and a percent (%) symbol for the answer. The intention was to collect data on how much practitioners might rely on each substance. This information is reported under section C.

Because of the ambiguity of this question, the information we collected here can only suggest trends and the perception of the practitioners at the moment the question was answered, though the responses are worth noting in relation to other information.

Replacements and Peer Review (D)

Respondents were asked, "What substance(s), if any, do you substitute for (substance) when it is unavailable or unacceptable?" In analyzing these results, it was determined that the substitute of choice was the one most frequently listed by practitioners. An expanded questionnaire was sent to an additional group of senior practitioners* that asked them to review the substitutes given by the survey population and provide details of substitutions by action. This group also provided guidance when there was little consistency in the substitutions offered for a particular substance from the respondents of the first survey. Therefore, every effort has been made to provide clinicians with relevant and peer reviewed information to aid them in choosing effective alternatives to the substances surveyed. This information is reported under section D.

....

RESULTS

Training

A total of 241 practitioners responded with information about training. Five different countries of training were represented, with 22 practitioners having received training from two or more countries, as follows:

USA	199
China	57
Taiwan	5
Korea	1
Australia	1
	263

---

* These 48 senior practitioners were comprised of those who had completed the original survey, had 10 or more years of experience, and some or all of their clinical training in China. Of these 48, 13 replied, which is a response rate of 12.5 percent. Six of these 13 final respondents agreed to discuss finer points via conference call and assist in reaching a consensus on the substitutions.

Overall, respondents listed 32 U.S. acupuncture/oriental medicine colleges from which they received training. At the time of their responses all of these colleges were accredited or in candidacy with the Accreditation Commission of Acupuncture and Oriental Medicine (ACAOM). Fifteen respondents named individuals with whom they personally studied. Nine different institutions in China were specifically identified, with other respondents identifying only the city and/or province in China where they trained.

Years in Practice

Of the 273 respondents who reported years in practice, the average totaled 7.6 years, with a combined total of 2,087.5 years in practice.

1. L ú Huì (Herba Aloes)

A. Establishing Usage

Yes	87	28.9%
No	210	69.8%
Blank	4	1.3%
	301	100.0%

B. Perceived Importance

Two hundred nine respondents (69.4% of the total survey population) indicated their perceived importance of *Lu Hui*.

CRUCIAL	2	1.0%
IMPORTANT	26	12.4%
HELPFUL	86	41.1%
MINIMAL	95	45.5%
Total	209	100.0%

C. Perceived Frequency of Use

Sixty-three respondents (20.9% of the total survey population) indicated how often they used *Lu Hui*. Of that group, the *average* perceived use was approximately 7.6 percent, making *Lu Hui* the tenth most frequently used substance surveyed.

D. Suggested Replacements

Of the sixty-eight respondents (22.6% of the total survey population) who provided one or more replacements for **Lu Hui**, **Da Huang** was the most frequently named substitute, with 36 citations. Senior practitioners provided the following suggestions for replacements appropriate to specific actions and indications for **Lu Hui**:

- To drain fire and guide out accumulation as in the formula *Geng Yi Wan*: **Da Huang.**

- To kill parasites and strengthen the stomach, the first choice was **Bing Lang** and the second choice was **Shi Jun Zi.**

- To clear heat and cool the Liver, as in the formula *Dang Gui Long Hui Wan*: **Jue Ming Zi and Zhi Zi** could be used. Senior practitioners acknowledged that this formula is not frequently used.

Summary

Practitioner responses indicate that **Lu Hui** falls somewhere between helpful and minimal importance to the practice of Chinese medicine. To protect *Aloe ferox* and *Aloe vera* var. *chinensis*, it would be prudent to use one of the many options listed above by action, or *Aloe vera barbadensis*, which undergoes certification through the International Aloe Science Council.

2. Gŏu Jĭ (Rhizoma Cibotii Barometz)

A. Establishing Usage

Yes	116	38.5%
No	177	58.8%
Blank	8	2.7%
	301	100.0%

B. Perceived Importance

One hundred eighty-nine respondents (62.8% of the total survey population) indicated their perceived importance of **Gou Ji**.

CRUCIAL	4	2.1%
IMPORTANT	39	20.6%
HELPFUL	87	46.0%
MINIMAL	59	31.2%
Total	189	99.9%

C. Perceived Frequency of Use

Ninety-six respondents (31.9 % of the total survey population) indicated how often they use **Gou Ji**. Of that group, the *average* perceived use was approximately 10.1 percent, making **Gou Ji** the seventh most frequently used substance surveyed.

D. Suggested Replacements

Of the seventy-four respondents (24.6% of the total population) who provided one or more replacements for **Gou Ji**, **Du Zhong** was the most frequently named substitute, with 43 citations. **Xu Duan** was a close second with 30 citations. Senior practitioners provided the following substitutions for specific actions of **Gou Ji**:

- To tonify the Liver and Kidneys and strengthen sinews and bones: **Du Zhong** or **Xu Duan**

- To expel wind and dampness: **Ba Ji Tian, Du Huo,** or **Wu Jia Pi.**

- While **Gou Ji** is rarely used to stabilize the Kidneys, **Bu Gu Zhi** or **Wu Wei Zi** can be used as substitutions for this purpose.

Summary

Respondents indicated by use and by opinions that **Gou Ji** has some importance in Chinese medicine, though this herb doesn't appear to be crucial. It is thought that present use is sustainable but scientists have recommended certain exporting restrictions to help reduce excessive use. As we have seen in the *C. barometz* profile, cultivation is possible.

3. Tian má (Rhizoma Gastrodia Elatae)

A. Establishing Usage

Yes	285	94.7%
No	15	5.0%
Blank	1	0.3%
	301	100.0%

B. Perceived Importance

Two hundred eighty-six respondents (95.0% of the total survey population) indicated their perceived importance of **Tian Ma**.

CRUCIAL	79	27.6%
IMPORTANT	164	57.3%
HELPFUL	37	12.9%
MINIMAL	6	2.1%
Total	286	99.9%

C. Perceived Frequency of Use

Two hundred thirty-four respondents (77.7% of the total survey population) indicated how often they use *Tian Ma*. Of that group, the *average* perceived use was approximately 16.7 percent, making *Tian Ma* the second most frequently used substance surveyed.

D. Suggested Replacements

Of the one hundred-seven respondents (35.5% of the total survey population) who provided one or more replacements for *Tian Ma*, *Gou Teng* was the most frequently named substitute, with 82 citations. Our panel of senior practitioners acknowledged that *Gou Teng* was an appropriate substitute for *Tian Ma*, but agreed that the fungus that grows with the plant, *Mi Huan Jun* can be substituted across the board, especially in prepared formulas.

Summary

It is clear that *Tian Ma* has a significant place in the practice of Chinese medicine and that an overwhelming majority of practitioners use it. While *Tian Ma* is cultivated, it is also taken from the wild. We suggest using one of the replacements above, particularly the fungus that has a symbiotic relationship with *Tian Ma*: *Mi Huan Jun*.

4. Xī Yáng Shēn (Radix Panacis Quinquefolii)

A. Establishing Use

Yes	240	79.7%
No	55	18.3%
Blank	6	2.0%
	301	100.0%

B. Perceived Importance

Two hundred sixty-one (86.7% of the total survey population) indicated their perceived importance of *Xi Yang Shen*.

CRUCIAL	55	21.1%
IMPORTANT	127	48.7%
HELPFUL	62	23.8%
MINIMAL	17	6.5%
Total	261	100.1%

C. Perceived Frequency of Use

One hundred ninety-six respondents (65.1% of the total survey population), indicated how often they use *Xi Yang Shen*. Of that group, the *average* perceived use was approximately 17.6 percent, making *Xi Yang Shen* the most frequently used substance surveyed.

D. Suggested Replacements

Of the one hundred-thirty respondents (43.2% of the total survey population) who provided one or more replacements for *Xi Yang Shen*, *Dang Shen* was the most frequently named substitute with 47 citations. *Tai Zi Shen* was a close second with 44 citations. Senior practitioners provided the following distinction between the 2 suggestions:

- Tonify qi and yin: *Tai Zi Shen*.
- Tonify the lungs and augment the qi, *Huang Qi* and *Dang Shen*.
- Strengthen the Spleen and tonify the Stomach: *Dang Shen*.
- Generate fluids and stop thirst: *Tai Zi Shen*.
- Benefit the Heart qi and calm the spirit: *Ren Shen, Zhi Gan Cao*.

Summary

It is clear that *Xi Yang Shen* is an important and frequently relied upon herb in clinical practice. The panel of senior practitioners recommended that while one can always use the above as replacements, practitioners could also request that the importer and/or manufacturer provide a certificate of cultivation. In addition, seeking out organic sources for *Xi Yang Shen* is optimal, and while more expensive, wild cultivated *Xi Yang Shen* would be the most supportive of biodiversity.

5. Shí hú (Herba Dendrobii)

A. Establishing Usage

Yes	222	73.8%
No	69	22.9%
Blank	10	3.3%
	301	100.0%

B. Perceived Importance

Two hundred fifty-four respondents (84.4% of the total survey population) indicated their perceived importance of *Shi Hu*.

CRUCIAL	17	6.7%
IMPORTANT	103	40.6%
HELPFUL	108	42.5%
MINIMAL	26	10.2%
Total	254	100.0%

C. Perceived Frequency of Use

One hundred seventy-four respondents (57.8% of the total survey population) indicated how often they use *Shi Hu*. Of that group, the *average* perceived use was approximately 13.8 percent, making *Shi Hu* the fifth most frequently used substance surveyed.

D. Suggested Replacements

Of the ninety-four respondents (31.2% of the total survey population) who gave one or more replacements for *Shi Hu*, *Mai Men Dong* was the most frequently named substitute with 43 citations. The next most frequently named substitutions were *Yu Zhu* and *Sha Shen* with 22 and 21 citations respectively. Senior practitioners provided some clarifications as to how these options may be used:

- To nourish Yin, clear heat, and generate fluids, *Mai Men Dong* was considered to be the best choice.

- To nourish Stomach Yin, the best choice was considered to be *Yu Zhu*.

- To brighten the vision, *Gou Qi Zi* was considered to be the best substitution, although *Shi Hu* is rarely used this way.
- To strengthen the lower back, *Nu Zhen Zi* would be the best substitution, although *Shi Hu* is rarely used for this purpose.

Summary

Practitioners perceive *Shi Hu* to be fairly important to the practice of Chinese medicine. While some sources report a recent increase in cultivation, it is unclear if this can match the demand for *Shi Hu*, especially given its unique functions. Practitioners can request a certificate of cultivation and use *Shi Hu* judiciously, substituting it when appropriate.

6. Bái jí (Rhizoma Bletillae)

A. Establishing Usage

Yes	168	55.8%
No	125	41.5%
Blank	8	2.7%
	301	100.0%

B. Perceived Importance

Two hundred twenty-seven respondents (75.4% of the total survey population) indicated their perceived importance of *Bai Ji*.

CRUCIAL	8	3.5%
IMPORTANT	72	31.7%
HELPFUL	105	46.3%
MINIMAL	42	18.5%
Total	227	100.0%

C. Perceived Frequency of Use

One hundred forty-eight respondents (49.2% of the total survey population) indicated how often they use *Bai Ji*. Of that group, the *average* perceived use was 11.8 percent, making *Bai Ji* the sixth most frequently used substance surveyed.

D. Suggested Replacements

Of the seventy-two respondents (23.9% of the total survey population) who gave one or more replacements for *Bai Ji*, *San Qi* was the most frequently named substitute with 22 citations, with *Xian He Cao* cited 16 times. Senior practitioners offered the following substitutions by action:

- To restrain the leakage of blood and stop bleeding, it was felt that either *Qian Cao Gen* or *Pu Huang* would be indicated for this function more than *San Qi*.

- To reduce swelling and generate flesh, *Mo Yao*, *Ru Xiang*, and *San Qi* were considered to be good replacements. .

Summary

Bai Ji represents a situation where it is difficult to ascertain whether its listing on CITES Appendix II is because of the "look alike" factor in order to control trade or if it is as endangered as other orchids are. While it might be endangered in the wild, it is very amenable to cultivation, as its profile in Chapter 5 suggests. Practitioners should learn about this herb by growing it, even though they may not want to harvest and prepare it for use and can request a certificate of cultivation if they choose to use it or replace it with one of the choices above.

7. Xióng Dǎn (Vesica Fellae Ursi)

A. Establishing Usage

Yes	29	9.6%
No	265	88.0%
Blank	7	2.3%
	301	99.9%

B. Perceived Importance

One hundred sixty five respondents (54.8% of the total population) indicated their perceived importance of *Xiong Dan*.

CRUCIAL	3	1.8%
IMPORTANT	26	15.8%
HELPFUL	32	19.4%

MINIMAL   104   63.0%
Total   165   100.0%

C. Perceived Frequency of Use

Twenty three respondents (7.6% of the total survey population) indicated how often they use *Xiong Dan*. Of that group, the *average* perceived use was 9.5 percent, making *Xiong Dan* along with *She Xiang*, the eighth most frequently used substance surveyed.

D. Suggested Replacements

Of the forty-six respondents (15.3% of the total survey population) who gave one or more replacements for *Xiong Dan*, *Xia Ku Cao*, *Niu Dan*, and *Zhu Dan* were the most frequently named, at 9 times each. After that, a wide variety of other choices with diminishing rates of commonality were offered. Overall, there seems to be little agreement on how to substitute *Xiong Dan*, which may reflect the surfeit of options available for the different actions of this substance. Senior practitioners recommend the following substitutions for specific actions of *Xiong Dan*:

- To clear heat and alleviate spasms, *Bai Shao, Di Long, Gou Teng, Shu Dan, Chi Shao Yao, Long Dan Cao,* and *Mu Dan Pi* are all appropriate choices.

- To clear heat and relieve fire toxicity, *Niu Huang* was considered the best choice, but *Huang Lian* could also be used to clear heat and relieve fire toxicity in the gastrointestinal tract.

- To benefit the eyes in patterns of Liver fire, *Jua Hua* was considered the best choice, but *Xia Ku Cao* and *Jue Ming Zi* could also be used.

- To reduce swelling, bile salts from pigs, cows, or other domestic cattle are perfectly appropriate, and alum can be used topically. For reducing pain, either *Yan Hu Suo* or *Chuan Xiong* is appropriate.

Summary

As indicated above, the majority of practitioners felt that *Xiong Dan* has minimal importance in Chinese medicine. With so many substitutions available, there is no need for practitioners to use bear bile. While only 10 percent of practitioners reported ever using bear bile, if these numbers are representative of international practice, they are significant enough to make a big impact on bear populations worldwide. As we saw from its' profile in Chapter 4, the conservation gains to all bear species from discontinuing the use of bear bile are too convincing to ignore. Our profession can make a real difference if we choose to discontinue the use of bear gallbladders, especially with such compelling and numerous substitutions as those listed above. Fortunately, the extraordinary cruelty of bear farming is becoming a subject of discussion recently* and serves to provide yet another inducement to avoid the use of bear bile altogether.

It is important to note that prepared formulas containing bear products have been shown to contain adulterants such as heavy metals and pharmaceuticals that are not listed on the label. Practitioners who use these formulas may be putting their patients at risk,** another reason to avoid using bear bile.

8. Xī Jiǎo (Cornu Rhinoceri)

A. Establishing Usage

Yes	22	7.3%
No	270	89.7%
Blank	9	3.0%
	301	100.0%

B. Perceived Importance

One hundred seventy-seven or (58.8% of the total survey population) indicated their perceived importance of *Xi Jiao*.

CRUCIAL	12	6.8%
IMPORTANT	33	18.6%
HELPFUL	35	19.8%
MINIMAL	97	54.8%
Total	177	100.0%

---

* Lau Y (2004) The Suffering on Bear Bile Farms. *The Mayway Mailer*, 5:1. Robinson J (2004) The Suffering of Bears – Part 2. *The Mayway Mailer*, 5:2.
** Ko R and Au A (1998) *1997-1998 Compendium of Asian Patent Medicines*. California Department of Health Services. This work shoed that numerous Chinese prepared formulas claiming tiger, rhino, bear or cow gallbladder and other animals, are associated with detectable levels of lead, mercury, arsenic and other chemicals or drugs.

C. Perceived Frequency of Use

Seventeen respondents (5.6% of the total survey population) indicated how often they used *Xi Jiao*. Of that group, the *average* perceived use was 16 percent, making *Xi Jiao* the third most frequently used substance surveyed.

D. Suggested Replacements

Of the eighty-three respondents (27.6% of the total survey population) who provided one or more replacements for *Xi Jiao*, *Shui Niu Jiao* was cited the most frequently at 44 percent. The second most cited substitution was *Sheng Di Huang* at 13 percent. Senior practitioners gave the following replacements for specific actions:

- To clear heat and relieve fire toxicity and cool the blood, either *Shui Niu Jiao* or *Sheng Di Huang* could be used.
- To clear heat and arrest tremors, either *Shui Niu Jiao* or *Gou Teng* could be used.

Summary

The majority of practitioners felt that *Xi Jiao* has minimal importance to the practice of Chinese medicine. However, it is disturbing that a small group of the respondents perceived such an excessive use of *Xi Jiao* since it is illegal. (Recall that in section "A" above, only 22 (7.3%) practitioners reported *ever* using this substance). While 5.6 percent of the practitioners using 16 percent of *Xi Jiao* in their practices may seem insignificant, if this is representative of international practice, the amount is very high, considering that use of rhino horn is illegal and is not in the prepared formulas that claim to contain it on their label. Further, if practitioners were actually using rhino horn, this amount of use would have an overwhelming impact on a vulnerable animal population. Unless these practitioners are purchasing rhino horn on the black market, the only other way they could perceive that kind of use is by recommending prepared formulas claiming to contain it. Unfortunately, patients who take these formulas may be ingesting unhealthy amounts of heavy metals with their herbs, since a link has been demonstrated between prepared formulas claiming rhino horn on the label and heavy metals.* The 1998 labeling provisions

---

* Ibid.

of the Rhinoceros and Tiger Conservation Act make it illegal to sell or buy rhino horn, as well as those products claiming to contain it.

Because there are practitioners who report using rhino horn, national and local professional organizations must improve efforts to help practitioners keep abreast of current trends and legal issues in the field. Since the use of rhinoceros horn or products claiming it on their label is illegal, this should be an ethics issue for all national and state organizations.

9. Hŭ Gŭ (Os Tigris)

A. Establishing Usage

Yes	19	6.3%
No	271	90.0%
Blank	11	3.7%
	301	100.0%

B. Perceived Importance

One hundred sixty-three or (54.2% of the total population) indicated their perceived importance of *Hu Gu*.

CRUCIAL	5	3.1%
IMPORTANT	21	12.9%
HELPFUL	25	15.3%
MINIMAL	112	68.7%
Total	163	100.0%

C. Perceived Frequency of Use

Eleven respondents (3.7% of the total survey population) indicated how often they used *Hu Gu*. Of that group, the *average* perceived use was 8.1 percent, making *Hu Gu* the sixth most frequently used substance surveyed.

D. Suggested Replacements

Of the fifty-three respondents (17.6% of the total survey population) who provided one or more replacements for *Hu Gu*, little consensus was demonstrated on which were most useful. The most frequently cited substitution was *Wu Jia Pi* with 12 citations. Dog bone was cited 9 times, and various species of cat bone were cited 6 times. Since wild cats are now also endangered, they are not reasonable substitutions, and dog bone is unacceptable to many people. Senior practitioners unanimously recommended using cow bone to replace *Hu Gu*, agreeing that the therapeutic treatment strategy here involves the use of calcium. Therefore, a calcium supplement could be taken in the form of microcrystalline hydroxyapatite concentrate (MCHC).*

Summary

As we can see, the majority of practitioners agree that *Hu Gu* has minimal importance to the practice of Chinese medicine. As with rhino horn, however, it is disturbing that even 3.7 percent of respondents could provide information as to their perceived use of tiger bone. This suggests that our national and state organizations are not keeping their members apprised of trends and legal changes in our field. As previously stated, the Rhinoceros and Tiger Conservation Act prohibits the purchase or sale of any tiger parts, and the labeling provisions of this act also prohibit the sale of herbal products *labeled* as containing tiger parts. In addition, these practitioners may be putting their patients at risk by recommending tiger bone products that, along with rhino horn and bear bile products have been shown to contain heavy metals and/or chemicals or drugs.**

As with rhino horn, the illegal use of tiger bone, or products claiming to contain tiger bone, should be an ethics issue for national and state professional organizations, as well as for licensure.

10. Shè Xiāng (Secretio Moschus)

A. Establishing Usage

Yes	76	25.2%
No	213	70.8%
Blank	12	4.0%
	301	100.0%

---

* According to Technical Services at Metagenics (a manufacturer of MCHC), microcrystalline hydroxyapatite complex is manufactured from bovine raw bone compound, minus the marrow. MCHC contains minerals as well as the protein collagen of the bone. Metagenics asserts that this form provides increased bio-availability. Their product comes from New Zealand free-range cattle.

** Ko R and Au A (1998) *1997-1998 Compendium of Asian Patent Medicines*. California Department of Health Services.

B. Perceived Importance

One hundred eighty-six respondents (61.8% of the total survey population) indicated their perceived importance of **She Xiang**.

CRUCIAL	17	9.1%
IMPORTANT	47	25.3%
HELPFUL	55	29.6%
MINIMAL	67	36.0%
Total	186	100.0%

C. Perceived Frequency of Use

Fifty-eight respondents (19.3% of the total survey population) indicated how often they use **She Xiang**. Of that group, the *average* perceived use was 9.5 percent, making **She Xiang** along with **Xiong Dan**, the eighth most frequently used substance surveyed.

D. Suggested Replacements

Of the fifty-six respondents (18.6% of the total survey population) who provided one or more replacements to **She Xiang**, **Bing Pian** was listed most frequently with 23 citations. **Shi Chang Pu** was second and was cited 21 times. Nevertheless, several problems exist with these replacements. First, **Bing Pian** is labeled for external use only, and secondly, **Shi Chang Pu** acts as a central nervous system *depressant*, while **She Xiang** acts as a central nervous system *stimulant*. Therefore, senior practitioners recommend the following replacements for **She Xiang**:

- To open the orifices, revive the spirit, and unblock closed disorders, **Su He Xiang** was considered to be the best substitution.

- To invigorate the blood, dissipate clumps, reduce swelling, and alleviate pain, either **Ru Xiang** or **Mo Yao** were recommended.

Summary

As can be seen in section B above, a majority of practitioners believe **She Xiang** is helpful to important in the practice of Chinese medicine. As we have seen in the species profile in Chapter 4, efforts at farming musk deer in China have not been successful. In addition, several animals end up being killed in order to get one pod of wild musk, making musk an unsustainable substance. Any use of musk will impact a fairly vulnerable population, and substitution is recommended in order to conserve these species.

11. Chuān Shān Jiǎ (Squama Manitis Pentadactyla)

A. Establishing Usage

Yes	117	38.9%
No	174	57.8%
Blank	10	3.3%
	301	100.0%

B. Perceived Importance

Two hundred-five respondents (68.1% of the total survey population) indicated their perceived importance of *Chuan Shan Jia.*

CRUCIAL	8	3.9%
IMPORTANT	65	31.7%
HELPFUL	62	30.2%
MINIMAL	70	34.1%
Total	205	99.9%

C. Perceived Frequency of Use

Eighty-seven respondents (28.9% of the total survey population) indicated how often they use *Chuan Shan Jia.* Of that group, the average perceived use was 7.3 percent, making *Chuan Shan Jia* the eleventh most frequently used substance surveyed.

D. Suggested Replacements

There was little consensus among the sixty-seven respondents (22.3% of the total survey population) who gave one or more replacements for *Chuan Shan Jia.* The one most cited—by 18 practitioners—was *Wang Bu Liu Xing.* The next two were *Zao Jiao Ci* and *E Zhu* cited 10 and 7 times respectively. The remaining suggested substitutions varied greatly. Senior practitioners recommended the following replacements based on specific actions:

- To disperse blood stasis and unblock menstruation, the best substitute would be *Lu Lu Tong.*

- To promote lactation, the best choice would be **Wang Bu Liu Xing**.
- To reduce swelling and promote the discharge of pus, as used in combination with **Zao Jiao Ci,** the best choice would be **Bai Zhi**.
- To expel wind-dampness from the channels, the best choice would be **Ji Xue Teng**.

Summary

As can be seen above, approximately half of the practitioners surveyed perceive **Chuan Shan Jia** helpful or important to the practice of Chinese medicine. From the pangolin species profile in Chapter 4, it seems that American practitioners use it less than their Chinese counterparts, making acceptance of substitutions in the United States easier, especially since there are many options with which to replace it. By discontinuing the use of **Chuan Shan Jia** and replacing it with other herbs, practitioners can make a significant contribution to the survival of pangolins in the wild.

12. Líng Yáng Jǐao (Cornu Antelopis)

A. Establishing Usage

Yes	78	25.9%
No	214	71.1%
Blank	9	3.0%
	301	100.0%

B. Perceived Importance

One hundred eighty six or (61.8% of the total survey population) indicated their perceived importance of **Ling Yang Jiao**.

CRUCIAL	10	5.4%
IMPORTANT	50	26.9%
HELPFUL	60	32.3%
MINIMAL	66	35.5%
Total	186	100.1%

C. Perceived Frequency of Use

Sixty-two respondents (20.6% of the total survey population) indicated how often they use **Ling Yang Jiao**. Of that group, the average perceived use was 6.7 percent, making **Ling Yang Jiao** the twelfth most frequently used substance surveyed.

D. Suggested Replacements

Of the seventy two respondents (23.9% of the total survey population) who gave one or more replacements for **Ling Yang Jiao**, **Gou Teng** was cited most frequently with 31 citations. Senior practitioners recommended the following:

- To extinguish wind and control spasms and convulsions: **Gou Teng** or domestic goat horn.
- To calm the Liver and anchor the yang: **Gou Teng** with **Bai Shao**.
- To clear the Liver and improve the vision: **Ju Hua** or **Jue Ming Zi**.
- To drain heat and relieve fire toxicity: **Huang Lian**.
- To clear damp-heat: **Long Dan Cao**.

Summary

The majority of practitioners perceive that **Ling Yang Jiao** has helpful to minimal importance in the practice of Chinese medicine. However, avoiding its use is crucial to help saiga survive in the wild. Because the male is targeted for hunting, this has created an imbalance in the animals' ability to reproduce, causing a serious population crash. All practitioners should replace **Ling Yang Jiao** with one of the above options as a way to conserve and protect these animals.

It is important to note that other than domestic sheep and goats, which are obviously not endangered, the additional substitutes given in our literature* for saiga horn also come from endangered animals. The Tibetan antelope (*panthelops hogsonii*) and serow (*capricornis sumatraensis*) are both on Appendix I (prohibited to trade) and the Mongolian (*procapra gutturosa*) and Tibetan (*procapra picticaudata*) gazelles and the goral (*naemorhedus goral*) are on Appendix

---

* Bensky D, Clavey S and Ströger E (eds.). (2004) *Chinese Herbal Medicine Materia Medica, 3ʳᵈ Edition.* Eastland Press, Seattle WA. pp. 967.

II. Another species given as a replacement is the goitered gazelle (*gazalla subgutturosa*) and is not listed on CITES but is considered endangered by the US Endangered Species Act and the IUCN. As we have seen from the precipitous decline of the saiga in Chapter 3, substituting one endangered species with another is shortsighted and only serves to increase pressure on other vulnerable species.

13. Hǎi Mǎ (Hippocampus)

A. Establishing Usage

Yes	40	13.3%
No	251	83.4%
Blank	10	3.3%
	301	100.0%

B. Perceived Importance

One hundred forty-five or (48.2% of the total survey population) indicated their perceived importance of *Hai Ma*.

CRUCIAL	2	1.4%
IMPORTANT	18	12.4%
HELPFUL	36	24.8%
MINIMAL	89	61.4%
Total	145	100.0%

C. Perceived Frequency of Use

Thirty respondents (10.0% of the total survey population) indicated how often they used *Hai Ma.* Of that group, the *average* perceived use was 6 percent, making *Hai Ma* the thirteenth most frequently used substance surveyed.

D. Suggested Replacements

Of the forty five respondents (15.0% of the total survey population) who gave one or more replacements for *Hai Ma*, there was very little consensus on any one substitution, with *Lu Rong* and *Yin Yang Huo* each being cited 9 times. After that, the suggestions varied greatly. Senior practitioners agreed that *Hai Ma* was mainly in prepared formulas that have little clinical application. One senior practitioner noted that the formulas with *Hai Ma* were "...silly and one never needs to use it."

Summary

The majority of respondents to this question perceived that *Hai Ma* had minimal importance to the practice of Chinese medicine, and senior practitioners also felt this way. As we saw in the Seahorse profile in Chapter 4, with Chinese medicine making up 90 percent of the trade in seahorses, avoiding their use would be a tremendous contribution to seahorse conservation. It is heartening to note that the Hong Kong Chinese Medicinal Merchants Association (HK-CMMA) has recommended seeking replacements for seahorses, in addition to other measures directed towards how they are harvested, to help conserve them. Practitioners in the United States can go one step better and stop using *Hai Ma* altogether, since there is little clinical need for using it.

It is important to note that pipefishes and pipehorses, (*Hai Long*) are on Appendix II, are also endangered and have comparable properties to seahorse and are used in similar ways.* Therefore it is reasonable to discontinue the use of these animals, since there is little need for them clinically.

14. Guī Bǎn (Plastrum Testudinis)

A. Establishing Usage

Yes	222	73.8%
No	72	23.9%
Blank	7	2.3%
	301	100.0%

B. Perceived Importance

Two hundred fifty respondents (83.1% of the total population) indicated their perceived importance of *Gui Ban*.

CRUCIAL	38	15.2%
IMPORTANT	108	43.2%
HELPFUL	73	29.2%

---

* Ibid. pp. 812.

MINIMAL   31   12.4%
Total   250   100.0%

C. Perceived Frequency of Use

One hundred seventy respondents (56.5% of the total population) indicated how often they used *Gui Ban*. Of that group, the *average* perceived use was 14.1 percent, making *Gui Ban* the fourth most frequently used substance in this survey.

D. Suggested Replacements

Of the one hundred-sixteen respondents (38.5% of the total survey population) who gave one or more replacements for *Gui Ban*, there were 38 citations for *Bie Jia*, with another 20 citations for "yin tonics" and 17 citations for *Nu Zhen Zi* to replace *Gui Ban*. After this, there was little agreement among the numerous other proposed substitutes. Senior practitioners felt that since *Bie Jia* (*Amydae sinensis*) is also endangered, this would *not* be a good choice. (Since *Bie Jia* was not included in the survey, many practitioners may not have known of its endangered status.) Senior practitioners suggested the following substitutions according to action:

- To nourish the yin and anchor the yang, a combination of *Bai Shao* with *Sheng Di* was recommended.
- To benefit the Kidneys and strengthen the bones, *Du Zhong* would be the best replacement.
- To cool the blood and stop yin deficient uterine bleeding, substitute with *Sheng Di* or *Di Yu*.

Senior practitioners agreed that *Gui Ban* does not need to be used to nourish the blood, tonify the heart, or to heal sores and ulcerations.

Summary

As can be seen above, the majority of practitioners believe *Gui Ban* is helpful to important in the practice of Chinese medicine. Given the intense pressure on turtles worldwide, and most particularly in Asia, we strongly suggest that practitioners replace *Gui Ban* with one of the substitutes given. If a practitioner chooses to use either soft or hard shell turtle, a certificate that verifies the animal's farmed status should be insisted upon.

Even though both soft-shell turtles and fresh water turtles (hard-shell) are farmed, there is strong evidence that these operations do not take pressure off wild turtles, which fetch higher prices. In March 2006 informal surveys of four turtle markets were done in Guongdong Province in southern China.* Approximately 70-75% of the total volume of turtles observed at these markets were farmed. However, one quarter of the traders had a substantial volume of wild-caught animals and one third of the 40 total species observed were native to the United States! Although the number of farmed species available is a positive trend, it is apparent that the wild-caught trade parallels the farming trade. Therefore, practitioners should be aware that farming may contribute to market forces that drive harvesting turtles from the wild. Because of this conservationists have recommended that all of Asia's turtle species without a listing at the present time to be listed on Appendix II** so that trade can be monitored for all of the species, because as one species gets hard to find in a particular location, others are used to fill the gaps.

....

Additional Species

The following is a list of Appendix II species that were not included in the survey. A mark (‡) indicates those species that were included in the species profiles of this book. Practitioners should consider substituting the following species, or ask for a certificate that verifies the cultivation or farming for the species in question. In addition, it is important to insist on accurate species specific labeling especially in the case of *E Jiao* and *Bie Jia* rather than the general or inaccurate nomenclature we often find.

   Cistanche deserticola—**Rou Cong Rong**
   ‡ *Aquilaria Lignam*—**Chen Xiang**
   ‡ *Amydae Sinensis*—**Bie Jia**
   ‡ *Euphorbiae Helioscopiae*—**Ze Qi**
   ‡ *Euphorbiae Kansui*—**Gan Sui**

---

* Van Dijk PP (2006) Market Survey Indicates that Farmed Species Dominate Chinese Markets but....*Asian Turtle News*. Asian Turtle Conservation Network.

** Asian Turtle Trade Working Group (1999) *Recommendations from the Workshop on Trade in Tortoises and Freshwater Turtles in Asia*. As of June 2006 Available at: www.traffic.org/turtles/recommendations.html

‡ *Euphorbiae seu Knoxiae*—**Da Ji**
‡ *Equus Asinus* spp.—**E Jiao**
Nardostachys chinense, N. jatamansi—**Gan Song**
Syngnathidae (various species in the family)—**Hai Long**

PART V

Therefore, wisdom is the way to nourish life; by following the four seasons, adapting to their climates, harmonizing the emotions, living in peace and contentment, and fine-tuning the yin and yang and hard and soft.
And in this way avoid pernicious influences to live a long and healthy life.

Chapter 9

THE ROLE OF CULTIVATION IN CONSERVING MEDICINAL PLANTS

Jean Giblette

The dried roots, barks, leaves, fruits, and other plant parts found on the shelves of the traditional medicine dispensary vividly display nature's abundance. Each herb, whether wild or farmed, originally came from a living organism within a dynamic community that shaped its healing potential. Through the years, herbs have represented health to the practitioners and patients using them. Conversely, human choices have affected the health of the plant communities where these herbs grow. These choices are the subject of this chapter.

Knowledge of how to harvest healing plants dates from ancient times, probably before agriculture began 10,000 years ago. Then, people were few, and wilderness was vast. Nevertheless, in the 21st century—with unprecedented human numbers, shrinking pockets of wild habitat scattered about the globe, and increasing industrialism—most medicinal herbs in China are still harvested from the wild (He and Sheng 1993). As a result, the capacity of many of these plant species to adapt to change, to continue to provide humans with medicine, and, for some, even to survive, is in jeopardy.

For Chinese medicine to sustain its metamorphosis into a world medicine, its students and practitioners must find creative solutions to the problem of medicinal plant conservation. They must develop a deeper understanding of how all those plants got into the jars on the dispensary shelves, just as they have educated themselves about how food reaches the supermarket, where it came from originally, and what was done to it in the process. Consciousness is the first step, followed by education, better choices, and collective action.

This chapter will first examine why plants are still harvested from the wild, and why wild plants are—or are perceived to be—of better quality. Because agriculture still presents a challenge for humankind, and our ability to conserve valuable wild plants is connected to these problems, we will summarize aspects of the history and contemporary redefinition of agriculture. Recommendations for ways that students and practitioners of Chinese medicine can help conserve medicinal plants will then be presented.

....

Wild Versus Cultivated

Since the beginnings of agriculture, people have shared an assumption that the medicinal efficacy of wild plants is reduced or absent once they are brought into cultivation. With the stubborn character of folklore, such beliefs reflect both our universal longing for a panacea and the will to survive that drives us to seek new cures.

Like other folk wisdom, however, the premium placed on wildness is only one facet of truth. The dichotomy of wild versus cultivated seems as old as the practice of agriculture itself. Theoretically, when a wild plant species is brought into cultivation, its gene pool is diminished, sometimes drastically. Depending on how the plant reproduces and how many individuals made up the original selection from the wild, the plant's ability to adapt to changing conditions and to keep itself healthy may be compromised.

Another aspect of biodiversity also affects plant quality. In general, agricultural ecosystems have been constructed as stripped-down versions of wild ecosystems. Most conventional agricultural practices reduce the numbers and varieties of microorganisms in the soil. The farmer may kill small and large animals competing for the crop and may grow only one crop in a large acreage (monoculture). Since plant nutrition is less a matter of taking in minerals and other nutrients directly from the earth than it is of feeding on the metabolic byproducts of literally millions of other organisms in their environment, any reduction in biodiversity in the environment affects plant health.

Agriculture's history shows a rather spotty record. When practiced badly—and never more so than today—devastation results. Even when practiced modestly with good intentions, agriculture without a holistic vision can lead to unintended negative effects. As industrial agriculture has intensified over the past 125 years, corrective interpretations have been available to those who would listen. Yet only recently—since the

1970s—has a counterforce gained momentum, a counterforce that has questioned all prevailing assumptions and established a series of alternative cultivation practices worldwide.

Nevertheless, as the 21st century begins, the new frontiers in agriculture are not fully visible to the general public, but instead remain the province of pioneers. Among this advance guard, new attitudes, experience, and research are in place, and the resulting practices demonstrate that the quality gap between wild and cultivated can be narrowed or closed.

....

A BRIEF HISTORY OF BAD AGRICULTURE

The roots of the "wild versus cultivated" problem run very deep and reflect our changing understanding of our relationship with nature. At present, when human population pressures have reduced wild habitat, and many medicinal plants have become rare or endangered, many observers regard agriculture as an ecological catastrophe, a problem so profound that a complete reinvention of the concept is underway.

The present crisis is a more widely dispersed version of an old one. Deforestation and plowing caused soil erosion in ancient Greece and Rome, as well as in central Mexico when maize cultivation began (Jackson 1980). Recent archaeological discoveries suggest that environmental degradation underlay the decline of civilizations in many other cases (Diamond 2003). Egypt, however, provides a contrasting example. There, regular flooding of the Nile took replenishment of soil fertility out of human hands until 1970, when the Aswan Dam was completed.

Some cultures fared better than others. Until the 20th century, China was a shining exception to the rule of careless stewardship. The Chinese sustained fertility for millennia, even though the land was intensively farmed, through a highly distributed, small-scale, closed-loop system that recycled everything, including human waste (King 1911).

Throughout the history of agriculture, a spectrum of practices has existed, now wider than ever, from pre-agricultural gathering to high-tech industrial agriculture. Along this continuum, biodiversity in the agricultural ecosystem is inversely proportional to the degree of industrialization (Badgley 2002).

The first synthetic fertilizers came into limited use in England in the 19th century. However, it was not until the end of World War II that the use of chemical products in agriculture became widespread. Huge chemical plants built for making explosives shifted easily into making nitrate fertilizers.

During the same period, a series of oversimplifications changed the practice of plant breeding, leading us into a cul-de-sac in which many of the world's major food crops have become dangerously dependent on chemicals. A group of scientists at the turn of the 20th century, influenced by the belated discovery of Gregor Mendel's life work, developed "pedigree" breeding (Robinson 1996), which produced desirable traits in certain crops. This practice deviated from quantitative or statistical approaches, which work with whole populations and assume the complex action of numerous factors in developing the kind of broad-spectrum resistance found in wild plants.

As an exercise in reductionism, the development of pedigree breeding can be compared to Galileo discounting friction and air resistance so that his measurements of falling objects fit his then-new theory of mechanics. His omissions were not considered important until the 1970s, when measurements became more accurate, and chaos theory showed how the irregularities of simple systems act as a creative process (Gleick 1987).

In the case of plant breeding, however, oversimplification has brought us ever closer to the edge of disaster. While 75 percent of agricultural biodiversity in the United States has been lost in the past century, our major food crops have been bred to resist only specific pests. The pests mutate, necessitating another application of chemicals and another round of breeding in an endless cycle. While profitable for the seed and chemical companies, the trend has been devastating to farmers.

From the vantage point of a century later, pedigree breeding can be seen as an artifact of incomplete understanding. In 20th century biology, including both genetics and ecology, the pace of scientific discovery has exceeded the descriptive power of the words we use, including the term "gene" (Keller 2001). But the profitability of the products created through oversimplification tends to perpetuate the mistakes. Genetic engineering of food crops can be understood as the next step in this sequence of reduction, an increasingly narrow focus on individual parts that disregards the integrity of the whole.

A crop with minimal genetic diversity can easily be wiped out by a single type of predator. The Irish potato famine, a well-known example, resulted in widespread human suffering and the deaths of a million people in three years. In 1845, a wind-borne fungus, *Phytophthora infestans*, arrived by accident (probably on a ship) to Ireland, where the poor relied on a potato monoculture. All plants were clones of a common ancestor, previously introduced from the New World in the late 16th century (Pollan 2001).

The human tendency to oversimplify, whether to save labor, make a profit, or through an attitude that regards nature as "other," works against us over the long term. The practices that have yielded quick profits in industrial agriculture are all reductionistic. Those practices described here, such as pedigree breeding, monoculture, and others—the systematic elimination of microorganisms through the use of artificial fertilizers, herbicides, and fungicides; genetic engineering; the consolidation of seed companies—have resulted in a continuous loss of biodiversity over the past century.

To repair the damage, we must re-learn how to work with nature. This challenge entails not so much a return to the old ways as a new awareness and respect for natural processes—an awareness we gain primarily through scientific investigation.

....

CORRECTIVE FORCES IN AGRICULTURE

With one-third of the world's arable land lost to erosion in the last 50 years, with 90 percent of U.S. cropland losing soil above replacement rates, worldwide pollution from agro-chemicals, declining fertility and continued outbreaks of famine and malnutrition, a colossal indictment of industrial-age agriculture is well underway. Beginning with Rachel Carson's seminal *Silent Spring*, published in 1962, the public has been put on alert.

Older prophets lived in our midst when the depredations of modern industrial agriculture began, and their criticisms supplied the theoretical basis for contemporary ecological practices. Among them was Sir Albert Howard (1873-1947), an English scientist who worked in India and wrote two classics of ecological agriculture published in 1940s: *An Agricultural Testament* and *The Soil and Health* (Barton 2001). In the United States, publisher Jerome I. Rodale (1898-1971) promoted Sir Howard's work and protected the public's access to information on natural approaches. Rudolph Steiner (1861-1925), Austrian philosopher and founder of Anthroposophy, also founded Biodynamics, which treats the farm as a whole organism and employs practices such as herbal preparations and use of lunar rhythms to stimulate natural forces (Steiner 1924). In Japan, Mokichi Okada (1882-1955) founded a philosophy called Shumei that gave rise to sustainable farming practices and alternative economic arrangements to support them.

These visionaries advocated stewardship in alignment with nature, creating a distinct counterpoint to prevailing reductionistic approaches. They each attracted a corps of followers that has grown steadily into the present day.

While industrial agriculture spread during the 20th century, the philosophical context changed to follow the direction that emerged after the theories of relativity and quantum mechanics eclipsed Newtonian physics. Holism, systems theory, and the development of the science of ecology in the second half of the 20th century contributed to the changing views of humankind's place in nature (Worster 1994).

The work of the visionaries supported senior, contemporary innovators in ecological agriculture. Masanobu Fukuoka, now 93 years old, a Japanese microbiologist who had a sudden epiphany and went back to the land, founded a series of practices known as Nature Farming (Fukuoka 1987). Inspired by Sir Albert Howard and others, a South African game warden named Allan Savory amassed several decades of observations of fragile grazing systems that demonstrate the counter-intuitive principle that grasslands protected from grazing actually suffer decline. He found that germination of plant species depends on the mechanical effect of animals' hooves breaking up the surface of the soil, as well as other subtle interactions (Savory and Butterfield 1999).

Australian farmer Bill Mollison became preoccupied with the cultivation of perennial plants for food and founded Permaculture ("permanent agriculture"), a practice that emphasizes design to fit the specifics of a particular place and allows for multiple uses of farm elements (Mollison 1998). In Permaculture and other ecological practices, wildness is considered an essential element in preserving biodiversity and the capacity of the system to adapt to changing conditions. Wildness can be maintained in small ways—in hedgerows that separate fields or in biostrips among rows in a mixed cropping system. Indeed, the re-creation of wildness has become the territory for astonishing innovation among our close contemporaries (Imhoff et al 2002).

Trained as a geneticist, Wes Jackson, whose innovative research at The Land Institute in Salina, Kansas, challenges the entire concept of soil tillage, is another contemporary leader in the corrective movement following nature as guide or instructor. He calls for "more people who will show us the practical possibility of a research agenda based on a marriage of agriculture and ecology." He also points out that in order to learn from nature, the process must be dialectical—we must ask questions and be prepared to have the questions revised by the answers (Jackson 1994).

THE RE-CREATION OF WILDNESS

The corrective forces, having gathered momentum in recent years, agree on the value of wildness and biodiversity for its own sake to compensate for what we do not yet understand about how individual species contribute to the whole. The interactions of a wide variety of species create a dynamic, self-regulating system that takes on a life of its own. As ecological farmers and gardeners recognize, beyond a threshold of effort, biodiversity increases without human interference. Life seems to attract life. "Pests" may be present, but they do not proliferate or attack healthy plants. The balance and resilience of the ecosystem approximates that of the wild.

However, given the extent of the destruction of medicinal plant habitat and other related worldwide threats, how do we maximize conservation without causing further damage? As biologist David Ehrenfeld pointed out 25 years ago, we must assign value to a threatened species to save it, yet it is "easier to develop value than it is to calculate the effects of our valuing" (Ehrenfeld 1998). Humans are part of natural systems, and when we interfere, even with good intentions, we bring along our incomplete ideas of utility and short-term gains, which can lead to unexpected consequences.

The paradox to which Ehrenfeld refers is demonstrated by the example of ginseng cultivation. While the Chinese learned about the North American species (*Panax quinquefolius)* through Jesuit missionaries in the early 18th century and sustained a substantial trade since then, cultivation of the plant in the United States did not begin until the 1870s (Foster 1999). A century later, cultivation was concentrated in Wisconsin, where the conventional practice produced an industry that grew the plants in monocultures under shade cloth, fertilized with agrochemicals and sprayed with fungicides to arrest the inevitable disease. Growers became concerned in the early 1990s over reports of falling levels of ginsenosides in their product (Acres USA 1995), yet restorative measures failed.

Meanwhile, although the amount of cultivated ginseng exported to China from Wisconsin amounted to over 2 million pounds in 1994, farmers in West Virginia complained about the persistence of wild ginseng poaching on their lands. The demand for wild ginseng was so great that local teenagers could bundle immature roots and sell them on the black market for $300 per pound. Law enforcement officers and the farmers themselves could not adequately patrol the hilly terrain. Some suggested that persuading potential poachers to become ginseng farmers was the only realistic solution (WV Herb Association 1996).

These occurrences suggest that a glut of inferior cultivated product produced an unintended consequence, at least in West Virginia at the time. It drove up the price of the wild root and aggravated the poaching problem, thwarting conservation efforts.

Since then, the Wisconsin farmers have fallen on hard times, largely due to competition from British Columbia and China itself. But recently a countertrend has emerged. Led by progressive farmers and landowners primarily in the Alleghenies, the art of ginseng cultivation has evolved from conventional (industrial) methods to "woods-cultivated," in which small areas of woodland are tilled and sometimes made into raised beds. Artificial fertilizer and other agrochemicals may or may not be used, according to the situation and choices made by the grower. (Buyers must learn to ask detailed questions concerning specific cultivation practices.)

However, "wild-simulated" or "wild-cultivated" methods are even more closely allied with nature. For those landowners fortunate enough to have inherited a natural population of ginseng with its own genetics, wild-cultivated ginseng means, in essence, wild. No outside seed is introduced, and interference is minimized (Jacobson and Burkhart 2004). Seed may be collected and either broadcast by hand or returned to the greenhouse, germinated, and the young seedlings set out in imitation of natural spacing, along with their preferred companion plants.

Recent efforts to learn from nature have produced a substantial body of research on ginseng in the wild. Observers have found that the plant seems to prefer certain tree species, with sugar maples at the top of the list. Sugar maples bring moisture to the surface and also concentrate calcium in their leaves, resulting in calcium-rich soil, high in organic matter with low pH levels. Characteristic companion plants—maidenhair, Christmas or rattlesnake fern, blue cohosh, red or white baneberry—indicate moisture levels (Beyfuss 2000). Overall ecosystem diversity ensures pest control.

Other research on the elaborate interdependence among plants in an ecosystem (Golley 1993), including work on the huge variety of soil microorganisms and their symbiotic roles, has led to the recognition that wild ginseng habitat is complex beyond our present understanding. However, stewardship is not only possible, but it is necessary to protect resources. Note that ecosystems with the plant companions, moisture levels, and climate preferred by ginseng are found in highly specific localities. Rather than force ginseng to grow where it is convenient for humans, we have moved toward a concept of first identifying ecological neighborhoods and then choosing crops that fit the locale. The neighbors who have previously established residence—the companion plants, microbes, pollinators, and predators—are both indicators and co-determinants of the qualities the plants will express. This principle holds for wetlands, pastures, prairies, drylands, alpine regions, and all the other ecosystems throughout the world.

....

ECONOMICS AND COMMUNITY CHOICES

The leading edge of ginseng production, with its advancements of the past 30 years, points the way toward resolving the perceived deficiency of cultivated medicinal plants. Yet agricultural ecosystems must always include the farmer. The economics of farming must become as sustainable as the ecology. This subject is too vast to treat in detail here, yet recent innovations in ecological agriculture include two market trends that bear mention.

Community-supported agriculture, which originated independently in Japan, came to the United States from Europe in the mid-1980s (McFadden 2003). This concept involves a group of shareholders who contract with a farmer on an annual basis for the harvest. The object is to support the farm by sharing the risk, with the produce (usually a variety of vegetables) as dividends. The principle is important to high-value crops such as medicinal plants because it allows the farmer to sidestep the commodity basis of production. A commodity is defined as equally valued units, none worth more or less than another. In commodity production, the major incentive for the producer is to hold down or decrease costs. In community-supported agriculture, however, advance payments create an incentive for the farmer to maximize quality and thereby retain shareholders.

A second trend is direct marketing, of which community-supported agriculture is a form. Direct marketing also includes farmers' markets or greenmarkets, farm stands, "u-pick" or customer harvesting, and internet marketing. The value of direct marketing is that it maximizes economic returns to the grower. Farmers' cooperatives that own their own processing plants and other market vehicles achieve the same result.

Embattled farmers in the United States, who now represent less than 2 percent of the population, use these measures to sustain themselves in the face of imports subsidized by devalued labor abroad and transported by artificially cheap fossil fuels. Customers who become aware of environmental issues are motivated to support these farmers with their business. Recently, communities have begun to take responsibility for supporting their farmers by passing "right-to-farm" laws, creating wholesale markets, and forming land trusts that preserve agricultural land.

Students and practitioners of herbal medicine are, of course, members of wider communities that may sustain ecological farmers with their food purchase choices. Because herbalists advise clients on dietary matters, practitioners have a responsibility to be thoroughly informed about the options available.

How Herbal Practitioners Can Conserve Medicinal Plants

Students and practitioners of Chinese medicine need to make a connection to medicinal plants that goes deeper than memorizing formulas or handling herbs in the dispensary. Botanical studies should be included in the sciences portion of the curriculum. But learning from texts and lectures has its limits.

Access to small gardens of the living plant species or larger collections within botanical gardens can be invaluable. Just as a picture is worth a thousand words, a five-sense experience of the whole plant deepens understanding of the herb's taste, nature, and affinities. Knowing something about the preferences and native habitat of the species can suggest how its healing properties developed. Observing traits the plant shares with its relatives helps develop a sense of the natural order and the ability to see patterns in nature.

The profession as a whole needs a means to identify quality attributes in medicinal plants—quality in terms of the characteristics and potency valued in a wild plant. Quality evaluation will become increasingly necessary as more herbs are cultivated outside Asia. While biochemical analysis can identify species and assess the number and strength of compounds in plant material, it does not at present address this problem. A research group in Minnesota has done ground-breaking work in this area, using a protocol from the food industry that promises an alternative, evidence-based method for the profession to assess quality in its medicinal plants (Hassel 2002).

Herbal practitioners who want to ensure continued access to high-quality medicinal plants must devise new ways to recognize and reward good stewardship. By learning about farming history and the contemporary lexicon, herbal practitioners can begin to specify the cultivation practices they believe to be appropriate. In this way, they can become an active force in the marketplace, capable of creating and enforcing standards of quality and supporting good farmers in the process.

Many people now interpret their own attitude shifts and behavioral changes as a matter of health, if not survival, for our food plants, animals, and human society. The traditional medicine practitioner must seek allies among those who are earth stewards and learn what others are doing to solve the problems of conservation. Only by understanding the full dimensions of the problem will herbal practitioners learn to make the right choices for themselves, teach their patients to do the same, and ensure a future for their medicine.

In making these connections with farmers, conservationists, and other earth stewards, herbal practitioners directly serve their own mission. As Sir Albert Howard declared more than 50 years ago in an acknowledgment of our interdependency, "the health of the soil, plants, animals and human beings ... is one great problem" (Howard 1947).

SOURCES

Acres USA (1995) Bulletin on the Wisconsin Ginseng Crop Improvement Project. *Acres USA: The Voice of Eco-Agriculture,* June 1995.

Badgley C (2002) Can agriculture and biodiversity coexist? In *Fatal Harvest: The Tragedy of Industrial Agriculture.* A. Kimbrell (ed.), Island Press, Covelo CA: pp. 279-284.

Barton G (2001) Sir Albert Howard and the forestry roots of the organic farming movement. *Agricultural History* 75:2, p. 168.

Beyfuss R (2000) Soil nutrient characteristics of wild ginseng populations in NY, ME and TN. In *American Ginseng Production in the Twenty-first Century* Conference Proceedings Sept. 2000, Cornell Cooperative Extension of Greene County, Cairo NY.

Diamond J (2003) The last Americans: environmental collapse and the end of civilization. *Harper's Magazine* Vol. 306 No. 1837, pp. 43-51.

Ehrenfeld D (1981) *The Arrogance of Humanism: The Conservation Dilemma.* Oxford Press, New York NY.

Foster S (1999) *American Ginseng.* Botanical Series No. 308, American Botanical Council, Austin TX.

Fukuoka M (1978) *The One-Straw Revolution: An Introduction to Natural Farming.* Rodale Press, Emmaus PA.

Gleick J (1987) *Chaos Theory: Making a New Science.* Penguin Books, New York NY.

Golley F (1993) *A History of the Ecosystem Concept in Ecology: More Than the Sum of the Parts.* Yale University Press, New Haven CT.

Hassel C et al (2002) Using Chinese medicine to understand medicinal herb quality: An alternative to biomedical approaches? *Journal of Agriculture and Human Values* 19: pp. 337-347.

Howard A (1947) *The Soil and Health.* Oxford University Press, London.

Imhoff D et al (2002) *Farming With the Wild: Strategies for Enhancing Biodiversity on Farms and Ranches*. Watershed Media, Philo CA.

Jackson W (1980) *New Roots for Agriculture*. University of Nebraska Press, Lincoln NE.

Jackson W (1994) *Becoming Native to this Place*. Counterpoint, Washington DC.

Jacobson M and Burkhart E (2004) *Opportunities from Ginseng Husbandry in Pennsylvania*. Penn State College of Agricultural Sciences, University Park PA.

Keller E (2001) *The Century of the Gene*. Harvard University Press, Cambridge MA.

King F (1911) *Farmers of Forty Centuries*. Rodale Press, Emmaus PA.

McFadden S (2003) Community farms in the 21st century: poised for another wave of growth? The New Farm, Rodale Institute. As of March 2006 available at: http://www.thenewfarm.org/features/0104/csa-history/part1.shtml

Mollison B (1988) *Permaculture: A Designer's Manual*. Tagari Publications, Tyalgum NSW Australia.

Pollan M (2001) *The Botany of Desire: A Plant's-Eye View of the World*. Random House, New York NY.

Robinson R (1996) *Return to Resistance: Breeding Crops to Reduce Pesticide Dependence*. agAcess, Davis CA.

Savory A and Butterfield J (1999) *Holistic Management: A New Framework for Decision Making*. Island Press, Washington DC.

He S and Ning S (1997) Utilization and Conservation of Medicinal Plants in China, With Special Reference to Atractylodes lancea. In *Medicinal Plants for Forest Conservation and Health Care*, pp. 109-115. G Bodeker, KKS Bhat, J Burley and P Vantomme (eds.) Food and Agriculture Organization of the United Nations, Rome (Non-wood Forest Products 11). As of August 2006, available at: http://www.fao.org/docrep/W7261E/W7261E13.htm

Steiner R (1924) *Agriculture: Spiritual Foundations for the Renewal of Agriculture*. Biodynamic Farming and Gardening Association, Junction City OR.

West Virginia Herb Association (1996) Breakout session on ginseng production. Annual Meeting, Jacksons Mill WV.

Worster D (1994) *Nature's Economy: A History of Ecological Ideas*. Cambridge University Press, Cambridge UK.

Chapter 10
Epilogue: "A Spiritual Pivot"

Elizabeth Call

Protecting biodiversity can feel overwhelming because of the many social and economic pressures that contribute to species loss. Because the problem is so widespread, we often don't know where to start or what to do. But "do" we must, for our own sake and for the future of humanity. The wisdom we exercise in using medicinal plants will not only nourish our health—it will nourish the health of our home, the Earth. That is why we should commit to altering our habits and expanding our perception of herbs to include how to give back to the plants and animals some of what they have given to us. In *The Heart* (Larre, et. al., 1991) Qi Bo says that when humans achieve balance and become quiescent, we can make our minds become one with nature and concentrate our Hearts. These words underscore the importance of connecting with nature not only through our intellects, but through our hearts as well. They also help focus our actions on how we are connected to nature, not separate from it and how we can recognize the sacred in conserving and collaborating with nature.

We have all experienced how we take care of something differently when we care *about* it. Fortunately, you have taken a first step in protecting biodiversity; you have educated yourself about the species covered here. You now know more about their unique lives and needs, and as a result, probably care more about them. The Taoists believed that education is wisdom (Campbell in Flowers, 1988). And in knowing more about some of the animals and plants used in medicine, you will be able to exercise foresight in your choices, thereby using wisdom "to nourish life." Your perspective has changed; you see your professional world from an expanded point of view. Consequently, there are concrete actions all of us can take immediately to avoid the "pernicious influence" of species loss and to help return species to their wild homes to live long and healthy lives.

Below are twelve actions that practitioners can choose from to support the biodiversity of Chinese medicinal plants. I hope you will choose to focus on at least two or three, as many of them are quite simple. Though some are changes that need to be made within our own educational and certification infrastructure, they can easily happen with our collective professional support and political will.

1. **Use the replacements suggested in this book when clinically appropriate.** This is one of the most powerful actions we can do right now to protect Appendix I and II species. This means that you may need to reassess some of the prepared formulas you use, or to call your supplier to ask some questions. For those practitioners using bulk raw herbs, the substitutions given in Chapter 8 can be easily implemented.

2. **Encourage herb companies to provide information on the supply chain for their herbs.** It is empowering to know where our herbs come from, how they are grown and propagated, if they are harvested from the wild and what, if any, conservation measures the farm or harvester takes to ensure sustainable production. This may uncover very positive efforts that we can support, and it can give herb importers a chance to highlight positive actions or discover practices that need to be changed. This information should not be limited to Appendix II species, but to all species. Many herb companies send out newsletters, and they could easily highlight a species in every letter.

3. **Support efforts to grow and produce Chinese herbs locally.** As was stated before, when we have a closer connection with a product, we care more about it. As outlined in Chapter 9, practitioners can participate in Community Supported Agriculture (CSA) or in direct marketing plans with growers. Such methods help farmers focus on the quality aspects of medicinal plant cultivation, with the security of knowing that their crops are sold. Some CSAs encourage participation from their customers in certain farm tasks, an activity that helps customers see first-hand the farmers' commitment to providing a superior product. See Resources for more information.

4. **Grow several medicinal plant species.** Growing just one or two species of medicinal plants can add depth to our understanding of

them. Many of the herbs in the Chinese materia medica also have culinary uses. And, as we are finding out more and more, many everyday western culinary herbs also have wonderful medicinal properties. Growing these herbs is an excellent way to learn about plants; touching them, smelling them, and nurturing them gives us a personal appreciation of their benefits. Since many of these species do well in containers and are easy to grow indoors or in a small space, even those with little experience growing plants or without access to a garden plot can experience the joy of using fresh herbs for food and medicine. Many communities have community gardens where one can have a small plot in which to work. If there are any community gardens in Asian neighborhoods, chances are that Asian participants may know about and grow some medicinal species.

5. **Support efforts to conserve, restore, and grow *native* medicinal plant species.** We can re-connect to our local ecosystems through our own North American native medicinal plant species. By doing this, we strengthen the "energetic flow" towards conservation, which ultimately will support conservation efforts in Asia. We can't expect people half a world away to be good land stewards if we are not doing the same in our own back yards. We have a perfect opportunity to model that commitment, since many of our native medicinal plants are disappearing from the wild from over-collection and poor land stewardship.

United Plant Savers (UpS) is an organization that was started by herbalist Rosemary Gladstar to address conservation of native medicinal plants. A partial list of United Plant Savers' contributions in this area follows (Gladstar, 2000):

- *Identifying which native medicinal plants are at risk.*
- *Raising public awareness of the current plight of at-risk native medicinal plants.*
- *Creating and managing botanical sanctuaries.*
- *Providing seeds and rootstock and information for replanting at-risk species.*
- *Replanting and restoring at-risk medicinal plants.*
- *Consulting with those who grow and harvest medicinal herbs regarding sustainable land-use practices.*

I suggest joining this group, or at least reading some of the books published by UpS on growing medicinal plants (see Resources). They provide a wealth of information on cultivation techniques, habitat, uses, and substitutions for plants on their "at-risk" and "to-watch" lists, in addition to advice on creating a medicinal plant sanctuary.

It is very satisfying to watch endangered or threatened native medicinal plants flourish in your own garden or land. Some of these plants are also loved by native birds, butterflies, and other animals, and they attract them to the garden, enhancing our efforts to care for and sustain biodiversity.

6. **Learn about collecting and using Chinese medicinal plants that grow as weeds in your local area.** The herbalist David Winston believes that we should use the "American Extra Pharmacopoeia" (Winston in Gladstar, et.al., 2000), which consists of the numerous Chinese herbs that grow wild in various local areas throughout the United States. Since many of these plants have naturalized here and have in some cases become invasive weeds, we should learn the proper way to harvest them and use them, not only for a "wild" source of fresh Chinese herbs, but to also reduce their impact on the local environments where they can compete with native plants. This action is an incredibly thrifty way to support biodiversity. It will give us an opportunity to see many Chinese herbs growing in the "wild," and we can learn to harvest them and work with fresh herbs. The use of these herbs would be sustainable to use, low cost, or even free, because of their local availability.

A word to the wise: Before collecting and using wild herbs, make an *absolutely* positive identification and be sure that the area in which you are collecting has not been contaminated with heavy metals or chemicals. It is imperative to learn these techniques from someone with experience in plant identification and wild herb harvesting.

Here is a partial list. For the full list see the book *Planting the Future* by Rosemary Gladstar.

Latin Name	Pin Yin Name
Polygonum aviculare	Bian Xu
Polygonum cuspidatum	Hu Zhang
Pueraria lobata	Ge Gen
Prunella vulgaris	Xia Ku Cao
Abutilon indicum	Mo Pen Cao

Aster tartaricus	Zi Wan
Bidens bipinnata	Gui Zhen Cao
Scirpus yagura	Jing San Leng
Commelina communis	Ya Zhi Cao
Cuscuta spp.	Tu Si Zi
Lonicera japonica	Jin Yin Hua/ Ren Dong Teng
Perilla fructescens	Zi Su Ye / Zi Su Zi
Tribulus terrestris	Ci Ji Li
Portulaca oleracea	Ma Chi Xian
Phragmites communis	Lu Gen
Dipsacus asperoides	Xu Duan
Raphanus sativus	Lai Fu Zi

7. **Encourage and support Botanical Studies as an adjunct to curricula in Oriental medicine.** This could be done with herb clubs, electives, field workshops, and other formats for students to connect directly with the plants. This will enable practitioners in the United States to be able to assess the quality of the herbs they use, and by so doing maintain access and control of our pharmacopoeia. In addition, this knowledge could eventually help to identify native replacements for many Chinese herbs.

8. **Encourage herb companies to provide more support for sustainable cultivation/harvesting in China.** For the foreseeable future, most Chinese herbs will continue to come from China. Buy from companies that can demonstrate their support for biodiversity there. While this relates to number 2 above, it is more than just giving information on the supply chain for an herb. It is about dealing with growers or collectors in China directly, and looking for ways to help them be good land stewards. While there are many middlemen in the trade (hence the lack of knowledge of the supply chain), how many companies get someone on the ground or farm to see where the herbs come from? Companies can look for ways to assist in creating botanical sanctuaries there, and they can help ensure that wild plants are harvested sustainably. Examples of this include dividing roots properly to ensure continued survival of the plant, harvesting aerial parts carefully, and distributing seeds in the area at the right time. Herb importers and companies have as much at stake in biodiversity as practitioners do. They can take the lead and work with people and organizations in China towards supporting biodiversity.

A thorny issue in the herb world has been the development of a certification process to ensure buyers that the product they are getting was sustainably harvested or grown. There are various pros and cons to this, ranging from the cons of cost and oversight, to the pros of the long-term advantage of consumers being able to vote with their dollars and choose a product that is sustainable. It is my personal belief that industry can do this if it secures partnerships with conservation organizations and creates a trade consortium. Often, oversight is seen as an inhibition to "free trade". But if trade is not sustainable, it really isn't "free" after all. In the future, when locally grown Chinese medicinals become more available, and with the emergence of a new generation of practitioners who have direct plant experience, a certification process may become a more attractive way for imported herbs to remain competitive.

9. **Support knowledge of biodiversity and replacements on national and state board exams for Chinese herbology.** Questions such as these on exams will ensure that the conservation information of Appendix I and II species is taught in herb programs. The National Commission for the Certification of Acupuncture and Oriental Medicine (NCCAOM) accepts questions for their exams via email. Visit their website for submission information, and compose a question based on this book for the national exam in Chinese herbology. Future generations of patients and practitioners may depend on this knowledge.

10. **Endangered species issues and their legalities should be an ethics issue for both state licensure and national certification.** As was seen in the survey reviewed in Chapter 8, there are those practitioners who continue to use products claiming to contain Appendix I species. All national and state professional organizations should have clauses that allow for disciplinary action if a practitioner is prosecuted for using Appendix I species or illegally obtaining Appendix II species. Even though compliance with United States law is implicit in licensure and ethics, I believe we need to be explicit in articulating support for those laws that pertain to the use of endangered species.

11. **We, as individuals and as a profession, need to start thinking about and relating to the natural world with our hearts and not just our heads.** Nature is not just a "business liquidation." The Earth is our home. We can care for the Earth and all of the won-

drous diversity here with our heart, recalling that the Heart in Chinese medicine connects us to others, allowing for intimacy, closeness and joy. We can extend this intimacy to the Earth and its resources. That way, we can better care for them, do our part to restore them, and use them in a respectful and sustainable way.

We can also engage in conservation by establishing partnerships with conservation organizations as a profession. We can personally join conservation organizations that have missions that speak to us. We can write letters to our leaders and representatives in support of conservation initiatives or against unsustainable policies. As compassionate health care providers, we need to take the broad view and recognize how unsustainable resource use has a direct negative impact on the health of our patients.

12. We can apply the Five Phases of Conservation right now. Whether or not anyone else appreciates the "Five Phases of Conservation," our own profession can still use this tool. We can evaluate species use within this paradigm, interweaving what we know about a species, the ecosystem in which it lives, the local community and national and international laws. If we start to learn more about the plants and see them as living beings, grow them and learn to provide them with the necessary conditions for their growth, we will learn more about their ecosystem. Using the plants as a foundation for our understanding, we will be drawn to how the Five Phases of Conservation impact them.

If we so choose, we can be strong, valuable contributors as the United States focuses increasingly on globalization, simply by addressing species conservation in our own backyards—in those regions of the country where we work and practice the healing arts.

And finally, we can recognize that our place in the web of life is not as the weaver, but as one of the many threads in the rich fabric of life here on Earth—an Earth on which we depend for our health, well-being and happiness. Rather than unravel this rich, beautiful and unique fabric with greed, selfishness and shortsightedness, we can seek to strengthen the fabric of life with prudence, altruism and joy knowing that we are stewards for another generation and another time.

SOURCES:

Flowers BS (ed.), (1988) *Joseph Campbell: The Power of Myth with Bill Moyers* Doubleday, New York NY.

Gladstar R and Hirsch P (eds.), (2000) *Planting the Future: Saving our Medicinal Herbs* Healing Arts Press, Rochester, VT

Larre C and Rochat de la Vallée E (1991) *The Heart: in Ling Shu Chapter 8.* Monkey Press, Cambridge, UK.

Contributing Authors and Reviewers

Sandra Altherr, Ph.D., is a biologist working on wildlife conservation issues and a founder of PRO WILDLIFE. She helped initiate the CITES discussion on the alarming status of Asian turtles.

Robert A. Blanchette, a professor at the University of Minnesota, St. Paul, is a forest pathologist and wood microbiologist researching tree defense mechanisms, deterioration processes of wood, and the biology of agarwood formation in Aquilaria trees.

Elizabeth Call is a licensed acupuncturist practicing in upstate New York and Vermont. She has studied Chinese herbal medicine with Andrew Gamble in New York City and has worked on bringing awareness of endangered species issues to the Chinese medicine community since 1996. Elizabeth was the Dean of Clinical Training at Tri-State College of Acupuncture from 1993 to 2000 and retains a faculty position there. She has been on the New York State board for acupuncture since 1999 and has served as chairwoman. In addition to enjoying her family, Elizabeth is also an organic gardener and is working on restoring grasslands, and native medicinal species to her family's rural land.

Sandra Cleva is a writer and editor with the U.S. Fish and Wildlife Service. She works with the Division of Law Enforcement.

Sarah Foster is a research biologist for Project Seahorse, based at the Fisheries Centre, University of British Columbia, Canada. She focuses on the use of life history to inform conservation and policy initiatives for seahorses.

Grace Ge Gabriel joined the International Fund for Animal Welfare (IFAW) in 1997 as China Country Director, and in that capacity she established the IFAW China office in Beijing, where she managed a wide array of wildlife conservation projects for bears, Asian elephants, and other species. Currently, she is IFAW's Deputy Director for Wildlife and Habitat. Born and raised in China, Ms. Gabriel trained as a journalist in China and the United States and also worked as a television producer in both countries. She is fluent in both Mandarin Chinese and English.

Jean Giblette is the director of High Falls Gardens (HFG), a farm-based educational enterprise founded in 1993 to advance the practice of Chinese medicine in North America through cultivation and study of the medicinal plants used in Asia. HFG supports botanical programs at various colleges of Oriental Medicine with its plant collection, the Student Gardens Program, research, lectures, field workshops, and publications. Ms. Giblette has a professional background in health administration and research. Since 1994, she has studied Chinese herbal medicine with Jeffrey C. Yuen in New York City.

Andrea Heydlauff recently graduated from the University of Arizona with a Master's Degree in Wildlife Science, after focusing on wildlife and human conflicts in northeastern Arizona. Since graduation, she has worked for the Asia Program with the Wildlife Conservation Society in New York.

Mary Maruca worked as a writer and editor for the U.S. Fish and Wildlife Service in the international program when this project was initiated and provided overall direction, support and editorial oversight.

Michael Spencer is a Thailand-based writer and photographer specializing in environmental journalism. He has prepared a number of investigative reports for WildAid on aspects of nature crime.

Partner Organizations

International Fund for Animal Welfare (IFAW) works to improve the welfare of wild and domestic animals throughout the world by reducing commercial exploitation of animals, protecting wildlife habitats, and assisting animals in distress. IFAW seeks to motivate the public to prevent cruelty to animals and to promote animal welfare and conservation policies that advance the well-being of both animals and people. More information is available at www.ifaw.org.

Project Seahorse is an international, interdisciplinary marine conservation organization. Its biologists and development specialists conduct fundamental biological research, empower communities, establish marine protected areas, manage subsistence fisheries, help to restructure international trade, advance environmental education, promote integrated policy, and redress habitat loss. More information is available at www.projectseahorse.org.

PRO WILDLIFE is a Germany-based organization dedicated to protecting wildlife from overexploitation, habitat destruction, and abuse. PRO WILDLIFE identifies and documents threats to the survival of wild species through international commercial trade and works to protect them, using scientific and legal research, advocacy, and education. The organization is committed to the enhancement, promotion, and strict enforcement of international legislation for the conservation and protection of species. PRO WILDLIFE is a member of the CITES Tortoises and Freshwater Turtles Working Group. More information is available at www.prowildlife.de/en/en.html.

U.S. Fish and Wildlife Service is a federal land managing agency under the Department of the Interior. Its mission is, "working with others, to conserve, protect, and enhance fish, wildlife, and plants and their habitats for the continuing benefit of the American people." The work of the agency dates back to 1871, when Congress first established the U.S. Fish Commission to study the nation's decreasing fisheries and recommend ways to conserve them.

WildAid, headquartered in San Francisco with small offices in the developing world, provides direct protection to wildlife in danger through wildlife law enforcement, habitat protection, care for confiscated animals, education, and community outreach. WildAid works to bring wildlife conservation to the top of the international agenda, to effectively and affordably protect wilderness areas, to ensure that endangered species populations rebound, and to enable people and wildlife to survive together. More information is available at www.wildaid.org.

Wildlife Conservation Society (WCS) has been dedicated to conserving the earth's biodiversity since its establishment in 1895 as the New York Zoological Society (NYZS). The Wildlife Conservation Society International Program believes in the intrinsic value of the diversity and integrity of life on Earth, and in the importance of wildlife and wilderness to the quality of human life. WCS saves wildlife and wild lands by helping to resolve critical problems that threaten key species and large, wild ecosystems around the world. More information is available at www.wcs.org.

Resources

High Falls Gardens
Box 125
Philmont, NY 12565

High Falls Gardens has an intern program and offers workshops on botanical studies, for more information see highfallsgardens.net.

To obtain information on how to order ecologically and sustainably grown Chinese herbs from the Medicinal Herb Consortium, see the following websites: www.sonomaherbs.org, localherbs.org, or highfallsgardens.net.

United Plant Savers
P.O. Box 400
East Barre, VT 05649

You can become a member and receive their newsletters packed with information on creating a sanctuary, nurseries that stock at-risk or to-watch medicinal plants, conferences, workshops, in-depth information on medicinal plants, and information about their books. Their website is www.plantsavers.org.

United States Fish and Wildlife Service

The following website contains the information on the testing of Chinese prepared medicinals: http://toltecs.lab.rl.fws.gov/lab/am/cover.htm.

Index

A

A. ferox Mill 157
A. vera (L.) Burm. f. 157
Agarwood **149**
    distribution 150
    biology 151
    threats 152
    conservation strategies/research 154
Agriculture 252
Ailuropoda melanoleuca 81, 92
Aloes 157
    distribution 158
    biology 159
    threats 159
    conservation strategies/research 160
    replacements/substitutions 226
Aloe vera L. var. *chinensis* 157
American Extra Pharmacopoeia 268
American Ginseng **163**, 262
    distribution 158
    biology 159
    threats 159
    conservation strategies/research 166
    replacements/substitutions 229
Animals (use of) 41, 275
Appendix I **14**, **201**
    species 42, 43, 44, 45, 47, 50, 58,
    77, 85, 91, 92, 95, 110, 211, 242, 260,
    270
Appendix II **14**, **201**
    species 42, 43, 46, 49, 58, 77, 85, 91, 92,
    95, 103, 110, 118, 129, 143, 152, 158,
    160, 166, 172, 175, 179, 181, 211,
    233, 242, 244, 246, 266, 270
Appendix III **14**, **203**
Aquilariae Lignum resinatum (see
    Agarwood)
Aquilaria sinensis 149
Asiatic Wild Ass **74**
    distribution 74
    biology 75
    threats 76
    conservation strategies/research 77

B

Bái jí (see Bletilla)
Bataguridae 55, 64
Bears 46, 48, 54, **81**, 202, 204
    distribution 81
    biology 82
    threats 83
    conservation strategies/research 84
    replacements/substitutions 233
Biē Jiǎ (see Asian Tortoises and Turtles)
Biodiversity, importance of 25
Bletilla **184**
    distribution 186
    biology 189
    threats 191
    conservation strategies/research 192
    replacements/substitutions 232
Bletilla ochracea Schltr 184, 189
Bletilla striata (Thunb.) Reichb. 184
Botanical Studies 269

C

Carrying Capacity 12
Ceratotherium simum 106
Ceratotherium simum cottoni 106
Ceratotherium simum simum 106
Carettochelyidae 55, 72
Chain Fern Rhizome **170**
    distribution 171
    biology 171
    threats 172
    conservation strategies/rsearch 172
    replacements/substitutions 227
Chelidae 55, 72
Chén Xiāng (see Agarwood)
*Chinese Herbal Medicine and
    Pharmacology* 45
Chinese Herbal Medicine Materia Medica
    45
Chinese Medicine
    term 8
    philosophy 21
    loss of biodiversity and, 26
Chuān Shān Jiǎ (see Pangolins)
Cibotium barometz 170

CITES permits 201
Community Supported Agriculture (CSA) 266
Conference of the Parties (CoP) 14, 201
Convention on International Trade in Endangered Species of Wild Flora and Fauna (CITES) 8, 200
Cornu Antelopis (see Saiga Antelope)
Cornu Rhinoceri (see Rhinoceros)
Cremastra **184**, 189
Cremastra variabilis (Bl.) Nakai 184
Cultivation 27, **251**

D

Deep ecology 34
Dendrobium **184**
    distribution 184
    biology 190
    threats 191
    conservation strategies/research 192
    replacements/substitutions 231
Dendrobium candidum Wall. ex Lindl. 184
Dendrobium chrysanthum Wall. 184
Dendrobium fimbriatum Hook. *var. oculatum* Hook. 184
Dendrobium loddigesii Rolfe. 184
Dendrobium nobile Lindl 184
Descartes, Rene 23
Dicerorthinus sumatrensis 106, 107
Diceros bicornis 106, 107

E

E. h. khulan 74, 75
E. h. khur 74, 75
E. h. luteus 74, 75
E. h. onager 74, 75
E. helioscopia L. 175
E. kansui Liou ex S.B. Ho 175
E. pekinensis Rupr. 175
Ecosystem 262
Ē Jiāo (see Asiatic Wild Ass)
Endangered Species Act 200, 203, **204**, 211, 243
Equus Asinus Linneus 74
Equus hemionus, hemionus 74
Euphorbias **175**, 177
    distribution 180
    biology 180
    threats 181
    conservation strategies/research 181
Exporting Wildlife 209
Extinction 14, **25**

F

Five Phases 3, 28
    of conservation **31**, 271
Food and Drug Administration 43, **214**

G

Gaia Hypothesis 28
Gān Suì (see Euphorbias)
Gastrodia 144, **184**
    distribution 187
    biology 190
    threats 191
    conservation strategies/research 192
    replacements/substitutions 228
Gastrodia elata Blume 184
Gelatinum Corii Asini (see Asiatic Wild Ass)
Global Medicine 49
Gŏu Jǐ (see Chain Fern Rhizome)
Guī Bǎn (see Asian Tortoises and Turtles)

H

Hǎi Mǎ (see Seahorses)
Helarctos malayanus 81, 92
Herba Aloes (See Aloes)
Herba Euphorbiae Helioscopiae (see Euphorbias)
Hippocampus spp. 123
Hǔ Gǔ (see Tigers)

I

Identification and Nomenclature 7
Integrated Worldview 24

J

Jīng Dà Jǐ (see Euphorbias)

L

Lacey Act 199, **208**
Law Enforcement 212, 273
Líng Yáng Jǐao (see Saiga Antelope)
Lovelock, James 28
Lú Huì (See Aloes)

M

Manis carssicaudata 99
Manis gigantean 99
Manis javania 99

Manis pentadactyla 99, 100
Manis temmenki 99, 100
Manis tetradactyla 99, 100
Manis tricuspis 99, 100
Marine Mammal Protection Act 200, **207**
Mechanistic Worldview 23
Medicinal Plant Conservation 174, 267
Melursus ursinus 81, 92
Migratory Bird Treaty Act 200, **206**
Moschus (see Musk Deer)
Moschus anhuiensis 93
Moschus beresovskii 93
Moschus chrysogaster 93
Moschus fuscus 93
Moschus moschiferus 93
Moschus sifanicus 93
Musk Deer 46, **93**
   distribution 93
   biology 94
   threats 94
   conservation strategies/research 95
   replacements/substitutions 238

N

National Commission for the Certification
   of Acupuncture and Oriental Medicine
   (NCCAOM) 223, 270
Native medicinal plants 267

O

Os Tigris (see Tigers)
Orchids 184

P

Panax quinquefolius 146, 163, 167
Pangolins 46, **99**, 202
   distribution 100
   biology 100
   threats 102
   conservation strategies/research 103
   replacements/substitutions 240
Panthera tigris 134
Pipe Fish(es) 46
Platysternidae 55, 70
Pleione 184
   distribution 186
   biology 189
   threats 191
   conservation strategies/research 192
Pleione bulbocodioides (Franch.) Rolfe
   184

Pleione yunnanensis Rolfe 184
Poaching 76, 77, 156, 166
Pseudobulbus Cremastrae seu Pleiones
   184

R

Radix Euphorbiae Kansui (see Euphorbias)
Radix Euphorbiae Pekinensis (see
   Euphorbias)
Radix Panacis Quinquefolii (see American
   Ginseng)
Red List **15**, 63, 74, 123, 127, 152, 159,
   165, 172, 181, 191
Regulation 10, 17, 209
Resource Conservation 209, 212
Rhino horn 43
Rhinoceros 106
   distribution 106
   biology 107
   threats 109
   onservation strategies/research 110
   replacements/substitutions 235
Rhinoceros and Tiger Conservation Act
   43, 44, **206**
Rhinoceros sondaicus 106, 107
Rhinoceros unicornis 106, 107
Rhizoma Bletillae (see Bletilla)
Rhizoma Cibotii Barometz (see Chain Fern
   Rhizome)
Rhizoma Gastrodiae (see Gastrodia)

S

Saiga Antelope 29, 46, **113**
   distribution 113
   biology 114
   threats 116
   conservation strategies/research 117
   replacements/substitutions 241
Saiga tatarica mongolica 113, 120
Saiga tatarica tatarica 113, 120
Seahorses 46, **123**
   distribution 124
   biology 124
   threats 127
   conservation strategies/research 129
   replacements/substitutions 243
Shān Cí Gū (see Pleione)
Shè Xiāng (see Musk Deer)
Squama Manis (see Pangolins)
Sustainable Use 7, 9

T

Testudinis Plastrum/ Trioycis Carapax (see
    Tortoises and Turtles)
Testudinidae 55, 63
Tīan Má (see Gastrodia)
Tigers 43, 44, **134**
    distribution 135
    biology 136
    threats 138
    conservation strategies/research 140
    replacements/substitutions 237
Tiger bone (see Tigers)
Tortoise (see Tortoises and Turtles)
Tortoises and Turtles (Asian) 55
    distribution 55
    biology 56
    threats 57
    conservation strategies/research 58
    replacements/substitutions 244
Tremarctos ornatus 55, 92
Trionychidae 55, 56, 70

U

United Plant Savers 266, 277
Ursus americanus 81, 91
Ursus arctos 81, 91
Ursus maritimus 81, 92
Ursus thibetanus 81, 91
US Department of Agriculture 211, 213
US Fish and Wildlife Service 166, 168, 199
US Wildlife laws 203

V

Valuation of Natural Resources 10
Vesica Fellea Ursi (see Bears)

W

Wildlife Trade 37, 209
World Conservation Union (IUCN) 8, **15**

X

Xī Jiǎo (see Rhinoceros)
Xī Yáng Shēn (see American Ginseng)
Xióng Dǎn (see Bears)

Z

Zé Qī (see Euphorbias)